UNDERSTANDING YEAR 5&6 MATHS

Author:

Merle Green B.Ed. T.C. (University of London)

PERSONAL ACKNOWLEDGEMENT:
The high standard of typesetting, layout, artwork and hundreds of complex illustrations are due to Anne McLean's expertise in the field of computing. The publisher would like to add a thank you for your time, patience, attention to detail, and the overall quality of your work.

Editor/Publisher:
W. S. Marlin
P.O. Box 568
Turramurra NSW 2074
Telephone (02) 214 4418

Note:
This book can be purchased directly from Accelerated Maths Learning by writing to the address shown above.

Typesetting by:
Anne McLean
Allambie Heights NSW 2100

Printed by:
Star Printery Pty. Limited
Erskineville NSW 2043

1st Edition April 1996

ISBN 1 875462 06 6

AUTHOR'S ACKNOWLEDGEMENT

Merle Green acknowledges the dedicated work of the groups in the various states and territories of Australia who produced their K–6 Mathematics curriculum documents.

Particular mention is made of 'Mathematics K–6' produced by the NSW Department of Education and 'Mathematics—a curriculum profile for Australian Schools', produced by the Curriculum Corporation.

This book provides a summary and interpretation of these documents for those interested in developing mathematical understanding in Primary School children.

'I see, I forget
I read, I know
I do, I understand'

TEACHERS

This book summarises the steps and stages by which Australian children acquire the necessary mathematical skills and concepts. It eliminates the need to wade through reams of paper in curriculum documents. It provides a clear, easy to follow summary for teachers to use which they can also confidently recommend to parents as it supports activities and exercises.

PARENTS

This book tells you what your child's teacher does not have the time to—the steps and stages by which each strand of mathematics is taught in schools.

It gives you the confidence to support your child by reinforcing what is being taught in school and to correctly provide assistance where weaknesses are identified.

B.ED., DIP. ED. STUDENT PRIMARY TEACHERS

This book provides a concise record of the steps to be taken and the activities suggested to support the acquisition of mathematical concepts. It is the perfect reference book for teaching practice and in the early years of teaching when there is so much to learn.

'teaching of others, teacheth the teacher'

AVAILABILITY OF BOOKS IN THIS SERIES

All of the books below incorporate the same quality presentation, format and philosophy. They can be purchased directly through Accelerated Maths Learning, but they are also available in over 180 educational bookshops throughout NSW and Australia. Almost every Dymocks bookshop; many Angus & Robertson; Collins, QBD Bookshops (in Queensland), Book City; Dominie; Bellbird; Five Senses; Nepean Educational Specialists; Duckworth's; Jacaranda Educational Supplies; etc, etc. Please phone us, if you want details of the closest bookshop near you.

❑ YEAR 1 & 2	ALL LEVELS
❑ YEAR 3 & 4	ALL LEVELS
❑ YEAR 5 & 6	ALL LEVELS
❑ YEAR 7	ALL LEVELS
❑ YEAR 8	ALL LEVELS
❑ YEAR 9 & 10	INTERMEDIATE
❑ YEAR 9 & 10	ADVANCED
❑ YEAR 11 & 12	MATHS IN SOCIETY
❑ YEAR 11/2 UNIT	PRELIMINARY
❑ YEAR 12/2 UNIT	HSC
❑ YEAR 11/3 UNIT	PRELIMINARY
❑ YEAR 12/3 UNIT	HSC

STATES OUTSIDE NEW SOUTH WALES

The first seven books in the above series would be very beneficial to students in all States, because the syllabus content is virtually identical throughout Australia up to the end of Year 10.

However, in Years 11 and 12, there are more significant variations in the syllabus between the States. Therefore, although many of the more senior books have been used with success by students in other States, you must keep in mind that the topics may not be followed in the same order, or with the same emphasis, as they are done in NSW.

FOR FURTHER INFORMATION AND BROCHURES
RELATING TO ANY OF THE TITLES ABOVE, PHONE:

(02) 214 4418

CONTENTS

THE IMPORTANCE OF PRIMARY MATHEMATICS HOW THIS BOOK HELPS—NOTES FOR PARENTS

'parents and patterns'

The study of mathematics aims to develop an understanding of why number, space and measurement concepts are useful in everyday living. Mathematics is not pages and pages of 'sums' (algorithms) which are either right, and are ticked, or wrong, and are crossed.

Each day of our lives we will use so many mathematical concepts and processes without realising that we are doing it. We constantly have to solve problems which involve mathematical thinking whether spatial, involving manipulating numbers or requiring an understanding of measurement in one form or another. We cannot get by without understanding the mathematical processes in all the major strands.

Unfortunately there are many parents and students who believe that it is sufficient to be able to manipulate numbers skilfully and accurately in the 4 operations of addition, subtraction, multiplication and division. This is untrue. An understanding of the different aspects of measurement and spatial awareness are essential in a well rounded person who is fully equipped for adult life.

It is during the primary school years that the foundations of mathematical understanding and attitudes to mathematics are laid down. It is therefore most important, indeed vital, that students develop understanding, confidence and enjoyment if they are to succeed later. By achieving success now it is probable that their skills will continue to grow and flourish throughout their secondary education.

Most parents are aware of these factors. Many would like to help, stimulate or extend their children towards greater understanding, enjoyment and success in mathematics. There are, however, several reasons why they feel unable to do so.

1. They may feel unqualified to help because the methods of teaching mathematics have changed so much since they were at school.
2. Some parents were weak in mathematics at school and therefore feel incapable of helping their children.
3. Because of this weakness there is the expectation that their children will also experience difficulties.
4. Most, if not all, parents are capable of helping their children, but are unsure of what is to be taught.
5. Parents are concerned that they are not aware of the methods being used by teachers.

Every child is an individual with unique levels and rates of development in the acquisition of knowledge in the different areas of the curriculum. These rates of development vary considerably within the individual. A child who has difficulty grasping certain mathematical concepts at the age of 8 may easily have a leap forward in mathematical maturity in the next few years. This series of books caters for these individual differences and rates. Your child may, for instance, be at a K–2 level of understanding in fractions and decimals, Years 3–4 level in addition and at Years 5–6 level in their understanding of the concepts of 2 and 3 dimensional shapes. This disparity is quite normal. Because this series is carefully graded, the needs of the individual are met. Simply assess the level the child has achieved and progress from there.

IT IS IMPORTANT THAT THE PRACTICAL PRECEDES THE WRITTEN, THE HANDS-ON BEFORE THE TEXT BOOK.

It is known that children learn with understanding from shared experiences, discussions and hands on activities. Rote learning is often forgotten and the facts cannot be transferred to other situations through a lack of understanding.

Work through each page yourself. Doing the activities will help you to understand the process and stages of development. You will also appreciate how important the sometimes very subtle steps are. You will also develop your owns ideas to add to the suggestions in the books. Only when *you* truly understand the processes can you help your children to learn.

Offer every opportunity for practical hands-on experiences in real-life, measuring the correct amount of ingredients for cooking, comparing sizes or masses for the best value whilst shopping. These experiences are invaluable because they show children how important and relevant mathematical skills are to their own lives. They also give you an opportunity to see how your children think so that you can use suitable strategies to help their learning. For example, some children need to write things down in order to learn and understand, others need to say them aloud. These and other methods are all acceptable.

This series empowers you with the ability to give appropriate support when a weakness is identified. Use the series to go right back to basics and slowly work through to the level of the child's class. Weaknesses develop from a lack of understanding of basic principles.

You can approach each concept at the right level for your child. By looking at the child's text book you can identify the level which has been reached. These books provide a means of accurately assessing whether your child has grasped the concepts being taught in school.

DON'T MISS OUT STEPS! It is not clever to miss out steps. It is not clever to miss out the practical activities. Taking part in practical, hands-on experiences is not a sign of weakness. Such experiences form the basis of the layering process of learning with understanding.

Being proficient in number manipulation is not enough. A good working *understanding* of measurement concepts is essential in everyday life. Well developed spatial awareness is an important life skill. If your child has mastered all the concepts in, for example, Number in one of these books then it is important to work on spatial and measurement concepts to bring them to year level rather than pushing into more advanced number concepts.

With students who are truly well above the average in ability it is advisable to introduce them to the many activities available which will extend their breadth of mathematical understanding by exploring sideways rather than forwards. These activities add to a student's understanding in a positive and challenging way rather than pushing them forward to a level for which they may not be ready thus encouraging negative attitudes. Educational bookshops have shelves full of excellent material to challenge such students.

The rate at which your children learn and the level to which they can reach with understanding at any given time are linked to mathematical maturity. *You cannot force these and make them go faster*. If difficulties are being encountered then stop for a while, work on another topic and return later to try again. When a child is pushed beyond his or her capabilities at that particular time, permanent attitudinal damage can result. It is much better to make haste slowly!

Assume your child knows nothing. Just because you know what you are talking about doesn't mean your child does. Follow the simple precise steps laid down in the books, constantly assess to be sure that concepts have been understood and then progress to the next stage. You can't go wrong!

Don't give answers; ask questions so that your children can find the answers for themselves. 'Let's just look at this bit again. What did you do here? How did you get that answer?' This teaches a child to self-assess and you can see the line of thinking.

Try not to say 'No!' or 'You're wrong!' The fault lies in the teaching not in the learning. If a child doesn't understand how can they be expected to be right? Go back a few steps, give more practical experiences, try a different line of questioning, approach the problem from a different point of view and your children may then see where they are meant to be heading. If not, try again later. Praise your children constantly and have fun discovering together.

By using this book you and the children in your care should;

- be given opportunities to experience graded activities which will aid the development of mathematical concepts
- come to understand all the basic concepts as a result of this practical involvement
- be able to understand why and how errors were made and have the ability to correct them.

THE FORMAT OF 'UNDERSTANDING YEAR 5 & 6 MATHS

This series of books provides a structured and clear idea of the syllabus and what a student is required to know.

Teachers and parents are able to see what skills should be developed over the two year period.

The series provides a means of overlap to cater for individual differences.

It is also an ideal reference for parents to consult when they wish to provide assistance in eliminating any weaknesses in understanding.

The syllabus for Years 5 and 6 has been divided into 3 major areas or strands: NUMBER, SPACE, MEASUREMENT, CHANGE AND DATA AND PROBLEM-SOLVING.

Each strand has been sub-divided into various substrands:

NUMBER: Numeration, Addition, Subtraction, Multiplication, Division, Fractions and Decimals, Money, Chance and Data.

SPACE: 3D, 2D, Position, Graphs.

MEASUREMENT: Length, Area, Volume, Mass, Temperature, Time.

CHANCE AND DATA: Investigations

PROBLEM-SOLVING: Strategies

Each strand is introduced with an explanation of its importance.

Each substrand is introduced with an explanation of what is to be learned and the vocabulary which is to be employed.

Each substrand is followed by a series of assessment procedures with concrete materials and 3 graded tests for which solutions are to be found at the back of the book. The tests enable parents and teachers to check to what extent concepts have been grasped.

The appendix contains pages which can be used as numeral and symbol cards and place value charts.

Those responsible for the education of children, whether parents or teachers, are introduced to activities which develop a real understanding of the different aspects of mathematics in an enjoyable yet meaningful way. The students come to this understanding by completing a series of activities.

This book introduces the language that students would be expected to use and the stages through which they pass on the way to acquiring understanding of mathematical concepts. Possible conversations have been included to show the kinds of thought processes which may be taking place or which should be encouraged in all areas of mathematical discovery.

Interlink the substrands as much as possible. They are not separate isolated entities.

The emphasis is on:

- discovery, and
- development of the ability to accurately identify which processes can be used to solve real-life problems together with an introduction to the uses of technology to simplify mathematical calculations.

This well structured book covers the syllabus topic by topic, explaining what is to be taught and how it is being taught in the classroom. It is a comprehensive, well presented, easy to understand mathematics summary book which is applicable to schools throughout Australia.

ESTIMATION/APPROXIMATION

It is absolutely vital to constantly encourage and develop the skill of estimation or approximation.

Well developed estimation skills give confidence to children. They learn to assess whether their answer is reasonable in relation to the estimated answer. This helps in both computation and problem-solving.

They learn to question whether their answer is logical. Would it really be reasonable that the combined weight of 4 adult elephants would be 1 200 kg?

Various techniques can be used.

1. Rounding off — 673 rounded off to the nearest hundred is 700
2. Rounding up and down — Shopkeepers round amounts up or down to the nearest 5 or 10 cents.
3. Clustering — Similar numbers or numbers which add to approximate multiples of 10 or 100 are grouped to make estimation easier.

   28 + 33 = about 30 + 30.
   The answer would be around 60.
4. Comparing — 'This pile is larger than that one'.

CONCRETE MATERIALS BASE 10

Base 10 wooden blocks are utilised in schools to represent units, tens, hundreds and thousands. Such blocks are available at educational stores. Some are also colour coded but they all incorporate the following principles:

A single cube represents one unit and is called a SHORT

A row of ten cubes joined together represents one ten and is called a LONG

A raft of ten longs joined together represents one hundred [10 tens (longs) or one hundred units (shorts)] and is referred to as a FLAT

A large cube made from ten flats joined together represents one thousand (10 flats or 100 longs or 1000 shorts) and is called a BLOCK

Children are able to SEE and FEEL that a flat is ten times greater than a long. They can also HEFT that a block has a greater mass than a flat. Such tactile and visual experiences facilitate progress towards and understanding of abstract mathematics. For this reason, wooden blocks are preferable to plastic blocks.

TABLES

Tables have been the bane of students' lives from time immemorial! Why is it that some students can recall the facts so easily and others really struggle? There are many reasons. Many students have not modelled the tables with concrete materials and so do not understand what is happening. Others need to model many times, over an extended period of time, to be able to retain the facts. Some have poor maths memories or have great difficult sequencing numbers so tables present a formidable, if not impossible, obstacle. Children whose mathematical readiness develops later have often formed the opinion that they can't do maths and therefore can't do tables. Confidence and self-esteem play an important part.

The thought of learning 121 tables facts from ×0 to ×10 can be very daunting. However, a closer look reveals that the task is less onerous than first appears. Taking little steps, one at a time, gives confidence and develops a positive attitude.

×0 table (0 × 0, 0 × 1, 1 × 0, 0 × 2, 2 × 0, etc.) eliminates 21 facts as the answer is always 0. (100 facts remain)

×1 table eliminates 19 facts as the number multiplied by 1 keeps the same value. (81 facts remain)

×10 table eliminates 17 facts as a '0' is added to the number multiplied by 10. (64 facts remain)

×2 table is fairly easy to remember. (49 facts remain)

×5 table answers are half the ×10 answers, or 5 × evens end in 0 and 5 × odds end in 5. (36 facts remain)

×9 table answers are 10 × the number minus the number, or alternatively;
Hold up the fingers and thumbs. For 4 × 9, counting the digits from the left, bend the 4th digit onto the palm.
Three digits remain on the left of the bent finger and 6 remain on the right. The answer is 36. (25 facts remain)

×4 table is related to the ×2 table. Double the ×2 answers. (16 facts remain)

×7 table answers are found by adding 5× the number and 2× the number. (9 facts remain)

The 9 facts remaining are:

3 × 3, 3 × 6, 3 × 8, 6 × 3, 6 × 6, 8 × 3, 8 × 6, 8 × 8

Of these 9 facts, 6 are reversing pairs.

The following technique is recommended to build confidence and skill levels.

CASSETTE PLAYER REPETITION

This technique involves students in helping themselves to learn and encourages them to have a go, safe in the knowledge that they can privately, and therefore comfortably, make mistakes.

1. The student slowly reads the table into the tape player.
2. Using headphones, the student reads the table many times whilst listening to the tape.
3. The student then reads the question part of the table onto the tape in sequence, leaving gaps between each fact.

   e.g. '3 × 4 equals . . .'

4. When the student has the confidence to try, he or she practises reading the question whilst listening to the tape and then saying and writing the answers. It can take lots of practice but there will be an improvement in most cases after a fairly short period of time which will build confidence.

5. The student then reads the questions out of sequence and practises saying and writing the answers.

6. Progress to mixing different tables together.

7. Make 100 square formats, writing the numbers 0 to 10 across the top and down the sides first in sequence and then later randomly. Many children have fun firstly trying to beat themselves in accuracy and then timing themselves trying to beat their time for a perfect square. (See Appendix for tables square format.)

This technique is excellent, empowering students to help themselves at their own pace and giving a real sense of achievement.

COMPUTER PROGRAMS AND CASSETTES/CDs
There are a number of computer programs and songs on tape and CD available which also can aid in the recall of tables.

A variety of fun activities used in a stress-free atmosphere can be most useful.

CALCULATORS

Calculators are useful tools in mathematics education giving opportunities for students to develop problem-solving skills, explore number patterns, place value, etc.

- Calculators provide answers quickly.
- They allow students to take risks and experiment with numbers—privately.
- Calculators frequently stimulate learning and interest in mathematical processes. 'Playing' with calculators offers opportunities for discovery.
- Calculators allow students to work through a problem without getting weighed down by calculations. The most important feature of problem-solving is understanding the processes/operations involved.
- Calculators allow students to explore problems involving large numbers which would otherwise require unnecessarily time consuming and unwieldy pencil and paper calculations.
- Calculators empower less able students who understand which operations are required to solve the problem without the need to personally manipulate the numbers.

However, there are four important points which should be made.

1. With simpler problems, the brain is often quicker than a calculator.
2. It is essential to estimate the answer to provide a check as to whether the calculated answer is a reasonable one to the particular problem.
3. If a student does not understand which operation, or series of operations, is needed to solve a problem, a calculator is useless.
4. Calculators do not eliminate the need to know tables!

COMPUTERS

Access to computers and programs varies considerably from school to school and home to home.

Computers can be excellent aids to the acquisition of mathematical concepts.

Computers can allow students to explore mathematics at greater depth and also develop problem-solving skills and spacial awareness with such programs as LOGO.

Many programs allow students to take risks and explore alternative strategies which will increase their mathematical understanding .

Many programs involve decision making and interpretation of information, generally promoting the use of the higher thinking skills such as analysing and evaluation.

Word-processing and design programs can be used to enhance presentation.

Graphing, data bases and spread sheets provide links with other curriculum areas.

Computers should not replace hands-on experiences or be used where calculators are appropriate.

NUMBER STRAND

'Experience is the best teacher'

INTRODUCTION

The ability to add, subtract, multiply, divide, to use money with confidence and to be familiar with parts of wholes expressed as fractions and decimals means the acquisition of life skills. These processes are not only essential to everyday living but also in science, medicine, economics, industry, business, etc. Adult life and employment need these skills.

It takes time and a great deal of practice to develop mathematical skills, some students needing much longer and much more practice than others. However, those who find their acquisition easy find it hard to understand and appreciate the difficulties of others. It is only through constant and continuing hands-on experiences over many years that understanding and confidence will develop.

In the past, the topics covered under the umbrella of 'number' have been learned by rote and pages and pages of 'sums' (algorithms) There is now the realisation that this method does not convey understanding and the processes are frequently not remembered for longer than a few days. Children develop understanding by experimenting and doing. This book emphasises this practical approach linked to written recording.

The many experiences suggested help to promote logical thinking and provide opportunities to develop the ability to communicate with others through numbers.

The art of mathematical communication not only involves numbers but also graphs, diagrams, tables, charts, etc. It is, therefore, essential that all students also develop spacial awareness and a familiarity with all aspects of measurement. To be able to manipulate numbers is not enough.

CONCRETE MATERIALS

Storage

Bowls, boxes, cartons, containers, jars, shoeboxes.

Objects for counting

Base 10 materials, beads, bottle tops, books, boxes, building blocks, buttons, calculators,cards, coins, corks, counters, dice, drinking straws, dry beans, gumnuts, leaves, Lego bricks, lids, macaroni, paddlepop sticks, paperclips, pegs, pencils, pebbles, pine cones, plasticine, plastic cups, plastic figures, rocks, rubber bands, screws, seeds, sewing thread reels, scissors, shells, soft toys, spoons, sticks, stickers, stones, toilet roll inners, toothpicks, toy cars, washers.

NUMERATION

Numeration means the reading, counting and calculating of numerals.

It is very important that the activities suggested in the previous volumes of this series are undertaken as an understanding of numeration is essential to all other sub-strands.

During Years 5 and 6 this understanding of numbers is extended to 1 million and beyond.

VOCABULARY

Digit, greater than, hundred(s), hundred thousands, infinite, infinity, less than, millions, number line, one(s), ordinal number, place, place value, ten million, ten(s), ten thousand, thousand, unit(s).

CONTENTS

Page

SPECIAL NUMBER PATTERNS

There are some groups of numbers in Maths which have special patterns. You must be able to recognise these patterns and also be able to name the different groups.

In streets, you will usually see even numbered houses on one side and odd numbered houses on the other side

Name of group	**Pattern**
Whole numbers	0, 1 2, 3, 4, . . .
Counting numbers	1, 2, 3, 4, 5, . . .
Even numbers	2, 4, 6, 8, 10, . . .
Odd numbers	1, 3, 5, 7, 9, . . .
Square numbers	4, 9, 16, 25, 36, . . . $1^2, 2^2, 3^2, 4^2$, etc.
Triangular numbers	1, 3, 6, 10, 15 . . .
	1, 1 + 2, 1 + 2 + 3, 1 + 2 + 3 + 4, etc.
Ordinal numbers	1st, 2nd, 3rd, 4th, . . .

NOTE: Triangular numbers can also be obtained from building up triangles from dots—this is how they got their name.

PLACE VALUE

Our number system today is based on the Hindu-Arabic system where the value of a number is determined by its place in a particular column.

For example, what does 3 520 697 really mean?

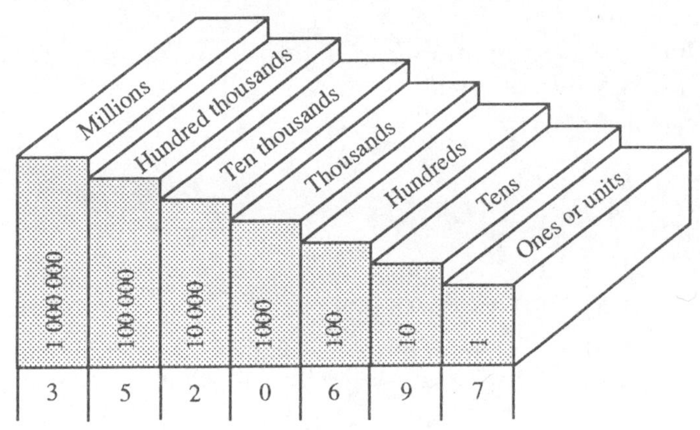

The place value of 2 is 20 000 or twenty thousand.
The place value of 6 is 600 or six hundred.

There are four ways of describing a whole number:

1. AS AN ORDINARY NUMERAL: 3 520 697
2. IN WORDS: Three million, five hundred and twenty thousand, six hundred and ninety seven.
3. IN EXPANDED NOTATION: $(3 \times 1\,000\,000\ ) + (5 \times 100\,000) + (2 \times 10\,000) + 0 \times 1\,000) + 6 \times 100) + (9 \times 10) + (7 \times 1)$.
4. IN EXPONENTIAL NOTATION: $(3 \times 10^6) + (5 \times 10^5) + (2 \times 10^4) + (0 \times 10^3) + (6 \times 10^2) + (9 \times 10^1) + (7 \times 1)$

ROMAN NUMERALS

When the Roman empire became powerful, its number system spread to many other countries. The system used a subtraction and addition idea. When a smaller unit appears before a larger one, it is subtracted from the larger one. When a smaller unit appears after the larger unit, it is added to the larger unit. Therefore the position of the symbols is important.

IV means 5 –1 = 4 whereas VI means 5 + 1 = 6

XL means 50 – 10 = 40 whereas LX means 50 + 10 = 60

1	2	3	4	5	6	7	8	9
I	II	III	IV	V	VI	VII	VIII	IX
10	20	30	40	50	60	70	80	90
X	XX	XXX	XL	L	LX	LXX	LXXX	XC
100	200	300	400	500	600	700	800	900
C	CC	CCC	CD	D	DC	DCC	DCCC	CM

1 000 = M

You will often get questions in tests which ask you to change from Roman to Hindu-Arabic, and vice versa.

Example: Change the Roman numerals into our own numerals:
(a) XXIV
(b) CXXVIII
(c) DCLXIV
(d) MDV

Solutions:
(a) 10 + 10 + 4 = 24
(b) 100 + 10 + 10 + 5 + 3 = 128
(c) 500 + 100 + 50 + 10 + 4 = 664
(d) 1000 + 500 + 5 = 1505

Example: Change these Hindu-Arabic numerals into Roman numerals:
(a) 37
(b) 213
(c) 1452
(d) 1992

Solutions:
(a) 37 = XXXVII
(b) 213 = CCXIII
(c) 1452 = MCDLII
(d) 1992 = MCMXCII

NUMBERS 1 000 TO 9 999

When writing numbers over 999, a space separates the thousands and the hundreds, e.g. 1 495

ACTIVITIES:

1. Explore the variety of ways 1 000 can be made. Use Base 10 materials.

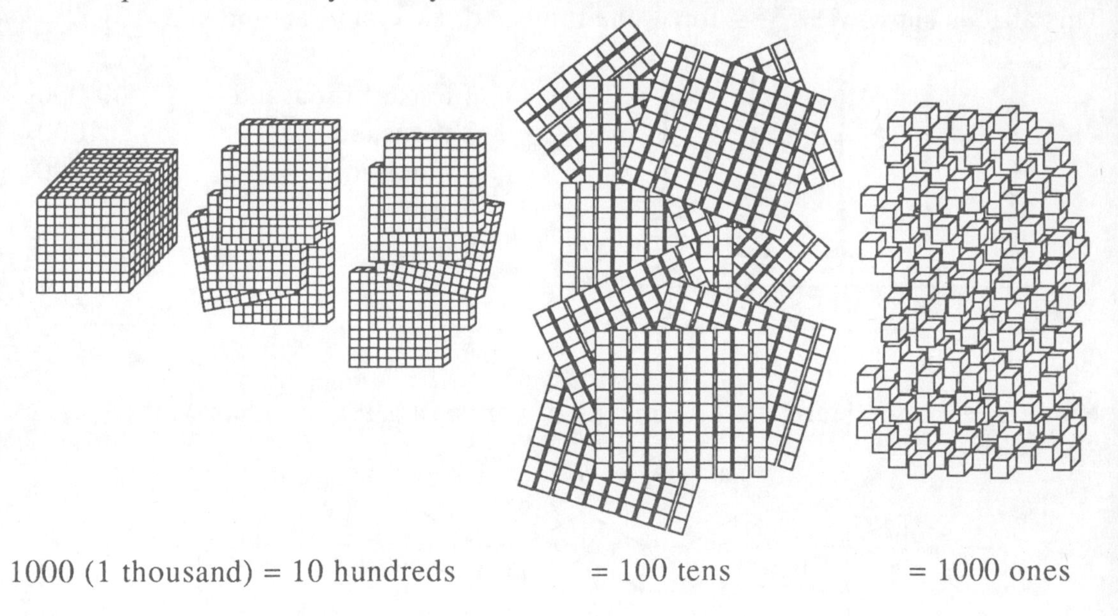

1000 (1 thousand) = 10 hundreds = 100 tens = 1000 ones

2. Represent three thousand and four hundred and six on an abacus.

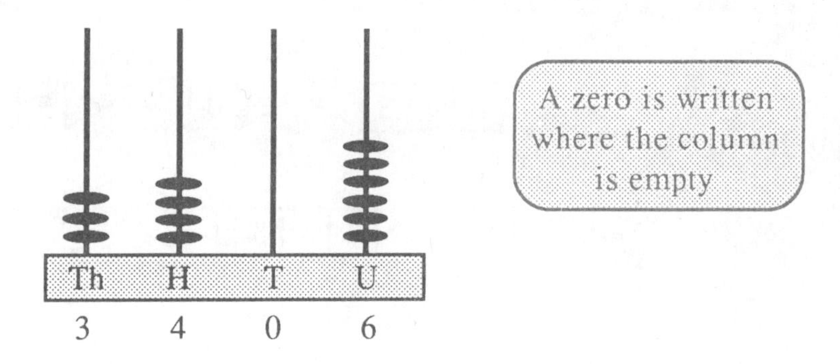

3. Count forwards to, and backwards from 9 999 by hundreds, fifities and tens. Read and write numbers from 1 000 to 9 999.

4. Place in order from largest to smallest, a selection of numbers between 1 000 and 9 999.

   e.g. 9 287, 7 782, 9 297, 9 645, 7 942, 4 983

5. What is the value of 2 in the number 4 728? (2 tens)

6. What is this number: 6 000 + 200 + 70 + 4? (6 274)

NUMBERS 10 000 TO 99 999

Crowds at large sporting occasions are usually counted in tens of thousands.

10 000 is the same as	10	thousands	or
	100	hundreds	or
	1 000	tens	or
	10 000	ones	or

This abacus shows 41 265—forty-one thousand, two hundred and sixty-five.

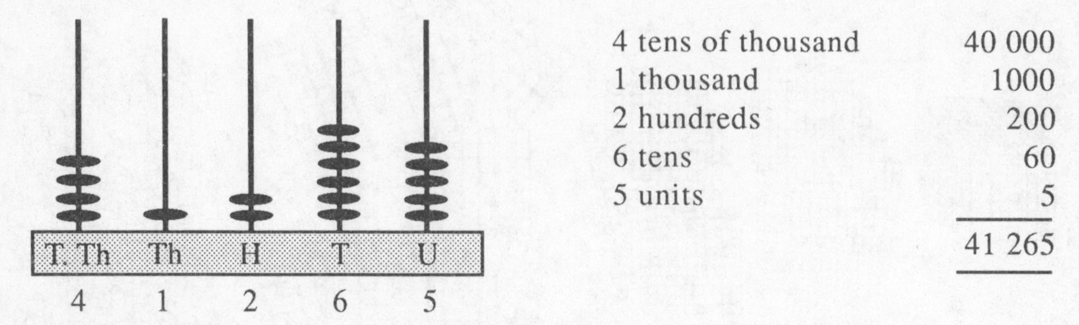

4 tens of thousand	40 000
1 thousand	1000
2 hundreds	200
6 tens	60
5 units	5
	41 265

Numeral expanders are a useful means of conveying that another way to see 24 307 is as:

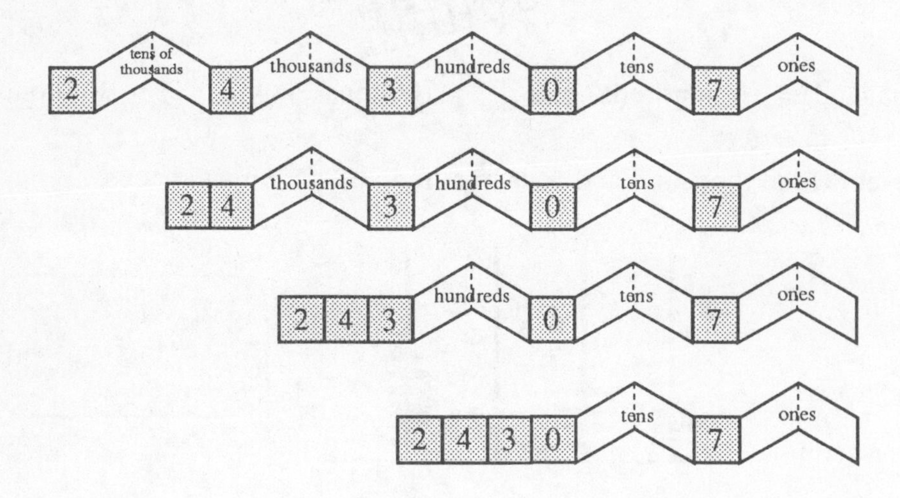

ACTIVITIES:

1. Read the odometer on the family car. Record the reading. Compare with other odometers.

2. Write as numerals:
   (a) 30 000 + 1 000 + 60 + 2 + 500 [31 562]
   (b) 8 + 7 000 + 30 + 20 000 [27 038]
   (c) Add 1 000 to the following: 49 225 [50 225]
   (d) Write the smallest possible number using these digits: 3, 9, 6, 2, 7 [23 679]

NUMBERS FROM 100 000 ONWARDS

The number of cars crossing Sydney Harbour Bridge in one year would be counted in hundreds of thousands, as would the populations of very large towns.

100 000 is the same as	10	ten thousands	or
	100	thousands	or
	1 000	hundreds	or
	10 000	tens	or
	100 000	ones	

This abacus shows 625 703, six hundred and twenty-five thousand, seven hundred and three.

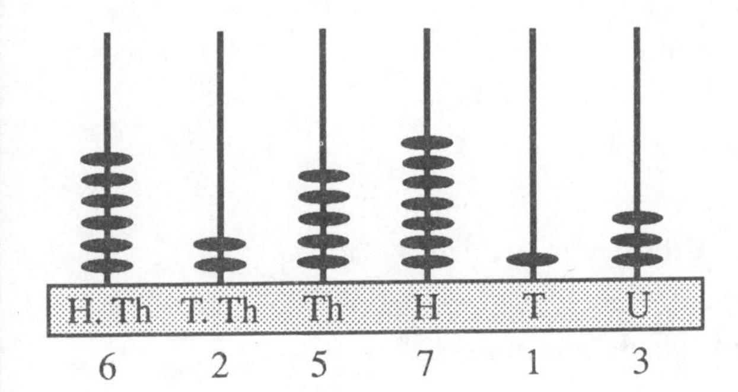

6 hundreds of thousands	600 000
2 tens of thousands	20 000
5 thousands	5 000
7 hundreds	700
0 tens	
3 units	3
	625 703

1 MILLION is one thousand thousands. It is written 1 000 000.

NOTE: A space is left between the millions and the hundred thousands as well as between the thousands and the hundreds.

The term **billion** is interpreted differently in different countries, which can cause confusion.

In Great Britain, a billion means a million million 1 000 000 000 000.

In America, a billion is regarded as one thousand million 1 000 000 000.

Australia use the same definition as America,that is, **one thousand million.**

ACTIVITY:
Research situations where large numbers are used: areas of countries, populations, national and intemational finance, etc.

NUMERATION ASSESSMENT

Students should understand the following ideas:

- define whole numbers, counting numbers, odd and even numbers, ordinal numbers, square and triangular numbers
- explain place value
- convert Hindu-Arabic numerals to Roman numerals, and vice versa
- identify numbers to 9 999 modelled in Base 10 materials
- use Base 10 materials to model numbers to 9 999
- use an abacus to model numbers to 9 999
- read numbers to 9 999 written in either words or numerals
- write spoken numbers to 9 999 in words and numerals
- count forwards and backwards to 9 999 by hundreds, fifties and tens
- give the place value of any digit in a four-digit number
- order several four-digit numbers in either ascending or descending order
- give the number which follows or precedes any given four-digit number
- repeat the above and similar activities for five-digit numbers
- repeat the above and similar assessments for numbers to a million and beyond

LEVEL 1 — NUMERATION

EASIER QUESTIONS

Q1. What number is:

(a) 100 more than 597? (b) 100 less than 1 521?
(c) 1 000 more than 2 674? (d) 1 000 less than 3 568

Q2. Write the numeral for twenty-seven thousand and twenty-seven.

Q3. What is the place value of 3 in the following numbers?

(a) 5 398 (b) 13 176 (c) 50 873

Q4. Write the numeral for 60 000 + 7 000 + 400 + 30 + 9.

Q5. Round off these numbers to the nearest thousand:

(a) 5 750 (b) 10 557 (c) 27 258

Q6. What number is:

(a) 1 000 more than 147 239 (b) 10 000 more than 63 012

Q7. Place these numbers in ascending order:

2 563 180; 376 428; 99 999; 1 000 202

Q8. Change to Roman numerals:

(a) 74 (b) 126 (c) 419

Q9. Change to our numerals (Hindu-Arabic):

(a) XCVII (b) CCCLXII (c) DXXXIX

LEVEL 2 — NUMERATION

AVERAGE QUESTIONS

Q1. What number is:

(a) 100 less than 4 050? (b) 2 more than 3 999?
(c) 50 less than 8 019? (d) 200 more than 1 850?

Q2. Write the numeral for:

(a)

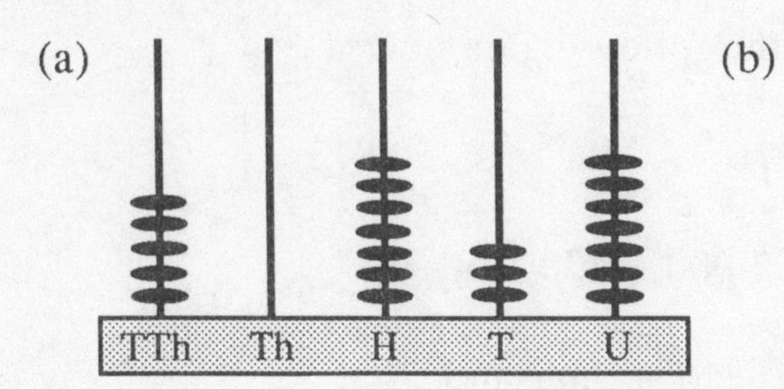

(b)

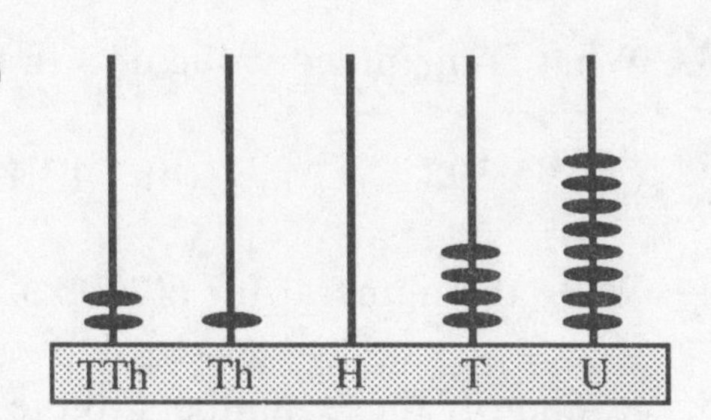

Q3. What is the place value of 3 in the following numbers?

(a) 175 703 (b) 435 540 (c) 392 161

Q4. Write the numeral for:

$(2 \times 100) + (7 \times 1\,000) + (5 \times 10) + (3 \times 10\,000)$

Q5. Round off these numbers to the nearest ten thousand:

(a) 56 390 (b) 112 628 (c) 376 192

Q6. What number is:

(a) 10 more than 18 007? (b) 5 less than 209 382?

Q7. Place these numbers in ascending order:

4 203 625, 4 099 958, 4 400 000, 4 199 986

Q8. Change to Roman numerals:

(a) 543 (b) 798 (c) 1 316

Q9. Change to our numerals (Hindu-Arabic):

(a) MCDXX (b) DCCCLXVIII (c) MCMXCV

LEVEL 3 — NUMERATION

DIFFICULT QUESTIONS

Q1. What number is:

(a) 400 more than 7 thousand, 4 ones, 6 hundreds and 2 tens?
(b) 2 more than nine thousand nine hundred and ninety-nine?

Q2. Write the numeral for:

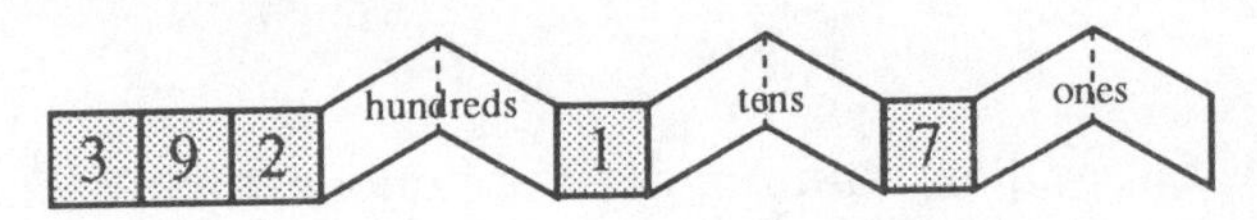

Q3. What is the place value of 6 in the following numbers?

(a) 560 483 (b) 649 205 (c) 16 190 253

Q4. Write the numeral for:

(a) $(2 \times 10^4) + (5 \times 10^3) + (3 \times 10^2) + (6 \times 10) + (0 \times 1)$
(b) $(9 \times 10) + (4 \times 10^2) + (5 \times 10^4) + (8 \times 1) + (1 \times 10^3)$

Q5. Round off these numbers to the nearest hundred thousand:

(a) 486 324 (b) 550 568 (c) 1 276 491

Q6. What number is:

(a) 100 000 more than 49 725? (b) 1 less than 100 000?

Q7. (a) Write 53 473 906 in words.
(b) Round off 53 473 906 to the nearest million.

Q8. Change to Roman numerals:

(a) 951 (b) 1 613 (c) 2 369

Q9. Change to our numerals (Hindu-Arabic):

(a) MXX (b) MMMDCI (c) MMDCCIV

ADDITION

By the end of these two years, it is anticipated that a student will usually have progressed to addition of two or more numbers containing up to four digits, with or without trading, and will feel confident about using numbers in these processes.

VOCABULARY

Add, addition, algorithm, altogether, column, digit, equals, estimate, flat, hundred, hundreds place, makes, one, ones' place, place, plus, short, sum, ten, tens' place, total, trade, unit, vertical.

There will be a significant proportion of students who will need to continue using concrete materials, either regularly or occasionally. As was explained in the previous book in this series, the use of concrete materials is an essential step in understanding the addition process, particularly when trading is involved. Where a Year 5/6 student is experiencing difficulties, it is recommended that reference be made to the processes covered in the previous volume and that these are practised thoroughly before attempting the next steps detailed below.

CONTENTS

EARLY EXPERIENCES

It is essential that addition practice not only begins in the very early years with the use of concrete materials (spoons, buttons, counters, paddle-pop sticks, blocks) but continues for a considerable number of years, depending on the needs of the individual student. The tactile and visual experience of using concrete materials ensures that students don't just learn by rote but through a thorough understanding. The visual impact of seeing that one line of buttons is longer than another and therefore contains more, the physical handling of materials reinforces the student's perceptions of relative amounts.

Therefore, an integral part of acquiring understanding of a process is a great deal of formal and informal handling of CONCRETE MATERIALS whether they are buttons, or later, Base 10 materials. Without such continuing experiences many students have difficulty forming concepts.

Opportunities for such activities arise constantly at home.

Example
I'm washing 6 red shirts and 4 blue shirts. How many shirts am I washing? Estimate the answer.

By seeing the shirts and actually counting them to find the answer a student is able to gradually acquire understanding of the process.

Another important skill which should be constantly encouraged from the earliest in addition practice is that of ESTIMATION. Every opportunity to develop the ability to estimate should be taken.

ADDITION UP TO 99

When the addition number combinations totalling up to 20 have been mastered the next stage is to repeat the process with addition combinations to 99.

It is unwise to progress until the combinations totalling to 20 are understood. Continuing opportunities should be given throughout the primary years to ensure their recall becomes automatic.

1. Always estimate the answer before solving.
2. Always check the function symbol (in this case it is +).
3. Always make sure the columns in the algorithm are straight with all the ones vertically above each other, the tens above each other, etc.

Example:
On Friday lunchtime, Little Red Hen's Chicken Barbecue sold 32 chickens, and on Friday evening, it sold 41 chickens. How many chickens were sold altogether on Friday?

Solution:
'This problem means about 30 chickens add about 40 chickens, so I estimate the answer to be about 70. I'll use longs and shorts to represent the chickens'.

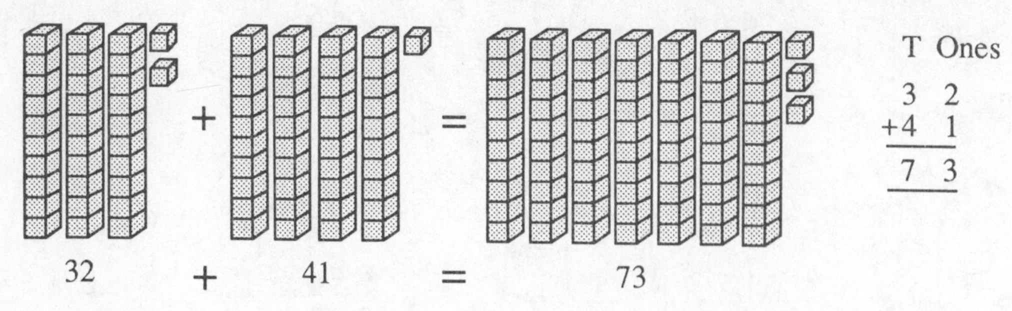

Little Red Hen's Chicken Barbecue sold 73 chickens altogether on Friday.

Example:
Rebecca sold 34 raffle tickets at school and 13 to her family. How many raffle tickets did she sell altogether?

Solution:
'I estimate that's about 35 and 15 which makes about 50.'

Longs and shorts are used to represent the raffle tickets. *(continued over)*

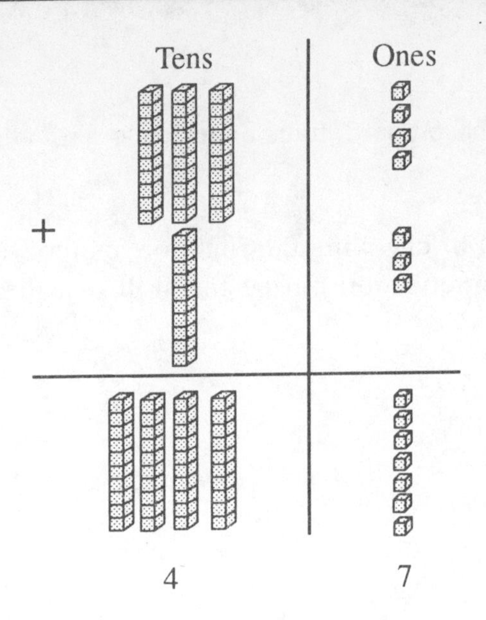

T Ones
3 4
+1 3
4 7

Rebecca sold 47 raffle tickets altogether.

Example:
Robert's team scored 56 tries in practice matches during the season and 35 tries in matches. How many did they score altogether?

Solution:

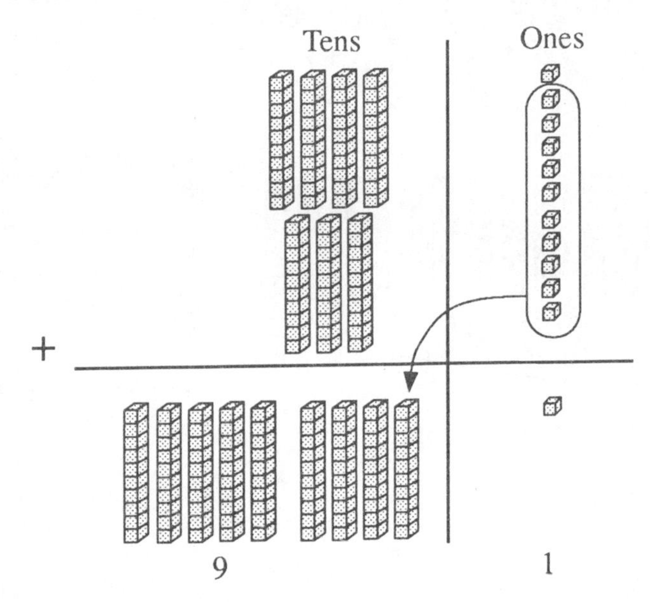

T Ones
1
5 6
+3 5
9 1
11

(i) Trade 10 shorts (ones) for a long (1 ten). One short remains. Transfer the long (ten) into the tens column. Total the tens.

(ii) In the algorithm, the 1 remaining one is written in the ones answer space. The ten is transferred to the top of the tens column. There is now a total of 9 tens which is written in the tens answer space.

Robert's team scored 91 tries.

ADDITION UP TO 999

Using Base 10 materials on a H T U base board gives experience with addition combinations totalling more than 100.

It is very important to get into the habit of checking the function symbol; in this case it is add. It is also important to practise and refine the skill of estimating the answer before actually working it.

Example:
A farmer owns 134 cattle, 212 sheep and 51 chickens. How many animals does he own?

(a) Function symbol?
(b) Estimate

Solution:

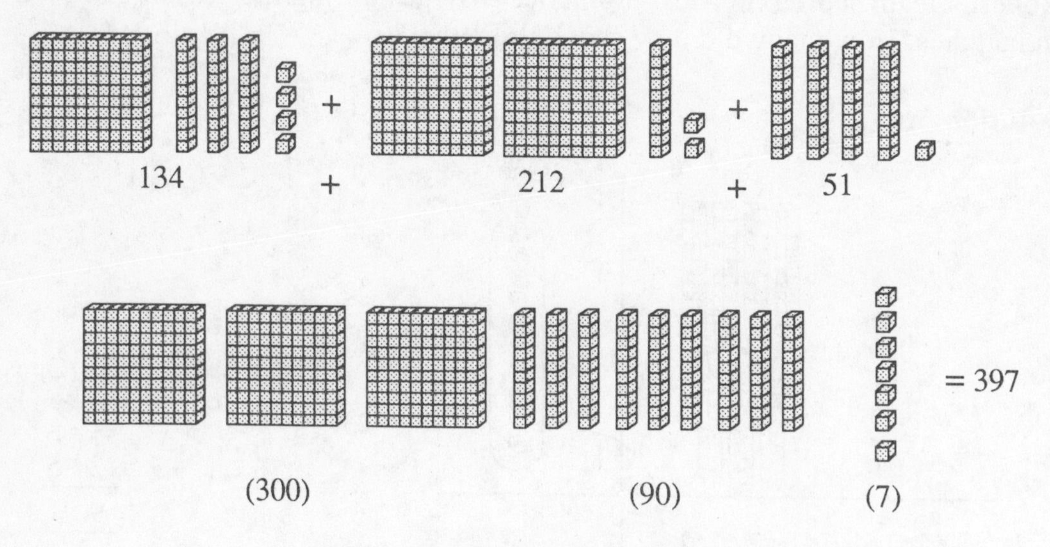

The farmer owns 397 animals.

WRITTEN ALGORITHMS

(a) Check the function symbol.
(b) Estimate the answer.

	H	T	Ones
		1	
		3	5
+	2	8	7
			2

Trading can take place

(a) Total the ones: 5 + 7 = 12
(b) Put this total beneath the answer line in the units column.
(c) The 1 ten belongs in the tens column. Write it at the top of the tens column.
(d) Write the 2 remaining units in the units answer space.

	H	T	Ones
	1	1	
		3	5
+	2	8	7
		2	2
			12

Trading can take place

(a) 1 + 3 + 8 = 12 tens
(b) Write the total beneath the answer line in the tens column.
(c) The traded 1 hundred belongs in the hundreds column and should be written at the top of the hundreds column.
(d) The 2 remaining tens are written in the tens answer space.

	H	T	Ones
	1		
		3	5
+	2	8	7
	3	2	2
	3	12	12

Trading not required

(a) Total the hundreds: 1 + 2 = 3.
(b) No trading is necessary.
(c) Write the 3 hundreds in the hundreds answer space.

Example:
34 children used the skateboard ramp on Friday morning and 87 used it in the afternoon and evening. How many children used the skateboard ramp on Friday?

Solution:

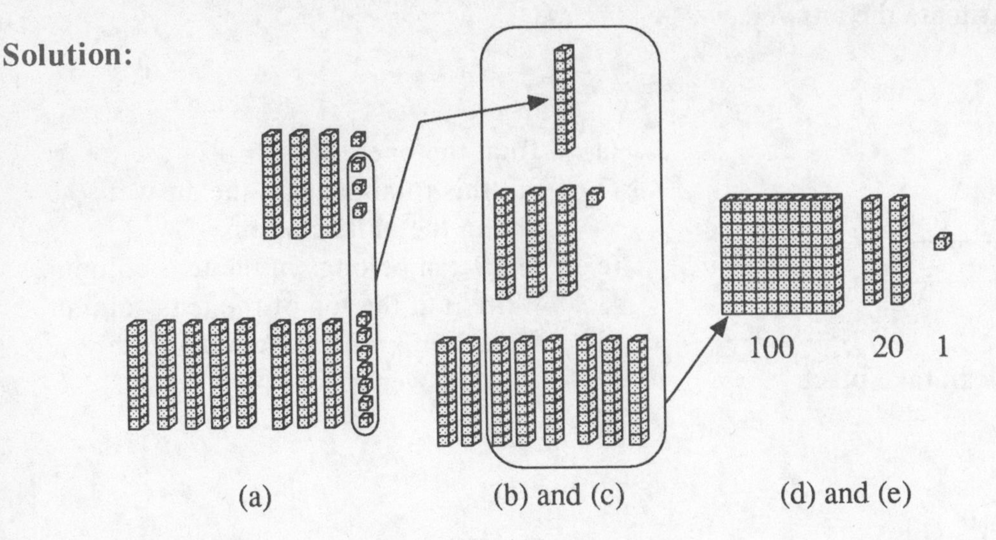

(a) (b) and (c) (d) and (e)

(a) Total the units. Trade 10 of the shorts (ones) for 1 of the longs (tens). 1 one remains.
(b) Place the long in the tens column. Total the tens. 12.
(c) Exchange ten of the longs (tens) for a flat (100). 2 tens remain.
(d) Put the flat in the hundreds column. Total the hundreds. 1 hundred.
(e) The total is 121.
(f) In the algorithm, the ones are totalled. The traded ten is placed at the top of the tens column and the remaining 1 one written in the ones answer space.
(g) The tens are totalled. The traded hundred is written at the top of the hundreds column and the remaining tens are written in the tens answer space. The total for the hundreds column is then written in the hundreds answer space.

H	T	Ones
1	1	
	3	4
+	8	7
1	2	1
	12	11

121 children used the skateboard ramp on Friday.

Example:
The nursery sold 83 plants on Friday, 156 plants on Saturday and only 9 on Sunday because of the storm. How many plants had the nursery sold?

Solution:

H	T	Ones
1	1	
	8	3
1	5	6
+		9
2	4	8
	14	18

NOTE: This kind of problem gives practice in putting the numerals into the correct place columns. All the units must be under units; next to them, all the tens must be under one another, etc. The use of grid paper makes this easier.

The nursery sold 248 plants.

ALGORITHMS TO 9 999 AND BEYOND

Working algorithms involving thousands and tens of thousands follows the same principles as outlined in the previous pages.

Examples:

	Th	H	T	Ones
	1		1	
	1	4	3	5
+	7	7	5	7
	9	1	9	2
		11	9	12

	Th	H	T	Ones
	1	1		
	3	6	6	2
+	4	9	7	5
	8	6	3	7
	8	16	13	7

ALGORITHMS EXPRESSED IN THE VISUAL WITHOUT CONCRETE MATERIALS

In testing situations where concrete materials are not available, students who need the support of the visual can feel very vulnerable. Such students should be encouraged to create their own visuals by drawing simple representations of Base 10 materials.

Example:

(a) Function symbol? +

(b) Estimate.

	H	T	Ones
		1	
	4	3	5
+	1	2	7
	5	6	2
			12

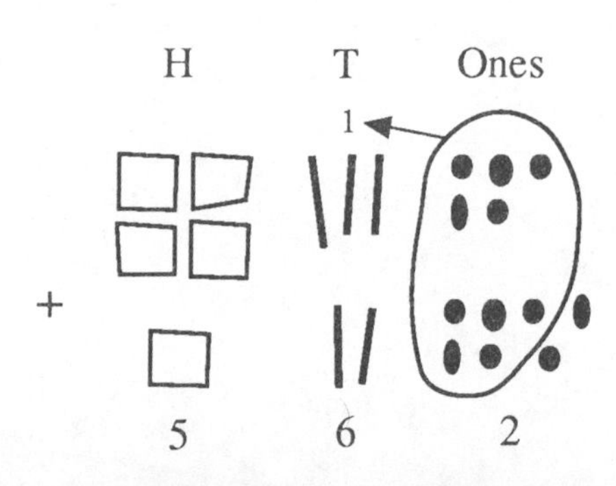

ADDITION ASSESSMENTS

Students should understand the following ideas:

- use concrete materials to represent addition problems, without and with trading, to total 99, estimating the answer before solving
- relate the above activities to numeral and symbol cards
- represent the problem with a written algorithm
- describe the process by which the problem was solved
- invent an addition problem to relate to a given algorithm
- repeat the above assessments with addition problems to 999
- repeat the above assessments with addition problems to 9 999 and beyond

LEVEL 1 — ADDITION

EASIER QUESTIONS

Q1. (a) $\begin{array}{r} 52 \\ +\ 46 \\ \hline \end{array}$ (b) $\begin{array}{r} 341 \\ +\ 38 \\ \hline \end{array}$ (c) $\begin{array}{r} 86 \\ +\ 58 \\ \hline \end{array}$

(d) $\begin{array}{r} 449 \\ +\ 63 \\ \hline \end{array}$ (e) $\begin{array}{r} 645 \\ +\ 332 \\ \hline \end{array}$ (f) $\begin{array}{r} 788 \\ +\ 659 \\ \hline \end{array}$

Q2. Set out, and then solve the following number sentences:

(a) 425 + 239

(b) 376 + 58

(c) 928 + 156

Q3. Andre's class collected 493 aluminium cans for recycling and Kurt's class collected 547 cans. How many cans were collected altogether?

Q4. Riverview Primary School has five Year 6 classes. 6A has 24 students, 6B has 22, 6C has 23, 6D has 21 and 6E has 21. How many Year 6 students does the school have?

Q5. Earlwood Scouts spent 3 days collecting rubbish from their local park. On each of the days they collected 96, 86 and 81 pieces of rubbish. How many pieces did they collect altogether?

Q6. In a multi-storey carpark there were the following number of cars on each of the 4 levels: level one—82; level 2—106; level 3—79 and only 14 on the roof. How many cars altogether in the carpark?

Q7. Drinks sold at the school fete were 121 orange juice, 276 colas and 85 chocolate milks. How many drinks were sold altogether?

AVERAGE QUESTIONS

Q1. (a)
```
  594
  685
+  73
-----

-----
```

(b)
```
  786
   69
+ 647
-----

-----
```

(c)
```
 1 529
   487
+  201
------

------
```

(d)
```
  6 348
  2 157
+   865
-------

-------
```

(e)
```
  4 369
  3 466
+ 5 038
-------

-------
```

(f)
```
 15 768
  3 543
+ 6 372
-------

-------
```

Q2. Set out, and then solve the following number sentences:

(a) 1 273 + 95 + 358

(b) 2 506 + 586 + 3 021

(c) 128 + 3 479 + 11 348

Q3. The populations of 3 towns are 11 295, 6 673 and 17 728. What is their total population?

Q4. McNalley Orchards harvested 15 093 apples, 12 348 oranges and 11 159 peaches. How many pieces of fruit did they harvest?

Q5. The local art competition gave $25 465 for 1st prize, $15 379 for 2nd prize and $11 425 for 3rd prize. What was the total amount of prize money?

Q6. The attendances at three consecutive football matches were 23 912, 26 478 and 35 246. What was the total attendance?

Q7. A salesman sells 4 cars on a Saturday. The cars cost $15 500, $27 900, $19 995 and $7 500. How much does he take altogether?

LEVEL 3 — ADDITION

DIFFICULT QUESTIONS

Q1. Find:

(a) 535 + 93 + 2 215 + 8

(b) 16 + 956 + 6 + 3 478 + 203

(c) 348 + 27 + 5 498 + 612 + 7

Q2.

(a)	(b)	(c)
7 261	36 618	678
23	1 925	5 364
248	49	53
+ 15 197	+ 5 250	+ 78 059
______	______	______

Q3. A city newspaper sold the following number of copies on four consecutive days; 187 479, 204 302, 165 297, 137 386. What is the total number of newspapers sold?

Q4. The area of NSW is 801 428 km^2, Victoria's area is 227 600 km^2, South Australia's area is 984 375 km^2 and the area of Tasmania is 67 800 km^2. What is the total area of the four states?

Q5. Bill and Mary have bought a new house for $230 000. They have also spent $18 950 on furniture, $5 655 on carpets, $11 983 on electrical appliances and $4 380 on painting the house. How much money have they spent in total?

Q6. A lottery paid $2 458 350 for first prize, $769 185 for second prize and $163 290 for third prize. What was the total prize money paid?

Q7. The populations of 4 large European cities are two million, five hundred and twenty thousand, 986 520, 7 856 830 and one million, two hundred thousand. What is the total population?

Q8. Popular Hollywood movies are judged by their ticket sales when first released. If a film takes $5\frac{1}{2}$ million dollars, 3.7 million dollars, $3\frac{1}{4}$ million dollars and 4 million dollars in its first 4 weeks, what is the total for ticket sales during this period?

SUBTRACTION

Subtraction means removing part of a group. The relationship between addition and subtraction should be clearly understood.

IT IS IMPERATIVE TO USE BASE 10 MATERIALS TO AID COMPREHENSION OF TRADING.

During Years 5 and 6 subtracting 2 digit numbers without and with trading and subtracting 3 digits without trading will be reinforced. When these stages have been **thoroughly mastered** progress can be made through subtraction, without and with trading, to 9 999 and beyond.

VOCABULARY

Blocks, difference, equals, exchange, flats, greater, how many left, how many less, how many more, how much change, leaves, left, less than, longs, minus, need to trade, plus some more, plus how many, remain, rename, shorts, smaller, subtract, swap, take away, the difference between, trade, what's left, what's the difference.

CONTENTS Page

SUBTRACTION TO 999 WITHOUT TRADING

By this stage, students should consistently be estimating the answer and should be totally familiar with trading. It is essential that they have experienced the activities suggested in earlier volumes in this series.

Listed below is the sequence through which students should progress.

1. $\begin{array}{r} 526 \\ -\ 215 \\ \hline \end{array}$ both numbers have 3 digits.

2. $\begin{array}{r} 765 \\ -\ \ \ 32 \\ \hline \end{array}$ smaller number has 2 digits.

3. $\begin{array}{r} 429 \\ -\ \ \ \ \ 5 \\ \hline \end{array}$ smaller number has 1 digit

4. $\begin{array}{r} 548 \\ -\ 330 \\ \hline \end{array}$ smaller number has 0 in the units column

5. $\begin{array}{r} 716 \\ -\ 503 \\ \hline \end{array}$ smaller number has 0 in the tens column

6. $\begin{array}{r} 643 \\ -\ 400 \\ \hline \end{array}$ smaller number has 0 in the tens and units columns.

7. $\begin{array}{r} 757 \\ -\ 247 \\ \hline \end{array}$ both numbers have the same digit in the units column.

- These algorithms should be written horizontally as well as vertically, e.g. 7 5 7 – 2 4 7 = ...
- Estimate, then use Base 10 materials to solve problems involving the subtraction of groups of hundreds, e.g. – 200, – 800.
- Link to length, area and time sub-strands.

SUBTRACTION TO 999 WITH TRADING

Algorithms should be written vertically and horizontally. **Continue to use Base 10 materials** .

The following examples demonstrate the different kinds of situation encountered when subtracting with trading. They will not necessarily be experienced in this order.

1. 3 digit minus 3 digit trading tens for units.

$$\begin{array}{cccc} & H & T & U \\ & 3 & 4 & 3 \\ - & 1 & 1 & 7 \\ \hline \end{array} \qquad \begin{array}{cccc} & H & T & U \\ & 3 & {}^{3}\not{4} & {}^{1}3 \\ - & 1 & 1 & 7 \\ \hline & 2 & 2 & 6 \\ \hline \end{array}$$

Trade one ten for 10 units
3 tens are left.
There are now 13 units
13 – 7 = 6
3 tens – 1 ten = 2 tens
3 hundreds – 1 hundred = 2 hundreds

2. 3 digit minus 3 digit trading hundreds for tens

$$\begin{array}{cccc} & H & T & U \\ & 5 & 1 & 7 \\ - & 2 & 5 & 3 \\ \end{array} \qquad \begin{array}{cccc} & H & T & U \\ & {}^{4}\not{5} & {}^{1}1 & 7 \\ - & 2 & 5 & 3 \\ \hline & 2 & 6 & 4 \\ \hline \end{array}$$

7 – 3 = 4
1 hundred is traded for 10 tens
4 hundreds are left
There are now 11 tens
11 tens – 5 tens = 6 tens
4 hundreds – 2 hundreds = 2 hundreds

3. 3 digit minus 3 digit trading tens for units, hundreds for tens

$$\begin{array}{cccc} & H & T & U \\ & 6 & 3 & 4 \\ - & 3 & 7 & 5 \\ \hline \\ \hline \end{array} \qquad \begin{array}{cccc} & H & T & U \\ & 6 & {}^{2}3 & {}^{1}4 \\ - & 3 & 7 & 5 \\ \hline & & & 9 \\ \hline \end{array} \qquad \begin{array}{cccc} & H & T & U \\ & {}^{5}\not{6} & {}^{12}\not{3} & {}^{1}4 \\ - & 3 & 7 & 5 \\ \hline & 2 & 5 & 9 \\ \hline \end{array}$$

1 ten is traded for 10 units
2 tens are left.
There are now 14 units
14 – 5 = 9
1 hundred is traded for 10 tens
There are 5 hundreds left
There are now 12 tens
12 tens – 7 tens = 5 tens
5 hundreds – 3 hundreds = 2 hundreds

4. 3 digit minus 2 digit trading tens for units.

	H	T	U
	7	4	1
−		3	8

	H	T	U
	7	${}^{3}\not{4}$	${}^{1}1$
−		3	8
	7	0	3

Trade one ten for 10 units
3 tens are left.
There are now 11 units
11 − 8 = 3
3 tens − 3 ten = 0 tens
7 hundreds − zero hundred = 7 hundreds

5. 3 digit minus 2 digit trading hundreds for tens

	H	T	U
	6	6	3
−		8	1

	H	T	U
	${}^{5}\not{6}$	${}^{1}6$	3
−		8	1
	5	8	2

3 − 1 = 2
Trade 1 hundred for 10 tens
5 hundreds are left
There are now 16 tens
16 tens − 8 tens = 8 tens
5 hundreds − zero hundreds = 5 hundreds

6. 3 digit minus 2 digit trading tens for units, hundreds for tens

	H	T	U
	4	3	3
−		7	5

	H	T	U
	4	${}^{2}3$	${}^{1}3$
−		7	5
			8

	H	T	U
	${}^{3}\not{4}$	${}^{12}\not{3}$	${}^{1}3$
−		7	5
	3	5	8

Trade 1 ten for 10 units
2 tens are left.
There are now 13 units
13 − 5 = 8
Trade 1 hundred for 10 tens
3 hundreds are left
There are now 12 tens
12 tens − 7 tens = 5 tens
3 hundreds − zero hundreds = 3 hundreds

SUBTRACTION—THE SPECIAL CASE WITH ZEROS

When a subtraction algorithm includes subtraction from a 3 digit number which has zeros in the units and tens columns, it is essential to use Base 10 materials to work through to the answer. Students need to manipulate the materials to be able to visualise the two stage process.

METHOD 1

```
  6 0 0     5 1 9 1
           ~~6~~ ~~0~~ 0
- 3 5 2    -3  5  2
-------    --------
-------     2  4  8
```

(a) I can't take away 2 from the units column.
(b) I can't exchange a ten for ones because there aren't any in the tens column.
(c) I can exchange 1 hundred for 10 tens, leaving five hundreds.
(d) There are now 10 tens. I can exchange 1 of the tens for 10 units. 9 tens are left.
(e) 10 – 2 = 8. Write 8 in the units answer space.
(f) 9 tens – 5 tens = 4 tens. Write 4 in the tens answer space.
(g) 5 hundreds – 3 hundreds = 2 hundreds.
600 – 352 = 248.

METHOD 2

```
             5  9
  6 0 0     ~~6  0~~ 10
- 3 5 2    - 3  5  2
-------    ---------
-------      2  4  8
```

(a) There are not any tens to trade.
(b) If I look at the hundreds and tens columns together, there are 60 tens.
(c) I can exchange 1 ten for ten units. There are 59 tens left. 59 tens = 5 hundreds and 9 tens.
(d) 10 – 2 = 8
(e) 9 tens – 5 tens = 4 tens.
(f) 5 hundreds – 3 hundreds = 2 hundreds.

NOTE: Method 2 is used when students fully understand that 5 hundreds are the same as 50 tens.

SUBTRACTION—NUMBERS WITH 4 OR MORE DIGITS

Use concrete materials if necessary and always estimate before solving.

The processes involved in subtraction involving 4 or more digit numbers are identical with those previously practised.

Students should be able:

- to subtract 1 000 from any given number
- to subtract from numbers with 4 or more digits both without and with trading.
- to use calculators to check answers.

An example follows which involves zeros.

(a)

$$\begin{array}{rcccc} & 9 & 0 & 0 & 1 \\ - & 4 & 6 & 7 & 2 \\ \hline \end{array}$$

(a) 1 need to trade 1 ten for 10 units.

(b)

$$\begin{array}{rcccc} & {}^{8}\not{9} & {}^{9}\not{0} & {}^{9}\not{0} & {}^{1}1 \\ - & 4 & 6 & 7 & 2 \\ \hline & 4 & 3 & 2 & 9 \end{array}$$

(b) (Method 1) 1 can trade 1 thousand for 10 hundreds, leaving 8 thousands. There are now 10 hundreds.
I can trade 1 hundred for 10 tens leaving 9 hundreds.
There are now 10 tens.
I can trade 1 ten for ten units leaving 9 tens.
There are now 11 units. 11 – 2 = 9
9 tens – 7 tens = 2 tens.
9 hundreds - 6 hundreds = 3 hundreds.
8 thousands – 4 thousands = 4 thousands.
9 001 – 4 672 = 4 329

(c)

$$\begin{array}{rcccc} & 8 & 9 & 9 & \\ & \not{9} & \not{0} & \not{0} & {}^{1}1 \\ - & 4 & 6 & 7 & 2 \\ \hline & 4 & 3 & 2 & 9 \end{array}$$

(c) (Method 2) There are 900 tens.
I'll exchange 1 ten for 10 units, leaving 899 tens.
There are now 11 units.
11 – 9 = 2 . . . etc.

SUBTRACTION ASSESSMENT

Students should understand the following ideas:

3 digit numbers to 999

- recognise the need to use subtraction to solve a given problem
- subtract whole hundreds from any given three-digit number
- record word problems involving 2 three-digit numbers using Base 10 materials, estimate answer and solve
- record problems involving 2 three-digit numbers without trading as written algorithms on grid paper, estimate answer, explain estimate, solve
- record problems involving 2 three-digit numbers with trading as written algorithms, horizontally and vertically, on grid paper, estimate answer, explain estimate, solve
- check answers with calculator
- create own real-life subtraction problems
- understand the three aspects of subtraction, (a) 'take away', (b) comparison, (c) 'counting on'

Subtraction facts to 9 999

- recognise the need to use subtraction to solve a given problem
- subtract whole thousands from any given four-digit number
- record word problems involving 2 four-digit numbers using Base 10 materials, estimate answer and solve
- record problems involving 2 four-digit numbers without trading as written algorithms on grid paper, estimate answer, explain estimate, solve
- record problems involving 2 four-digit numbers with trading as written algorithms, estimate answer, explain estimate, solve
- check answers with calculator
- create own real-life subtraction problems

Subtraction involving five or more digits

- recognise the need to use subtraction to solve a given problem
- record problems involving 2 five or more digit numbers without trading as written algorithms, estimate answer, explain estimate, solve
- record problems involving 2 five or more digit numbers with trading as written algorithms, estimate answer, explain estimate, solve
- check answers with calculator
- create own real-life subtraction problems

LEVEL 1 — SUBTRACTION

EASIER QUESTIONS

Q1. (a) $\begin{array}{r} 437 \\ -\underline{326} \end{array}$ (b) $\begin{array}{r} 876 \\ -\underline{143} \end{array}$ (c) $\begin{array}{r} 539 \\ -\underline{325} \end{array}$

Q2. (a) $\begin{array}{r} 6\,788 \\ -\underline{4\,553} \end{array}$ (b) $\begin{array}{r} 8\,747 \\ -\underline{2\,237} \end{array}$ (c) $\begin{array}{r} 5\,179 \\ -\underline{4\,048} \end{array}$

Q3. Bassville has a population of 96 792 and Rockley has a population of 35 420. How many more people live in Bassville than in Rockley?

Q4. Before starting on a holiday the odometer in the Koupparis' family car read 47 258 km. When they returned it read 53 679 km. How far had they travelled?

Q5. (a) $\begin{array}{r} 45 \\ -\underline{28} \end{array}$ (b) $\begin{array}{r} 63 \\ -\underline{37} \end{array}$ (c) $\begin{array}{r} 172 \\ -\underline{46} \end{array}$

Q6. Red Robin Pet Shop had 121 budgies. They sold 56 budgies. How many do they have left?

Q7. Mark has saved $81 in his piggy bank. If he spends $38, how much does he have left?

Q8. 82 of the 675 adults in a country town are blood donors. How many do not give blood?

Q9. A school of 838 students has 485 boys. How many are girls?

Q10. James had 653 stamps in his album. He gave away 29, had 15 stolen, bought 34 more and sold 18. How many stamps does James have now?

LEVEL 2 — SUBTRACTION

AVERAGE QUESTIONS

Q1. (a) $\begin{array}{r} 576 \\ -\ 58 \\ \hline \end{array}$ (b) $\begin{array}{r} 659 \\ -\ 374 \\ \hline \end{array}$ (c) $\begin{array}{r} 924 \\ -\ 125 \\ \hline \end{array}$

Q2. (a) $\begin{array}{r} 6\ 195 \\ -\ 4\ 834 \\ \hline \end{array}$ (b) $\begin{array}{r} 8\ 352 \\ -\ 5\ 634 \\ \hline \end{array}$ (c) $\begin{array}{r} 8\ 500 \\ -\ 5\ 746 \\ \hline \end{array}$

Q3. (a) $\begin{array}{r} 18\ 135 \\ -\ 565 \\ \hline \end{array}$ (b) $\begin{array}{r} 57\ 004 \\ -\ 6\ 482 \\ \hline \end{array}$ (c) $\begin{array}{r} 130\ 567 \\ -\ 18\ 496 \\ \hline \end{array}$

Q4. In Sydney 15 385 homes were completed in 1993. In 1994 the number had increased to 17 128. How many more homes were completed in 1994?

Q5. In five years the population of Garyton increased from 49 623 to 61 412. By how many has the population increased?

Q6. A new Ford costs $21 450. A new Daihatsu costs $5 980 less than a Ford. How much does the Daihatsu cost?

Q7. (a) 6 423 – ☐ = 2 508

(b) ☐ – 1 578 = 1 834

Q8. A Jumbo Jet has the space to carry 436 passengers. If it has 69 empty seats how many are on board?

Q9. A 5 000 L tank is filled with water but overnight 653 litres of water escapes through a broken joint. How much water is left in the morning?

LEVEL 3 — SUBTRACTION **DIFFICULT QUESTIONS**

Q1. (a) 804 − 628 (b) 700 − 352 (c) 715 − 389

Q2. (a) 6 403 − 1 858 (b) 9 021 − 979 (c) 18 138 − 9 989

Q3. (a) 105 643 − 97 565 (b) 2 341 021 − 548 635 (c) 43 200 100 − 2 598 647

Q4. Before leaving on her Queensland holiday Borgy read 135 710 kilometres on her car's odometer. When she returned the odometer read 139 107 kilometres. How far had Borgy travelled?

Q5. In the library, the computer reported that of the 125 319 books in the library 38 579 were on loan. How many books were still on the shelves?

Q6. Queensland has an area of 1 272 200 square kilometres and South Australia has an area of 984 375 square kilometres. How much larger in area is Queensland?

Q7. What number is 49 998 less than 100 000?

Q8. Mars is 227 940 000 km from the sun while Earth is only 149 600 000 km from the sun. How much further from the sun is Mars than Earth?

Q9. Beach Airlines expected a profit of $32 million but fell short of this figure by $8 729 000. Mountain Airtours expected a profit of $25 million but fell short by $2 576 000. Which airline made the most profit and by how much?

MULTIPLICATION

Multiplication means the process of finding a number that is the result (the product) of adding a given number of equal groups.

Before progressing to the stages outlined in this section it is imperative that all the stages which have been listed in the previous two volumes of this series have been thoroughly covered. During Years 5 and 6 formal multiplication is introduced and this needs a strong foundation. This process is explored through to multiplication of 2 digits by 2 digits.

VOCABULARY

Altogether, approximately, check, choices, estimate, explain, guess, how many, hundreds, multiple, multiplied by, multiply, number patterns, ones, possibilities, product, tens, ten thousands, thousands, times, trade, twice as many, units.

The product is produced when two numbers are multiplied together.

e.g. $5 \times 4 = 20$

The product of 5 and 4 is 20.

CONTENTS

RELATING THE CONCRETE TO THE WRITTEN ALGORITHM—INFORMALLY

Example:
The teacher received 4 boxes of chocolates and there were 12 chocolates in each box. How many chocolates did he receive? (Estimate before solving.)

Solution:

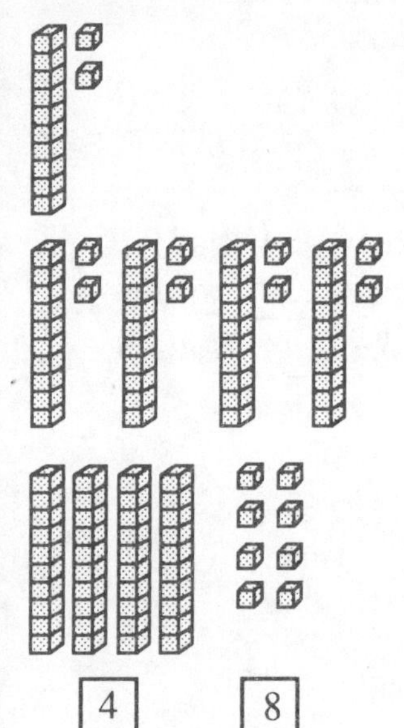

'One long and two shorts (1 ten and 2 units) represent the chocolates in each box'.

'There are 4 boxes'.

'There are 8 units so I don't need to trade. There are 4 tens which make 40. Altogether there are 48, so there must be 48 chocolates'.

'Using the numeral and symbol cards I'd put this':

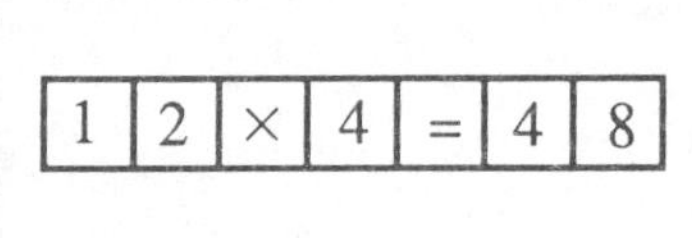

T	U
1	2
×	4
4	8

Example:
The children of Kimber Primary School are travelling by bus to camp. 34 children travel on each of 4 buses. How many children travel to camp? (Estimate before solving.)

Solution:

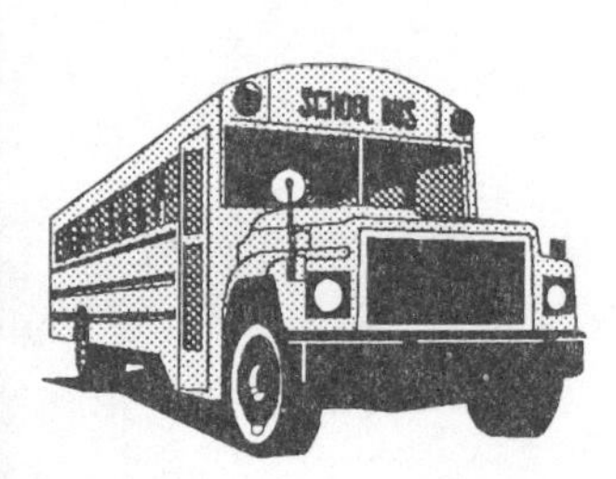

'4×4 units = 16 units. I can trade 10 of them for 1 ten, leaving 6 units. 4×3 tens = 12 tens. Add the 1 ten I made. Now there are 13 tens. I can trade 10 tens for 1 hundred, leaving 3 tens'.

	3	4
	×	4
1	3	6

One hundred and thirty-six children travel to camp.

NOTE: The same principle applies to 1 digit times 3 digits.

THE FORMAL EXTENDED ALGORITHM

Example:
Each carton of bottles of orange juice contains 48 bottles. The store had three cartons delivered. How many bottles of orange juice were delivered? (Estimate before solving.)

Solution:

This problem means there are three groups of eight bottles and three groups of 40 bottles.

$$\begin{array}{r} 40 \\ \times\ 3 \\ \hline 120 \end{array} \qquad \begin{array}{r} 8 \\ \times\ 3 \\ \hline 24 \end{array}$$

3 groups of 8 bottles make 24 bottles
3 groups of 40 bottles make 120 bottles
3 groups of 48 bottles make 144 bottles

Using numeral and symbol cards:

$$\begin{array}{r} 48 \\ \times\ 3 \\ \hline 24 \\ 120 \\ \hline 144 \end{array}$$

144 bottles of orange juice were delivered to the store.

Example:
The egg producer had 3 boxes each containing 144 eggs to deliver to the market. How many eggs was he delivering? (Estimate.)

$$\begin{array}{r} 144 \\ \times\ 3 \\ \hline 12 \\ 120 \\ 300 \\ \hline 432 \end{array}$$

Solution:

The egg producer was delivering 432 eggs to the market.

THE CONTRACTED ALGORITHM

(a) Use Base 10 materials.
(b) Write the extended form of the algorithm.
(c) Write the contracted form of the algorithm.

Example:
The cinema was fully booked for three nights at the start of the season for the block-buster new movie, with 124 people watching each night. How many people saw the movie during these three screenings? (Estimate the answer.)

Solution:

$$\begin{array}{rrr} 1 & 2 & 4 \\ & \times & 3 \\ \hline & 1 & 2 \\ & 6 & 0 \\ 3 & 0 & 0 \\ \hline 3 & 7 & 2 \\ \hline \end{array} \qquad\qquad \begin{array}{rrr} 1 & 2 & 4 \\ \times & {}_{1} & 3 \\ \hline 3 & 7 & 2 \\ \hline \end{array}$$

Example:
285 people visited the new light show in the Imperial Cave at Jenolan on each of the first five days. How many people altogether saw the light show during these days? (Estimate.)

$$\begin{array}{rrrr} & 2 & 8 & 5 \\ & & \times & 5 \\ \hline & & 2 & 5 \\ & 4 & 0 & 0 \\ 1 & 0 & 0 & 0 \\ \hline 1 & 4 & 2 & 5 \\ \hline \end{array} \qquad\qquad \begin{array}{rrrr} & 2 & 8 & 5 \\ \times & {}_{4} & {}_{2} & 5 \\ \hline 1 & 4 & 2 & 5 \\ \hline \end{array}$$

1 425 people saw the light show during the first five days.

PARTNERING

Clothes combinations and canteen choices are favourite topics for partnering problems. 'Tree' diagrams are useful in solving this type of problem.

Michelle has 3 different coloured blouses—red, blue and yellow and two different coloured skirts—white and green. How many different outfits can she wear? (Estimate before solving.)

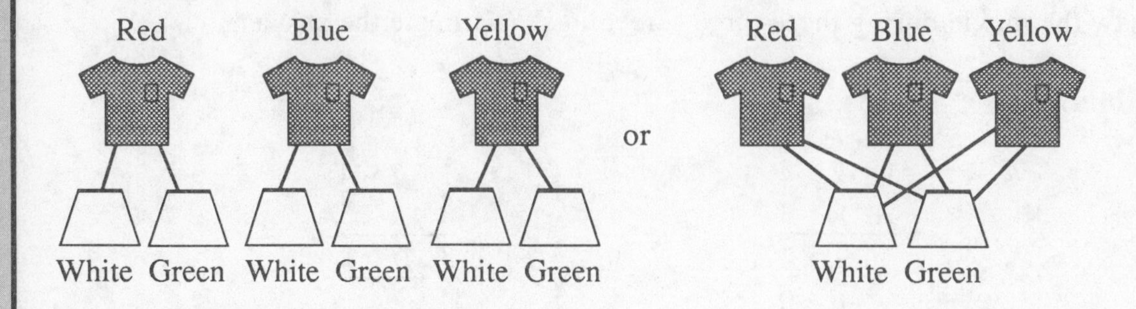

There are 6 possible combinations.

Michelle also has grey shoes and black shoes. How many different combinations now? (Estimate before solving.)

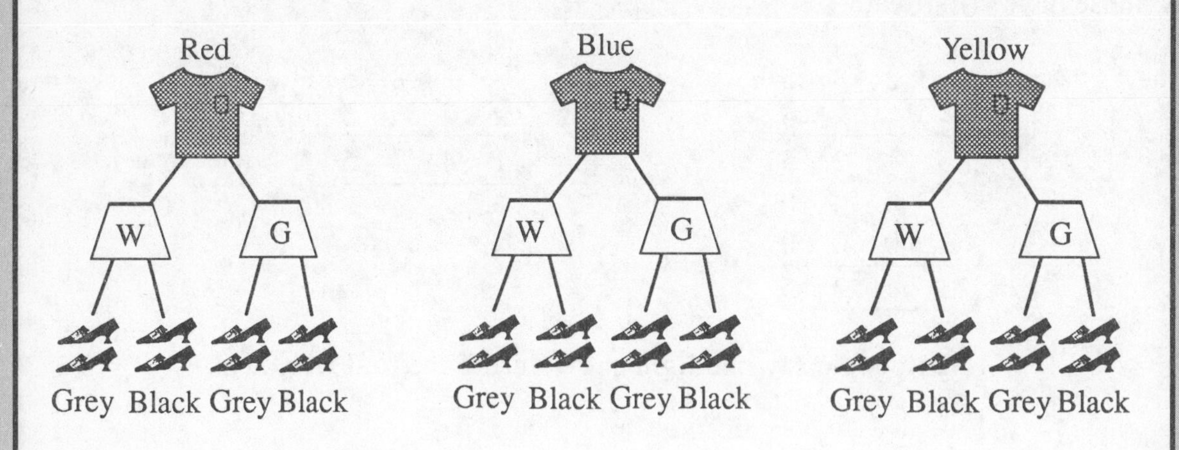

Now there are 12 different outfits.

Using many similar examples students should come to see for themselves that this type of problem can be solved using multiplication.

$3 \times 2 = 6$ outfits. $3 \times 2 \times 2 = 12$ outfits.

MULTIPLYING BY 2 DIGITS

Students will need plenty of experience using Base 10 materials to extend number facts that they already know.

They should be encouraged to look for patterns.

For example:

$2 \times 6 = 12$
$2 \times 60 = 120$
$2 \times 600 = 1\ 200$

$20 \times 6 = 120$
$20 \times 60 = 1\ 200$
$20 \times 600 = 12\ 000$

$10 \times 30 = 300$
$20 \times 30 = 600$

$10 \times 400 = 4\ 000$
$20 \times 400 = 8\ 000$

$60 \times 30 = 1\ 800$

$70 \times 400 = 28\ 000$

Example:
Using Base 10 materials solve 17×13. (Estimate the answer.)

Solution:

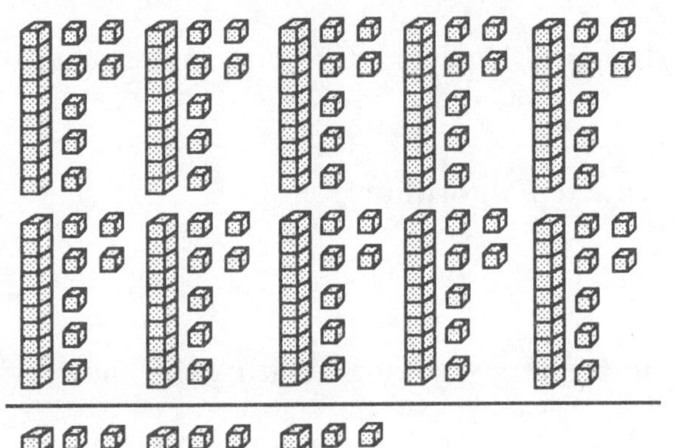

This means 10 groups of 17 = 170

This means 3 groups of 17 = 51

∴ 13 groups of 17 = 221

Record with numeral and symbol cards and, later, record by writing.

	1	7
×	1	3
1	7	0
	5	1
2	2	1

or preferably

	1	7
×	1	3
	5	1
1	7	0
2	2	1

then later

$$\begin{array}{r} 17 \\ \times\ 13 \\ \hline 51 \\ 170 \\ \hline 221 \\ \hline \end{array}$$

MULTIPLICATION ASSESSMENT

Students should understand the following ideas:

Concrete to algorithm—informal

- having estimated the answer, use drawings or Base 10 materials and place value charts to solve multiplication problems informally—1 digit × 2 digit and 1 digit × 3 digit.
- record the above problems with numeral and symbol cards

Concrete to extended algorithm

- demonstrate understanding of multiplication by modelling a problem with concrete materials and recording the process with numeral and symbol cards
- solve multiplication problems using extended algorithms

Contracted multiplication algorithm

- model multiplication problems with concrete materials and record the process with numeral and symbol cards
- estimate then solve these multiplication problems and write the answer using extended algorithms
- record these problems using the contracted algorithm

Partnering

- use tree diagrams to solve partnering problems after estimating the answer
- relate partnering problems to multiplication

Two-digits × two-digits and beyond

- make a reasonable estimate then solve two-digits × two-digits and beyond multiplication problems using the extended algorithm
- use calculators for checking answers and for problems involving larger numbers

LEVEL 1 MULTIPLICATION

EASIER QUESTIONS

Q1. What is the product of 6 and 5?

Q2. (a) $\begin{array}{r} 12 \\ \times\ 5 \\ \hline \\ \hline \end{array}$ (b) $\begin{array}{r} 27 \\ \times\ 6 \\ \hline \\ \hline \end{array}$ (c) $\begin{array}{r} 233 \\ \times\ 4 \\ \hline \\ \hline \end{array}$

Q3. (a) $\begin{array}{r} 73 \\ \times 14 \\ \hline \\ \hline \end{array}$ (b) $\begin{array}{r} 24 \\ \times 21 \\ \hline \\ \hline \end{array}$ (c) $\begin{array}{r} 43 \\ \times 25 \\ \hline \\ \hline \end{array}$

Q4. Daniel has 8 packets of lollies. If each packet contains 38 lollies, how many does Daniel have altogether?

Q5. The local 'Plant Power' nursery sells an average of 87 plants each day. How many plants would they sell in 14 days?

Q6. A plane makes 30 flights each week, each flight carrying 48 passengers. How many passengers are carried each week?

Q7. A carton contains 12 eggs. How many eggs in 25 cartons?

Q8. At the school canteen they sell rolls or sandwiches with either salad, cheese or ham in them. How many different combinations of rolls or sandwiches can be made?

Q9. At a drinks bar, orange, lemon or cola are sold in large, medium or small glasses. How many different drinks are sold?

Q10. Shirts are sold with long or short sleeves in the following colours: white, blue, grey or green. How many different shirts are sold?

LEVEL 2 MULTIPLICATION AVERAGE QUESTIONS

Q1. (a) $\begin{array}{r} 16 \\ \times 14 \\ \hline \end{array}$ (b) $\begin{array}{r} 37 \\ \times 23 \\ \hline \end{array}$ (c) $\begin{array}{r} 48 \\ \times 27 \\ \hline \end{array}$

Q2. What is the product of 9 and 13?

Q3. (a) $\begin{array}{r} 68 \\ \times 32 \\ \hline \end{array}$ (b) $\begin{array}{r} 76 \\ \times 45 \\ \hline \end{array}$ (c) $\begin{array}{r} 116 \\ \times 15 \\ \hline \end{array}$

Q4. The baker baked 275 loaves of bread each day for a fortnight. How many loaves were baked?

Q5. Melina travels a total of 38 km to and from work every weekday. In 35 weekdays how many kilometres does she travel?

Q6. There are 48 oranges in a box. How many oranges in 36 boxes?

Q7. Tina can travel to either Brisbane, Melbourne or Alice Springs for her holiday. She can travel by either bus, train or car. How many combinations of holiday can she choose between?

Q8. Mr Brewster bought 49 metres of carpet at $128 per metre. How much did he pay for the carpet?

Q9. The baker makes different loaves using 4 different types of flour. The loaves come in 4 different shapes. How many different types of loaf are available?

Q10. Wet suits are made differently for men and women, in three different thicknesses of material and 3 different lengths. How many suits are available?

LEVEL 3 MULTIPLICATION DIFFICULT QUESTIONS

Q1. What is the product of:

(a) 30 and 10? (b) 500 and 20? (c) 80 and 700?

Q2. (a) $\begin{array}{r} 245 \\ \times 28 \\ \hline \\ \hline \end{array}$ (b) $\begin{array}{r} 632 \\ \times 47 \\ \hline \\ \hline \end{array}$ (c) $\begin{array}{r} 896 \\ \times 78 \\ \hline \\ \hline \end{array}$

Q3. Miguel delivered 23 boxes of apple juice, each box containing 25 bottles, and 25 boxes of orange juice, each box containing 28 bottles. How many bottles of juice did Miquel deliver altogether?

Q4. On their outback holiday, the Goard family could travel by camel, horse or 4-wheel drive; stay in tents, cabins or motels; and either cook their own food or have the food prepared by a caterer. How many different combinations of holiday were available to the Goard family?

Q5. At summer camp, the kitchen served 78 children. Each child received three meals every day.

(a) How many meals were served by the kitchen each day?
(b) How many meals were served over a fortnight?

Q6. Martin gets paid $425 per week. How much does he get each year (i.e. 52 weeks).

Q7. How far did McBean's coach travel in March if it travelled 650 km each day?

Q8. Ford compact cars are painted in 9 different colours. They are made with petrol or diesel engines, saloons or coupes, with or without air conditioning. How many different models are available.

DIVISION

Division means sharing objects into equal groups.

Having learned to write number sentences incorporating the division symbol and memorised the basic division facts up to 100, a student progresses through dividing a 2 digit number by a 1 digit number or 10, without or with trading, to dividing by a 2 or more digit divisor using a calculator.

VOCABULARY

divide, divided by, dividend, division, divisor, equals, group, groups of, how many, is equal to, number facts, quotient, remainder, remaining, share(s), tables.

> The quotient is the answer to a division problem.
> e.g. $8 \div 2 = 4$. The quotient of 8 and 2 is 4.

CONTENTS

Page

DIVISION OF 2 DIGIT NUMBERS BY SINGLE DIGITS OR 10—WITHOUT AND WITH TRADING

$8 \div 2$ and $2\overline{)8}$ mean: Eight divided into 2 groups or 8 divided by 2. The total number of objects is 8. Share them into two groups.

THE STAGES

$45 \div 5 = 9.$ $\quad \begin{array}{r} 09 \\ 5\overline{)45} \end{array}$

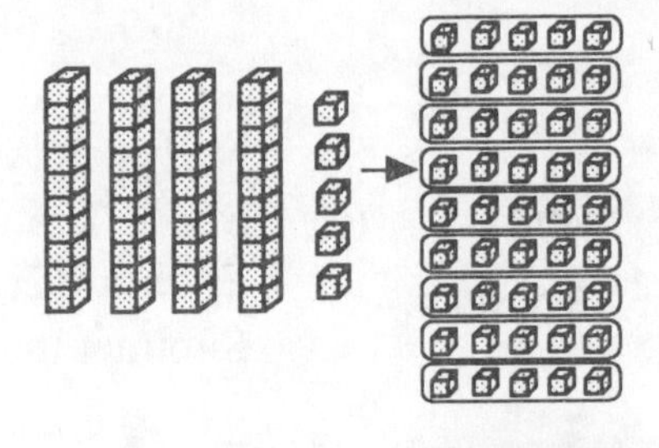

Single digit answers, without a remainder,

$47 \div 5 = 9\ r2.$ $\quad \begin{array}{r} 09\ r2 \\ 5\overline{)47} \end{array}$

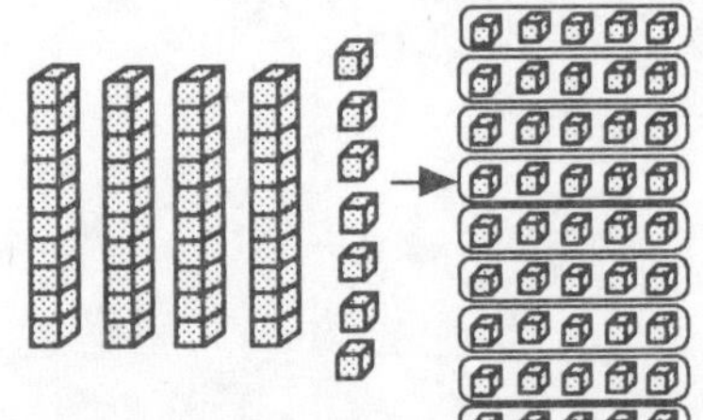

and with a remainder.

$54 \div 3 = 18.$ $\quad \begin{array}{r} 18 \\ 3\overline{)54} \end{array}$

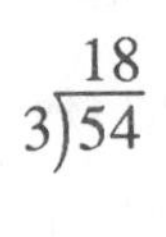

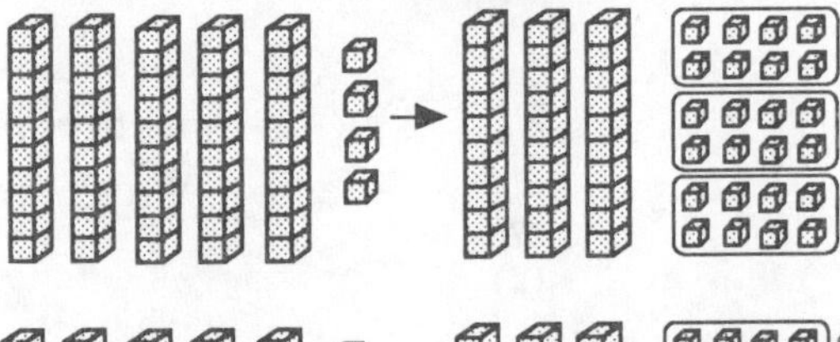

Double digit answer, without a remainder,

$56 \div 3 = 18\ r2.$ $\quad \begin{array}{r} 18\ r2 \\ 3\overline{)56} \end{array}$

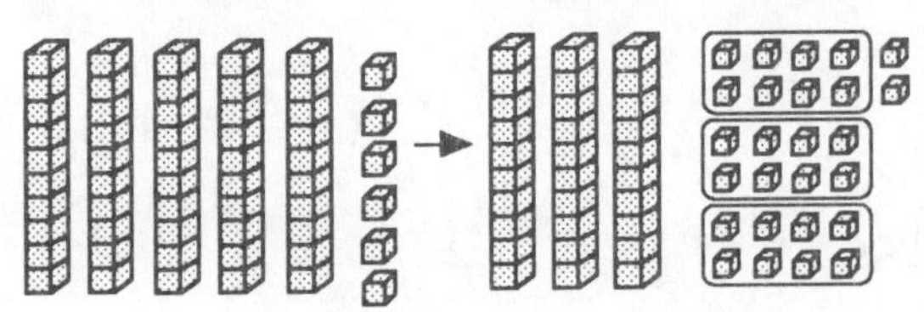

and with a remainder.

Practise both single and double digit answer algorithms with increasingly large remainders.

For example:

$80 \div 10 = 8$ $\quad \begin{array}{r} 08 \\ 10\overline{)80} \end{array}$ Dividing by 10, without

$87 \div 10 = 8\ r7.$ $\quad \begin{array}{r} 08\ r7 \\ 10\overline{)87} \end{array}$ and with remainders.

ACTIVITY:

Find the missing digits is an excellent way to assess understanding of the division process.

e.g. $\begin{array}{r} 1\ 3\ r\ 7 \\ 7\overline{)\square\square} \end{array}$

RELATING BASE 10 MATERIALS TO THE WRITTEN ALGORITHM

Example:

Students in Class 5G at McCarthy Primary School collected $75 during their Charities Week. Miss Ward, the teacher, wanted to share this money equally between 5 charities. She asked Skye and Amy to work out how much each charity should receive.

Solution:

$75 \div 5 = \ldots$ or $5\overline{)75}$

(a)

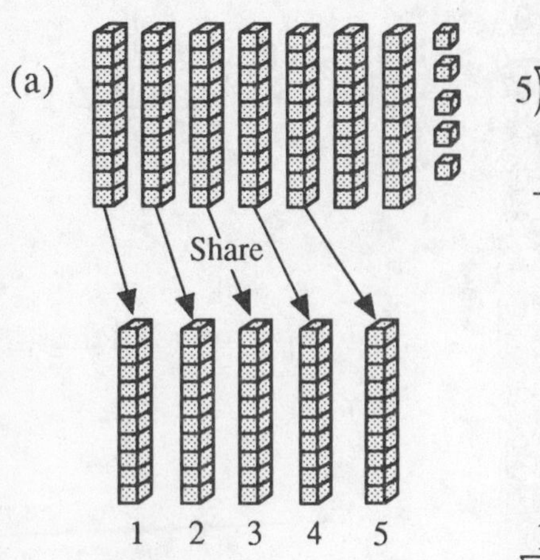

$$\begin{array}{r} 1 \\ 5\overline{)75} \\ 5 \text{ tens} \\ \hline \end{array}$$

(a) Share 7 tens between 5 charities.
Each will receive 1 ten,
Subtract these 5 tens from the 7 tens.

(b)

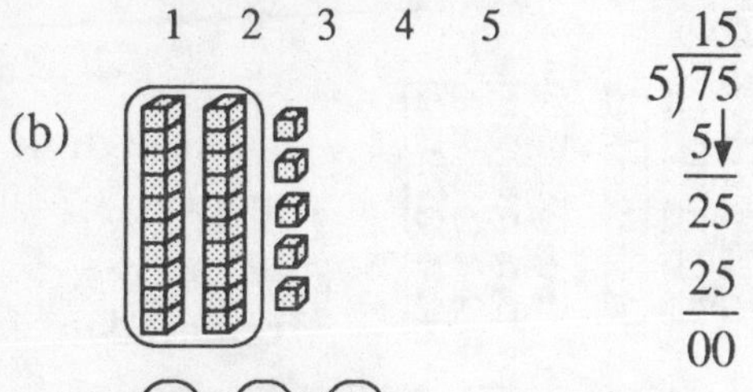

$$\begin{array}{r} 15 \\ 5\overline{)75} \\ 5\downarrow \\ \hline 25 \\ 25 \\ \hline 00 \end{array}$$

(b) There will be 2 tens left to trade for twenty units.
Altogether there will be 25 units.

(c)

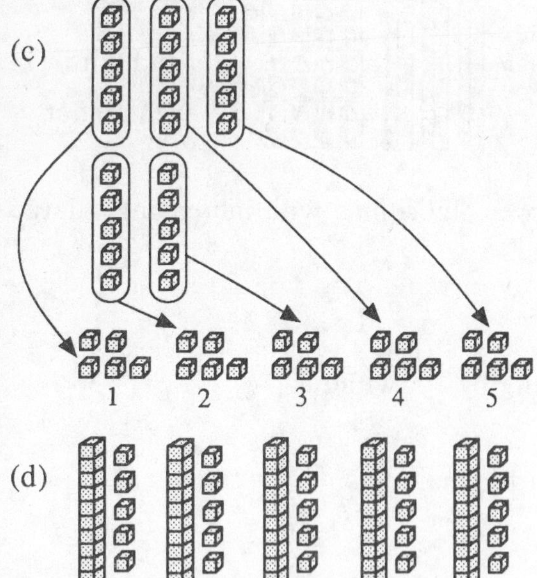

(c) 25 units shared between 5 gives 5 each and no remainder.

(d)

1 2 3 4 5

(d) Each charity will receive $15.

NOTE: It is important to use this visual process with Base 10 materials.

Do not use the terms 'goes into' or 'carry' as they are meaningless.

DIVISION OF NUMBERS WITH 3 OR MORE DIGITS BY SINGLE DIGIT NUMBERS OR 10, WITHOUT AND WITH TRADING

Concrete materials should be used to clarify the written algorithm.

There are many different kinds of division which involve slightly different processes. They are listed below.

1. $\begin{array}{r} 213 \\ 3\overline{)639} \end{array}$ All digits multiples of the dividing number (divisor).

2. $\begin{array}{r} 124 \\ 3\overline{)37^{1}2} \end{array}$ Trading has to take place between, e.g. hundreds and tens and/or tens and units, without a remainder.

3. $\begin{array}{r} 137\,\text{r}1 \\ 4\overline{)5^{1}4^{2}9} \end{array}$ Trading has to take place and there is a remainder.

4. $\begin{array}{r} 096 \\ 6\overline{)57^{3}6} \end{array}$ The hundreds digit in the three digit number to be divided (dividend) is less than the divisor.

5. $\begin{array}{r} 243\,\text{r}1 \\ 3\overline{)7^{1}3^{1}0} \end{array}$ There are zeros in the dividend, without and with remainders.

6. $\begin{array}{r} 048 \\ 10\overline{)4^{8}8^{8}0} \end{array}$ Division by 10 follows the same process. Begin with numbers without remainders.

7. $\begin{array}{r} 102 \\ 7\overline{)714} \end{array}$ The three digit answer has a zero in the tens column.

For numbers greater than 1 000, remember to leave a space between the thousands and hundreds digits.

The division process with larger numbers is identical with that demonstrated above.

OTHER METHODS OF DIVISION

In this section on division, we shall look at the more simple problems where the divisor is a smaller number, less than 10.

Example (i): A small lottery win of $936 has to be shared between 4 friends. How much will each person get?

Solution: The above question is a division problem of $936 ÷ 4.

```
    234
4 )936
   8
   13
   12
    16
    16
     0
```

STEPS:

(i) $9 \div 4 = 2$ Write in the answer 2
(ii) $2 \times 4 = 8$
(iii) $9 - 8 = 1$
(iv) Bring down the 3
(v) $13 \div 4 = 3$ Write in the answer 3
(vi) $3 \times 4 = 12$
(vii) $13 - 12 = 1$
(viii) Bring down the 6
(ix) $16 \div 4 = 4$ Write in the answer 4
(x) $4 \times 4 = 16$
(xi) $16 - 16 = 0$
(xii) There is no remainder

Each person will get exactly $234.

Example (ii):

```
   272 r 1
3)817
  6
  21
  21
   07
    6
    1
```

STEPS:

(i) $8 \div 3 = 2$ Write in the answer 2
(ii) $2 \times 3 = 6$
(iii) $8 - 6 = 2$
(iv) Bring down the 1
(v) $21 \div 3 = 7$ Write in the answer 7
(vi) $7 \times 3 = 21$
(vii) $21 - 21 = 0$
(viii) Bring down the 7
(ix) $7 \div 3 = 2$ Write in the answer 2
(x) $2 \times 3 = 6$
(xi) $7 - 6 = 1$
(xii) Can't do $1 \div 3$
(xiii) Record the remainder of 1

Divisor is 3
Dividend is 817
Quotient is 272r1

DIVISION BY TWO DIGIT NUMBERS

In Primary School, there are 2 methods which are used for long division by 2 digit numbers—CONTRACTED FORM which was shown on the previous page, and PREFERRED MULTIPLES. Both methods are shown in the example below, but it should be noted that the 'contracted form' is used more widely, particularly when students reach high school.

CONTRACTED FORM:

```
     213  r 14
 24)5126
    48
     32
     24
      86
      72
      14
```

STEPS:

(i) 5 ÷ 24 can't be done
(ii) 51 ÷ 24 = 2
(iii) 2 x 24 = 48
(iv) 51 – 48 = 3
(v) Bring down the 2
(vi) 32 ÷ 24 = 1
(vii) 1 x 24 = 24
(viii) 32 – 24 = 8
(ix) Bring down the 6
(x) 86 ÷ 24 = 3
(xi) 3 x 24 = 72
(xii) 86 – 72 = 14
(xiii) Can't do 14 ÷ 24
(xiv) Record the remainder

Answer = 213 remainder 14.

PREFERRED MULTIPLES:

24)5126	
–2400	100
2726	
2400	100
326	
–240	10
86	
–72	3
14	213 r 14

Steps: One obtains easy multiples of 24 (e.g. 2400 and 240) and keeps on subtracting until a remainder is left. The multiples are then added up in the right hand column as shown, plus a possible remainder.

Answer = 213 remainder 14.

DIVISION ASSESSMENT

Students should understand the following ideas:

Division symbol
- say, read and write a division number sentence containing the division symbol
- understand what each component in a sharing number sentence means
- understand what each component in a grouping number sentence means
- represent problems as number sentences using numeral and symbol cards

Division facts to 100
- model a division number sentence and explain the link with multiplication
- use numeral and symbol cards to record a division number sentence and the corresponding multiplication number sentence

Division symbol
- recognise when division is needed to solve a problem
- understand the meaning of both division symbols
- solve problems involving a two-digit number divided by a 1-digit number without and with trading
- solve problems involving a two-digit number divided by 10 without and with trading

Division of numbers with 3 or more digits
- estimate then solve problems involving division of three-digit numbers by a single-digit number, without and with trading
- estimate the answer then divide three-digit numbers by 10, without and with trading
- use a calculator to check to solve division problems involving division by two digit numbers

LEVEL 1 DIVISION

EASIER QUESTIONS

Q1. (a) $4\overline{)36}$ (b) $5\overline{)65}$ (c) $6\overline{)79}$

(d) $3\overline{)144}$ (e) $7\overline{)148}$ (f) $4\overline{)256}$

Q2. (a) Which number when divided by 3 gives an answer of 9?

(b) 48 divided by which number gives an answer of 4?

Q3. Mr. Cooper's school collected $224 during the year. If the money is to be shared equally between 7 charities, how much will each charity receive?

Q4. Nicola has 232 bottles and 8 boxes. If she packs an equal number of bottles into each box, how many bottles are in each box?

Q5. Tiffany is making fruitbaskets for the school fete. She has 196 pieces of fruit and 9 baskets.

(a) How many pieces of fruit in each basket, if each basket is to have the same number?

(b) How many pieces of fruit are left over?

Q6. (a) $3\overline{)3972}$ (b) $2\overline{)4278}$ (c) $4\overline{)4890}$

Q7. A pack of 52 cards is dealt to 4 players. How many cards does each player receive?

Q8. 900 g of meat is fed equally to 4 dogs. How much does each receive?

Q9. 5 full buses transport 210 pupils, how many are on each bus?

LEVEL 2 DIVISION

AVERAGE QUESTIONS

Q1. (a) $46 \div 2 = \square$ (b) $68 \div 4 = \square$ (c) $51 \div 3 = \square$

Q2. (a) $573 \div 4 = \square$ (b) $675 \div 6 = \square$ (c) $432 \div 8 = \square$

Q3. (a) $6\overline{)9253}$ (b) $9\overline{)3563}$ (c) $7\overline{)5896}$

Q4. Mangoes are packed in layers, each layer containing 8 mangoes. How many layers are needed to pack 768 mangoes?

Q5. An orchard contains 9 rows of apple trees. If there are 1 467 trees in the orchard, how many trees are in each row?

Q6. Mrs Davidson has $10 507 to share equally between her 7 grandchildren. How much does each child receive?

Q7. (a) $55 \div 10$ (b) $100 \div 10$ (c) $125 \div 10$

Q8. 296 red lollies and 343 blue lollies have to be shared between 9 bags.

(a) How many red lollies and blue lollies will each bag contain?

(b) How many lollies of each colour remain?

Q9. (a) $\begin{array}{r} 2\ 3 \\ 3\overline{)\square\square} \end{array}$ (b) $\begin{array}{r} 1\ 9 \\ 4\overline{)\square\square} \end{array}$ (c) $\begin{array}{r} 1\ 6\ 0 \\ 5\overline{)\square\square\square} \end{array}$

Q10. In a seven hour day a bricklayer lays 805 bricks. How many does he lay in each hour?

Q11. 8 apples and 12 oranges cost $3.40. If the apples cost 20c each, how much is 1 orange?

LEVEL 3 DIVISION

DIFFICULT QUESTIONS

Q1. (a) $78 \div 10$ (b) $900 \div 10$ (c) $753 \div 10$

(d) $300 \div 7$ (e) $500 \div 6$ (f) $1\,000 \div 8$

Q2. (a) $8\overline{)\square\square}$ = 1 0 r 5 (b) $4\overline{)\square\square}$ = 1 6 r 3 (c) $3\overline{)\square\square\square}$ = 0 8 6 r 1

Q3. (a) $13\overline{)1\,573}$ (b) $17\overline{)52\,736}$ (c) $32\overline{)15\,382}$

Q4. Tennis balls are packed into boxes, each box containing 24 balls. How many boxes are needed for 552 balls?

Q5. 1 694 head of cattle have to be separated into 14 different paddocks. How many cattle should be herded into each paddock?

Q6. $35 343 raised at a Telethon is to be given to 21 charities. If the amount is shared equally, how much will each charity receive?

Q7. The 490 children in Waltham Primary School were divided into 35 groups for the centenary celebration beach picnic. How many children were in each group?

Q8. 93 lollies were shared between 17 girls and 21 boys. Each boy received 2 lollies. How many did each girl receive?

Q9. 14 packets of biscuits, each containing 12 biscuits, were opened and placed on 9 plates. If one plate contained 6 more biscuits than the other plates, how many biscuits were on this plate?

ORDER OF OPERATIONS

Mathematicians around the world have agreed on a definite order of doing brackets and the 4 operations (+ − × ÷), otherwise confusion would occur.

For example, which is the correct answer?

$$6 + 2 \times 4 = 14 \quad \text{OR} \quad 6 + 2 \times 4 = 32$$

THE AGREED ORDER OF OPERATIONS

> Firstly, work out the answer to the brackets.
>
> Secondly, work out any division and multiplication as they occur from left to right.
>
> Thirdly, work out any addition and subtraction as they occur from left to right.

This is often remembered by students as:

B	**O**	**D**	**M**	**A**	**S**
Brackets	of	Division	Multipli-cation	Addition	Subtraction

Example (i)

	$6 + 2 \times 4$	Multiplication first
=	$6 + 8$	Addition next.
=	14	

Example (ii)

	$18 - 3 \times 4 + 1$	Multiplication first
=	$18 - 12 + 1$	Then addition & subtraction as they occur
=	$6 + 1$	from left to right.
=	7	

Example (iii)

	$(3 + 18) - 40 \div 5$	Brackets first
=	$21 - 40 \div 5$	Division next.
=	13	Subtraction last.

ORDER OF OPERATIONS

LEVEL 1 — EASIER QUESTIONS

Q1. (a) $6 \times 5 + 3$ (b) $6 + 5 \times 3$
(c) $9 + 8 \div 4$ (d) $10 - 3 \times 2$
(e) $4 \div 2 + 8$ (f) $15 - 4 \div 2$

Q2. (a) $(6 + 2) \div 4$ (b) $15 \div (2 + 3)$
(c) $5 \times (8 - 5)$ (d) $(18 - 6) \times 2$
(e) $(7 + 5) \div 6$ (f) $4 \times (6 + 5)$

LEVEL 2 — AVERAGE QUESTIONS

Q1. (a) $2 + 8 \div 4 + 3$ (b) $12 - 3 \times 2 + 4$
(c) $5 + 4 - 3 \times 2$ (d) $18 \div 6 + 5 - 2$
(e) $16 - 9 \div 3 - 3$ (f) $4 \times 2 + 6 \times 3$

Q2. (a) $(2 + 8) \div (5 - 3)$ (b) $(2 + 8) \div 5 + 3$
(c) $14 + 2 \times (3 + 4)$ (d) $21 - 16 \div (3 + 1)$
(e) $(3 + 4) \times (8 - 5)$ (f) $(16 - 9) \times 5 - 20$

LEVEL 3 — DIFFICULT QUESTIONS

Q1. (a) $7 \times 8 - (16 - 6 \div 2)$ (b) $7 \times 6 + 4 \times 2 - 15 \div 3$
(c) $(5 + 4 \times 6) - 3 \times 4$ (d) $5 + 3 \times 6 - 11 + 5 \times 4$

Q2. (a) $96 - [(15 \div 3) - (45 \div 15)]$ (b) $[72 \div (17 - 8)] \times 3 + 8$

FRACTIONS AND DECIMALS

Fractions and decimals describe equal parts of a whole.

Fractions and decimals are extremely difficult concepts for students to master. It is very important not to introduce them until the individual student is ready, because otherwise a 'can't do!' attitude is frequently adopted. It is, therefore, vital that the stages outlined in Book 1 and 2 are covered slowly and with great care.

Concrete materials are an essential component in the acquisition of these concepts and should under no circumstances be neglected.

The relationship between fractions and decimal factions is explored during the final two primary years. Progress is made from investigating hundredths and tenths (emphasising the importance of place value) through to the ordering and recording of decimal fractions, plus the four operations. Percentage is also investigated

VOCABULARY

Biggest, check, decimal point, discount, divide, estimate, factors, fifth, four point two, fraction, greater than half, hundredths, interest, kilometre, less than, metre, multiply, nonsignificant, one dollar and fifteen cents, one place to the right, ones, per cent, percentage, place value, product, quarter, significant, smallest, tenths, third, three point seven kilometres, zero point zero seven.

CONTENTS Page

FRACTIONS RECORDED AS DECIMALS

43 out of a hundred or 43 hundredths can be written as 0.43

0.43 is the decimal way of writing 43 hundredths.
This is read as **zero point four three**.

The zero fills the space where there are no units to record. It means 'No whole ones and 43 hundredths'.

ACTIVITIES:

1. Repeat or adapt previous activities recording results in decimal form.

2. A useful link can be made with the measuring and graphs substrands. Students measure their height or their arm span. These measurements are then recorded in decimal form.

Lauren's arm span measures 1 metre and 27 centimetres. This would be recorded 1.27m.

1 metre 27 centimetres
or 1.27 m

1	**.**	**27**
whole number of metres	decimal point	hundredths of a metre

Lauren would say, 'My arm span measures 1.27 metres. Your arm span is 1.12 metres which is 1 metre and 12 centimetres. Your arm span is narrower than mine by 15 cm. That means 15 hundredths of a metre narrower which we'd write 0.15 and read zero point one five.'

Graph the heights or arms spans of members of the group.

3. Link with the money sub-strand for recording amounts of money in decimal form.

$1.65 means one dollar and 65 cents (65 hundredths of a dollar).

LINKING TENTHS AND HUNDREDTHS

Students should investigate how many longs are needed to cover a flat.
10 longs are needed to cover a flat
Each long represents one tenth of a whole flat

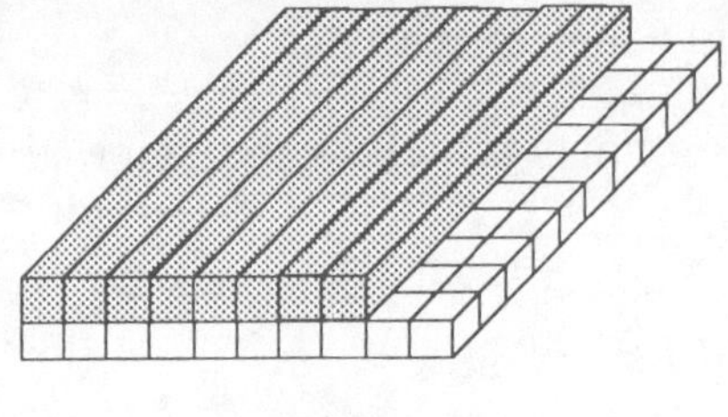

This model shows 8 longs out of ten longs.
It represents 8 tenths of a whole.

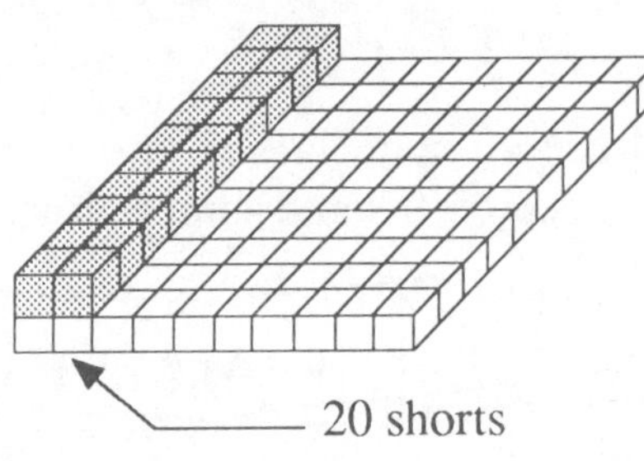

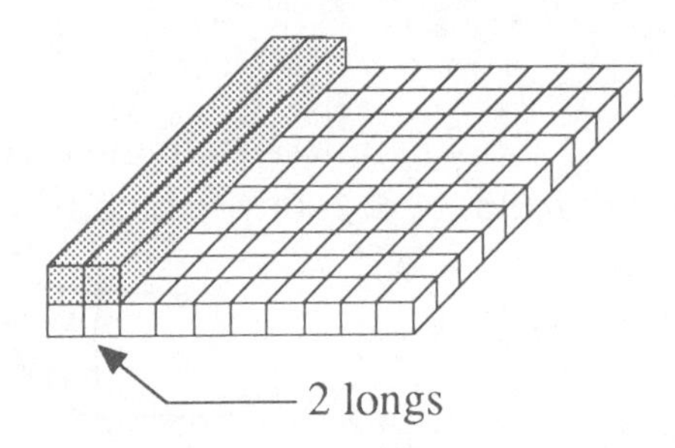

20 shorts cover the same part of a flat as 2 longs.

Examples:

1. How many longs are the same as:
   (a) 50 shorts? (b) 90 shorts?
   Model the answers with Base 10 materials.

2. How many shorts are the same as
   (a) 3 longs? (b) 7 longs? (c) 9 longs?
   Model the answers with Base 10 materials.

3. Describe each of these models in 5 different ways.

(a)

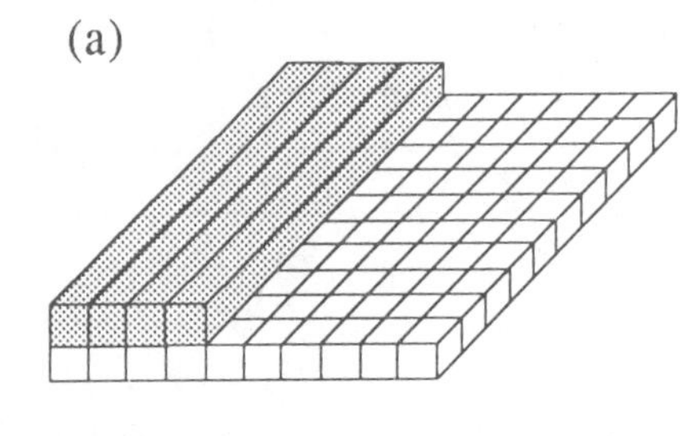

(b)

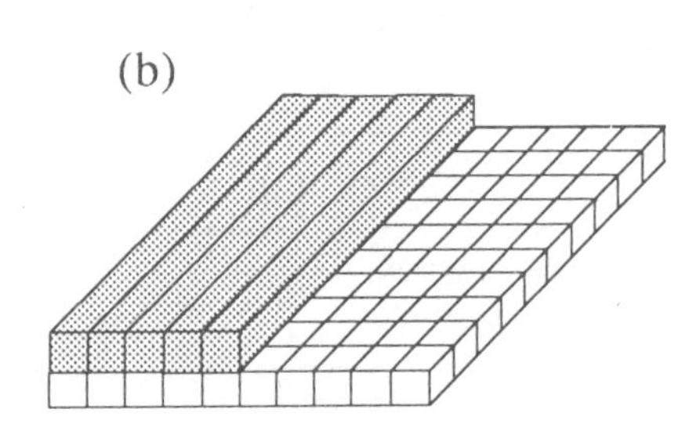

Solutions:

1. (a) 5 longs, (b) 9 longs.
2. (a) 30 shorts; (b) 70 shorts; (c) 90 shorts.
3. (a) 4 longs; 4 out of 10; 4 tenths; 40 shorts; 40 hundredths.
   (b) 5 longs; 5 out of 10; 5 tenths; 50 shorts; 50 hundredths.

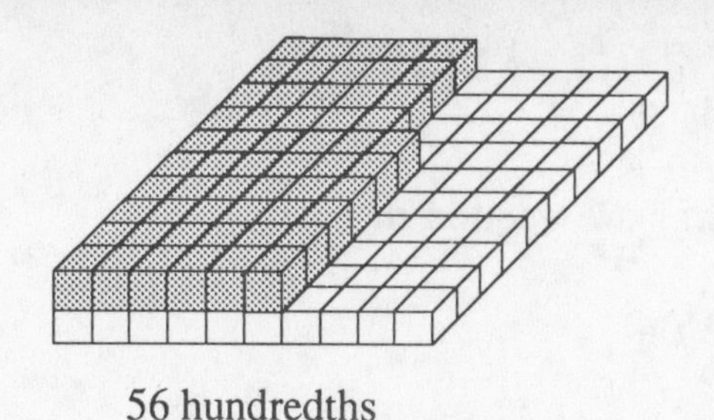

56 hundredths   5 tenths and 6 hundredths

56 hundredths (shorts) is the same as 5 longs and 6 shorts which is the same as 5 tenths and 6 hundredths.

5 tenths and 6 hundredths is the same as 56 hundredths.

ACTIVITIES:

1. Students should model similar examples with Base 10 materials.
2. Use numeral expanders to reinforce the link between tenths and hundredths.

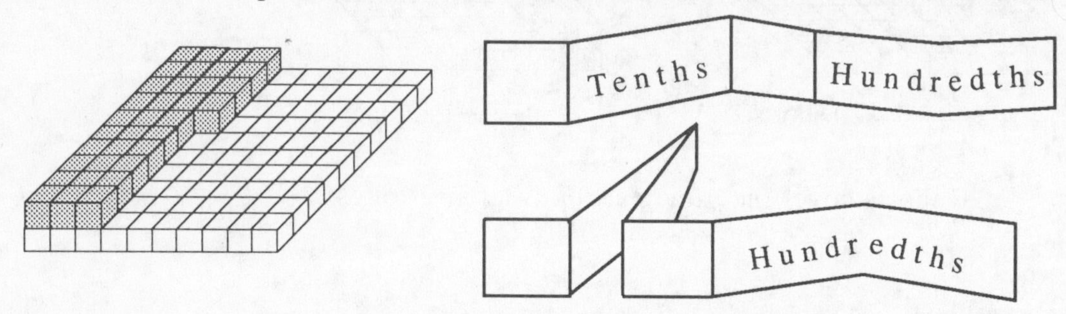

3. (a) Make models of hundedths with Base 10 materials.
   (b) Represent on grid paper as hundredths,and tenths and hundredths.

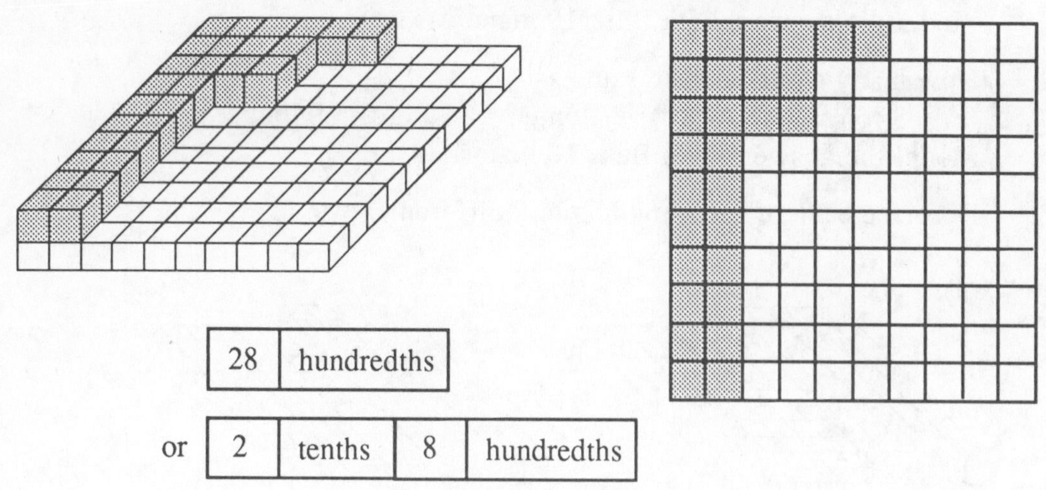

4. Each member of a small group makes a Base 10 model of a fraction with longs and describes using the term 'tenths'. The group discusses and compares their models, and then orders them according to the number of tenths.

5. Link to the money strand. In modelling fractions of a dollar, use 10 cent coins as tenths of a dollar. Students work in pairs to model examples for each other.

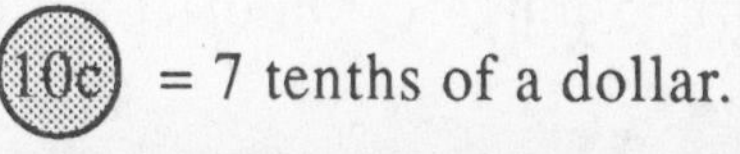

DECIMAL FRACTIONS—PLACE VALUE

As has been emphasised before, a clear understanding of place value is essential in mathematics.

While students should be acquiring this understanding regarding whole numbers, this should now be extended to decimal place values.

It is important to constantly revise and reinforce this with all students.

A decimal place value chart should be used.

ones		tenths	hundreths
	•		

The decimal point separates whole numbers to the left of the point from parts of numbers to the right of the point.

It is essential to link written decimals with Base 10 materials. Use numeral and symbol cards on a place value chart before writing.

ACTIVITIES

1. In pairs, students verbally give decimal fractions, sometimes including units, tenths and hundredths for their partner to model using flats for whole numbers, longs for tenths and shorts for hundredths, e.g.

'73 hundredths'

'Zero point seven three'

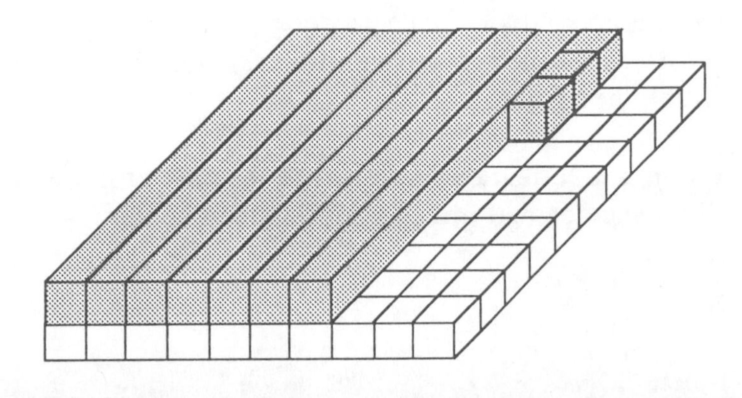

2. Model a decimal fraction then represent it on a hundred square grid paper. Use numeral and symbol cards on a place value chart to record.

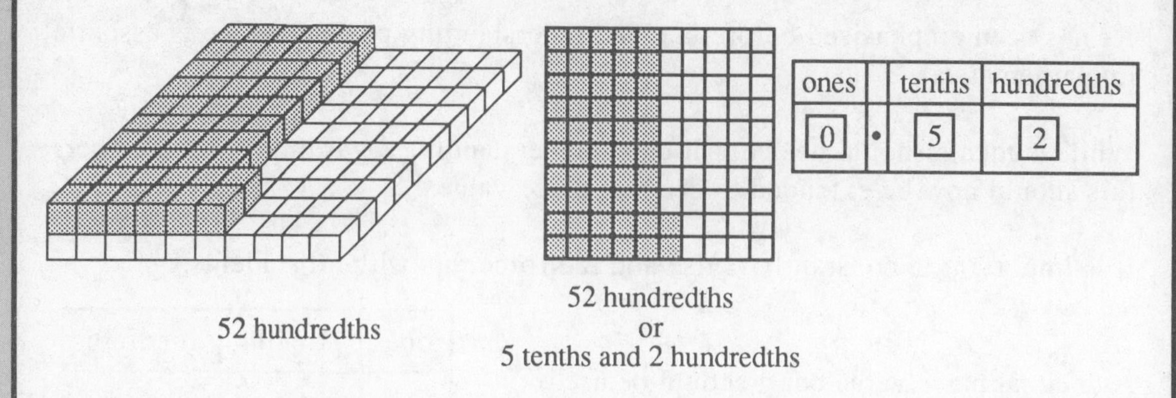

3. Use an abacus to model decimal fractions.

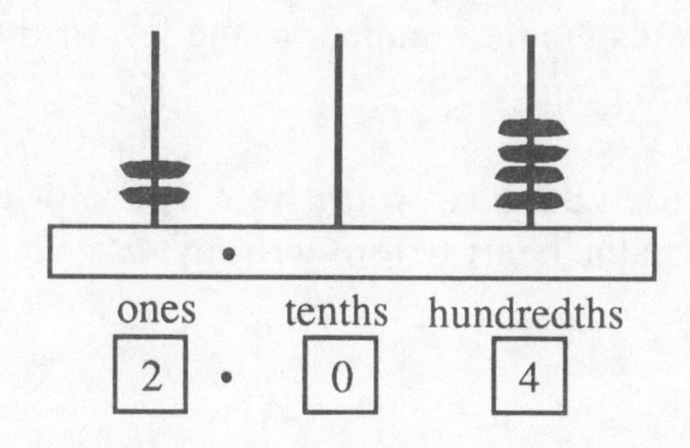

4. Predict and, with calculators, explore what happens when you repeatedly add one hundredth to the previous number. Begin at, e.g. 0.01, and add 0.01. Keep pressing the addition button and 0.01 will repeatedly be added on.

   Predict what happens after (a) 0.09; (b) 0.1; (c) 0.19.

   Discussion should follow these explorations.

   Repeat, adding one tenth—0.1—repeatedly.

5. In pairs or groups, explore length and money sub-strands.
   (a) Make a number of measurements, e.g. the height of doors in the classroom—the classroom door, cupboard doors, locker doors, etc. Record in decimal form and as metres and centimetres. Compare and order the results. Graph the results.

   (b) Using a supermarket leaflet, read the cost of items advertised for sale. Write the decimal prices as dollars and cents.

WRITING DECIMAL FRACTIONS

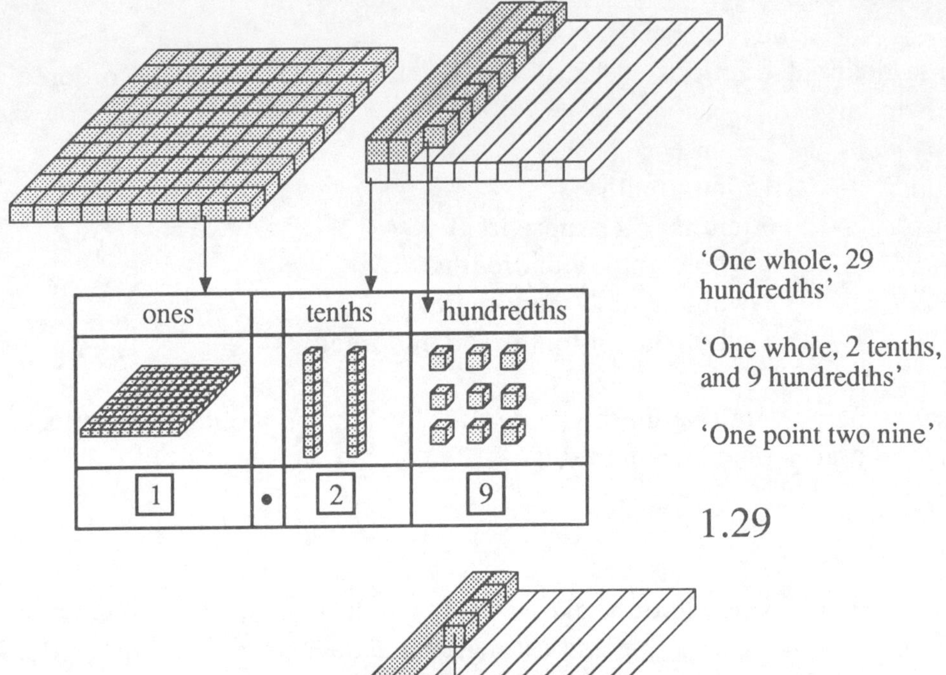

'One whole, 29 hundredths'

'One whole, 2 tenths, and 9 hundredths'

'One point two nine'

1.29

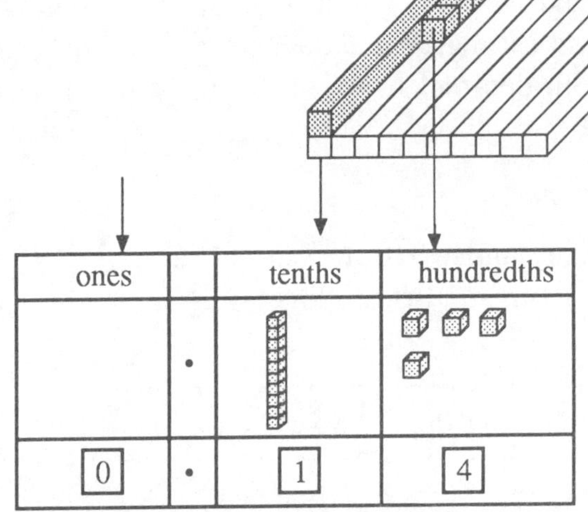

'14 hundredths'

'1 tenths, and 4 hundredths'

'Zero point one four'

0.14

N.B. Zero is placed in the ones place when there are no ones.

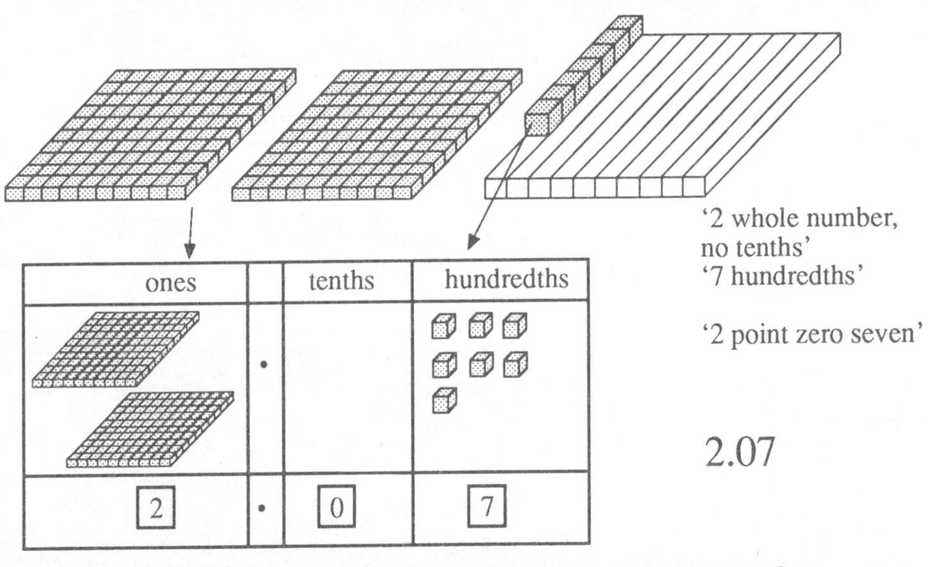

'2 whole number, no tenths'
'7 hundredths'

'2 point zero seven'

2.07

N.B. Zero is placed in the tenths place when there are no tenths.

DECIMAL FRACTIONS—COMPARE, ORDER AND COUNT

The following decimal fractions 0.15, 0.6, 1.27, 1.4, 1.13, would be ordered from smallest to largest:

0.15	—	15 hundredths
0.6	—	6 tenths (60 hundredths)
1.03	—	1 whole and 3 hundredths
1.27	—	1 whole and 27 hundredths
1.4	—	1 whole and 4 tenths (40 hundredths)

Like must be compared with like. In this case, all the examples should be examined with the decimal places read as hundredths.

Activities:

1. Each student in a small group take a small handful of plastic coins from the coin box. Look at each pile and estimate the value. Using trading, model the total for the pile and record in decimal form. Order the amounts from smallest to largest or vice versa.

2. Students each write a sum of money under $10 in decimal form. Share with the group and order the amounts from smallest to largest.

   $0.75 $1.15 $9.03 $7.00 $6.30 $1.70

3. In a small group, each student should measure an object with a metre rule or measuring tape. (Lengths of stride, each other's height.) Measurements are shared and discussed and also reported in as many ways as possible.

   The measurements are written in decimal form on cards and then ordered from smallest to largest or vice versa. Record as a graph.

WATCH OUT FOR PLACE HOLDER ZEROS.

WRITING COMMON FRACTIONS

In the previous book in this series, students began writing common fractions. Ensure those suggested activities have been experienced before progressing.

The bottom number of a fraction, the denominator, shows into how many equal parts the whole, e.g. pizza, chocolate bar, circle, square, has been divided.

The top number of a fraction, the numerator, shows how many of these equal parts have been coloured in, not coloured in, or eaten!

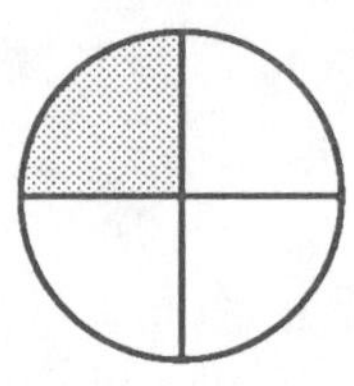

The shaded area in the circle represents 1 part out of 4 equal parts.

This is written in fraction form as

$\frac{1}{4}$ ← numerator / ← denominator

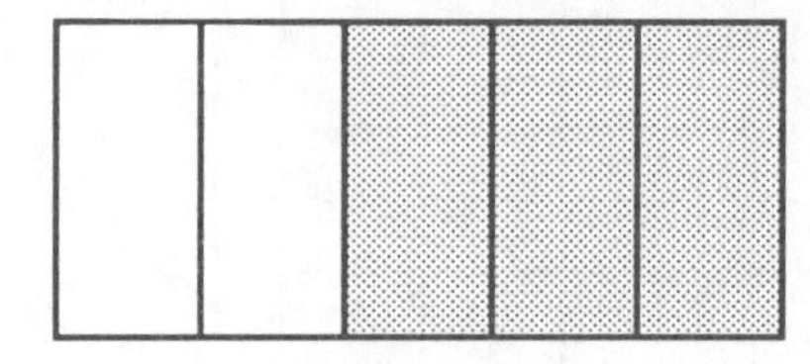

The shaded area in the rectangle represents 3 parts out of 5 equal parts.

This is written in fraction form as:

$\frac{3}{5}$ ← numerator / ← denominator

Surveys provide data which can be interpreted as fractions.

When surveyed 27 of the 30 children in 5T preferred the summer to the winter. 27 out of the 30 preferred the summer.

This could be shown by writing $\frac{27}{30}$

30 is the total number of children in 5T. 27 shows how many of these children preferred the summer. It therefore follows that:

$\frac{3}{30}$ preferred winter $\frac{30}{30}$ is the whole class

Activity:
Students conduct their own surveys and record the results as common fractions and also as graphs. Suitable topics would be favourite programs, sports or food.

PERCENTAGES

Percentage is really a special fraction which can always be written as hundredths. Percentages occur many times in everyday living. For example, exam marks in different subjects are usually written on a report as a percentage. In order to understand what a percentage means, look at the shaded squares in the diagram below.

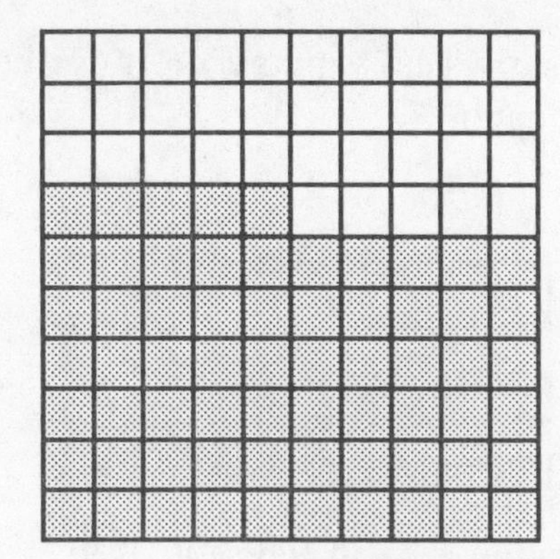

65 hundredths

or 65 out of 100

or $\frac{65}{100}$

We call this 65 per cent.
This is usually shortened to 65%.

'Per cent' is written as '%'.
It means: hundredths

OR: out of 100

OR: per hundred

Examples: What percentage has been shaded in the large squares shown below:

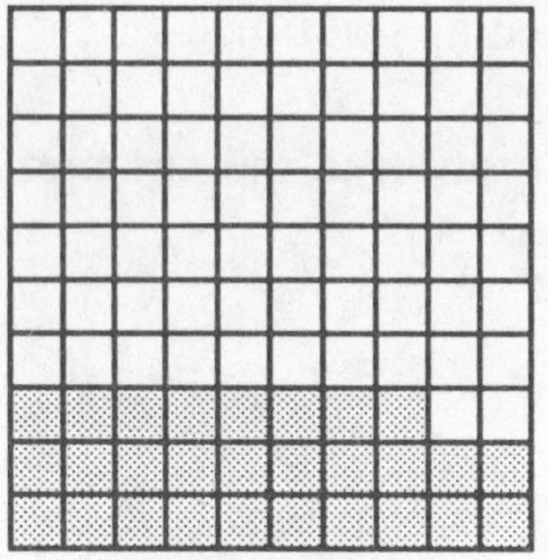

28 hundredths
or 28%

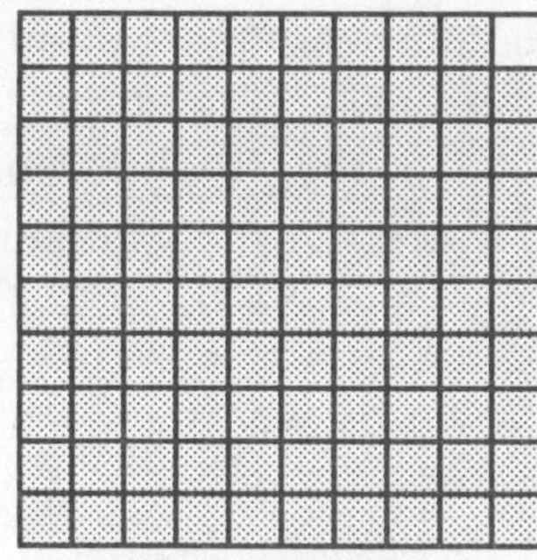

99 hundredths
or 99%

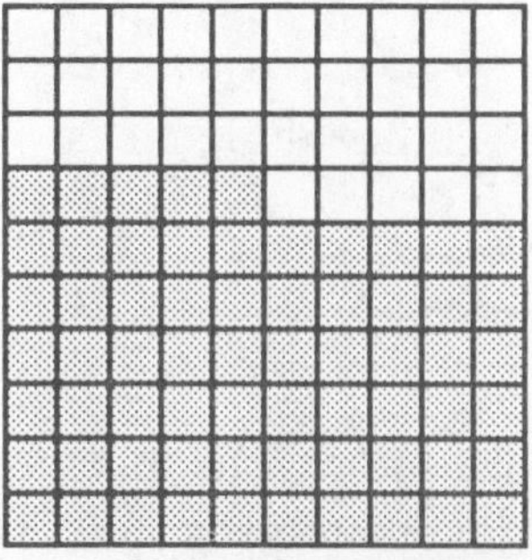

65 hundredths
or 65%

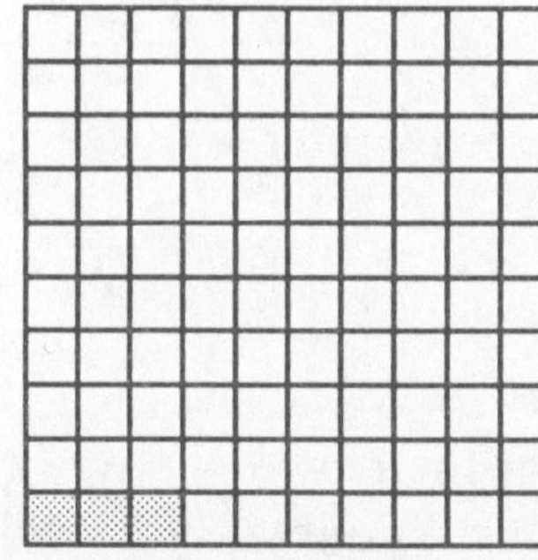

3 hundredths
or 3%

ONE WHOLE IS 100%

In any particular question about percentages, keep in mind that the total percentages in the question must add up to 100%. This idea is best understood by working through the examples below.

Example (i): Jenny scored 85% in Maths test. What percentage did she get wrong?

Solution: As all percentages in a question add up to 100%, Jenny must have 100% – 85% = 15% wrong.

Example (ii): A class consists of 60% boys. What percentage are girls?

Solution: 40% of the class are girls because the total percentage of the class adds up to 100%. 100 – 60 = 40.

Example (iii): Stanton Primary School has 3 choices for summer sport: swimming, tennis or cricket. 32% of the students choose to play tennis and 47% choose to do cricket. What percentage of the students will be swimming?

Solution: Tennis + cricket = 32% + 47% = 79%

Total percentages must add up to 100%.

100 – 79 = 21

Therefore 21% must be doing swimming.

Example (iv): Craig got 67%, 71% and 78% in 3 separate English exams. What was his average mark?

Solution:

$$\text{Average} = \frac{67 + 71 + 78}{3}$$

$$\frac{216}{3}$$

$$= 72\%$$

To find the average of the three percentages, add up all the percentages and divide the total by 3.

ACTIVITIES:

1. Using newspapers, magazines, brochures, etc., make a collection of pictures, photographs or labels showing percentages or fractions, Students should discuss items in the collection.

50% off	5% interest	$\frac{1}{3}$ off sale	$\frac{1}{2}$ price sale

2. Using grid paper, colour in specified percentages. Share these with a partner who should read the percentage represented on the grid. e.g.

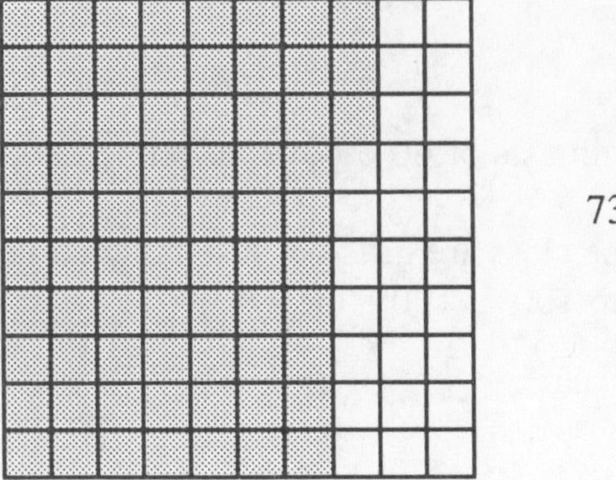

73%

3. Using the above grids, label each one in as many different ways as possible.

73 hundredths

73 out of one hundred.

$\frac{73}{100}$

7 tenths and 3 hundredths

0.73

73%

4. Play trading games involving tenths and hundredths.

Take a handful of Base 10 materials containing longs and shorts. Estimate how many flats (units), longs (tenths) and shorts (hundredths) the handful can be traded for. Sort and trade. Record the answer in decimal form.

e.g. 3.76

Other group members do likewise.

Order the sorted handfuls from smallest to largest or vice versa.

WRITING PERCENTAGES AS FRACTIONS

'Per cent' means 'out of a hundred', 'hundredths' or 'per hundred'.

> To change a percentage into a fraction, write the percentage number over a hundred.

Example (i): Change 50% into a fraction

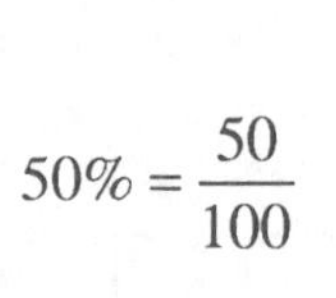

$$50\% = \frac{50}{100}$$

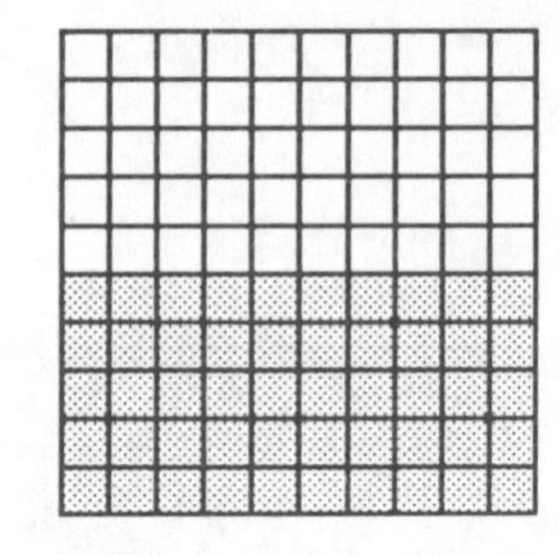

From the shading in the diagram it can be seen that this fraction, $\frac{50}{100}$, could be written more simply as $\frac{1}{2}$.

Example (ii): Change 25% into a fraction

$$25\% = \frac{25}{100}$$

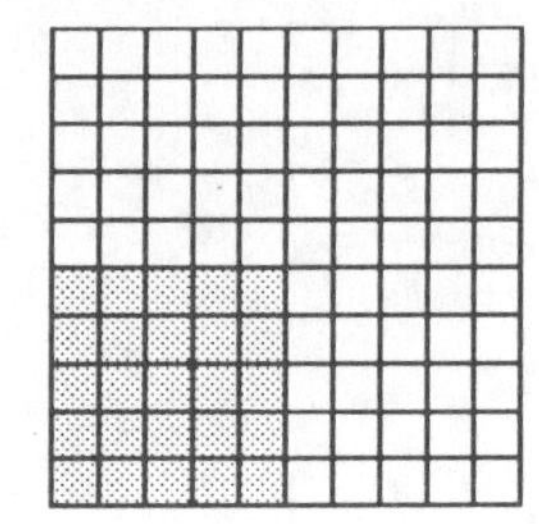

From the shading in the diagram it can be seen that this fraction, $\frac{25}{100}$, could be written more simply as $\frac{1}{4}$.

Example (iii): Change 70% into a fraction

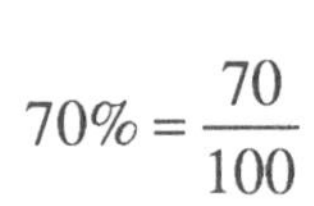

$$70\% = \frac{70}{100}$$

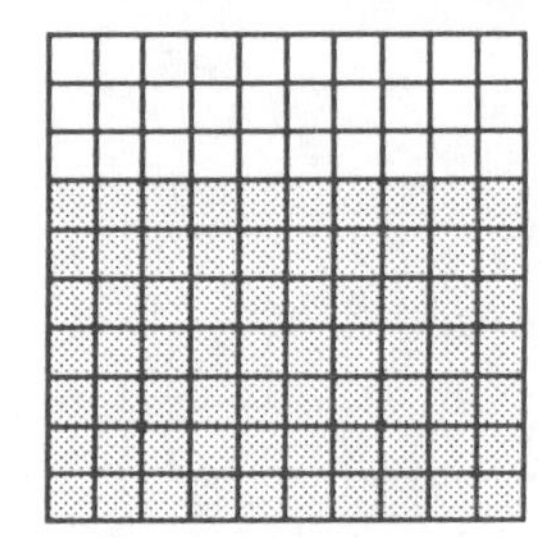

From the shading in the diagram it can be seen that this fraction, $\frac{70}{100}$, could be written more simply as $\frac{7}{10}$.

Example (iv): Change $\frac{80}{100}$ to a percentage.

This is simply the opposite of the rule at the top of the page.

$$\frac{80}{100} = 80\%$$

WRITING PERCENTAGES AS DECIMALS

Look at the shaded squares in the diagram below.

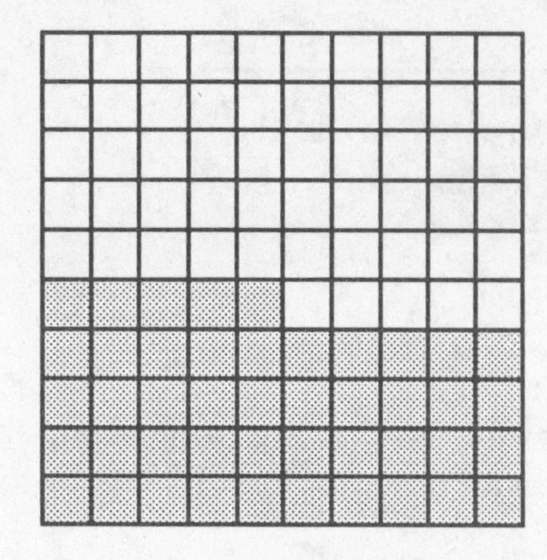

45 hundredths, or 45 out of 100 or $\frac{45}{100}$, have been shaded.

As a decimal, we would write 0.45.

As a percentage, we would write 45%.

Therefore 45% means the same as 0.45

To change a percentage into a decimal, write the number as hundredths, and then it is easy to see what decimal it is.

Example (i): Change 35% to a decimal.

$$35\% = 35 \text{ hundredths} = \frac{35}{100} = 0.35$$

Example (ii): Change 8% to a decimal.

$$8\% = 8 \text{ hundredths} = \frac{8}{100} = 0.08$$

Example (iii): Change 0.75 to a percentage.

This is the opposite of the rule shown above. Firstly change the decimal back into hundredths, and then write it as a percentage.

$$0.75 = \frac{75}{100} = 75\%$$

CHANGING SIMPLE FRACTIONS TO A PERCENTAGE

Students should now be aware that percentages are a number of hundredths and that 100% is a whole or the total.

100% means a whole.

To convert a fraction to a decimal it must first be converted to hundredths.

Express $\frac{12}{20}$ as a percentage.

Since both $\frac{20}{20}$ and $\frac{100}{100}$ make a whole,

then $\frac{1}{20}$ must be the same as $\frac{5}{100}$.

So, $\frac{12}{20}$ must be $\frac{12 \times 5}{100} = \frac{60}{100} = 60\%$.

This progresses to: $\frac{12}{20}$ $\frac{\square}{100}$

To change 20 to 100
multiply by 5.

It is necessary to change the numerator (12) in the same way as the denominator (20); multiply it by 5.

$$\frac{12}{20} \xrightarrow{\times 5} \frac{60}{100} = 60\%$$

Example: Write $\frac{3}{4}$ as a percentage.

Solution:

$$\frac{3}{4} \xrightarrow{\times 25} \frac{75}{100}$$

multiply the denominator, 4,
by 25 to change to 100.
Multiply the numerator by 25.

$$\frac{3}{4} = \frac{75}{100} = 75\%.$$

THE CONNECTION BETWEEN PERCENTAGES, DECIMALS AND FRACTIONS

As you have already seen, we can write hundredths in 3 different ways which all have exactly the same meaning. To make this idea very clear, we have shaded in different amounts of the larger squares in the diagrams below. On the right hand side, the EQUIVALENT (means equal) percentage, decimal and fraction of the shaded area has been given.

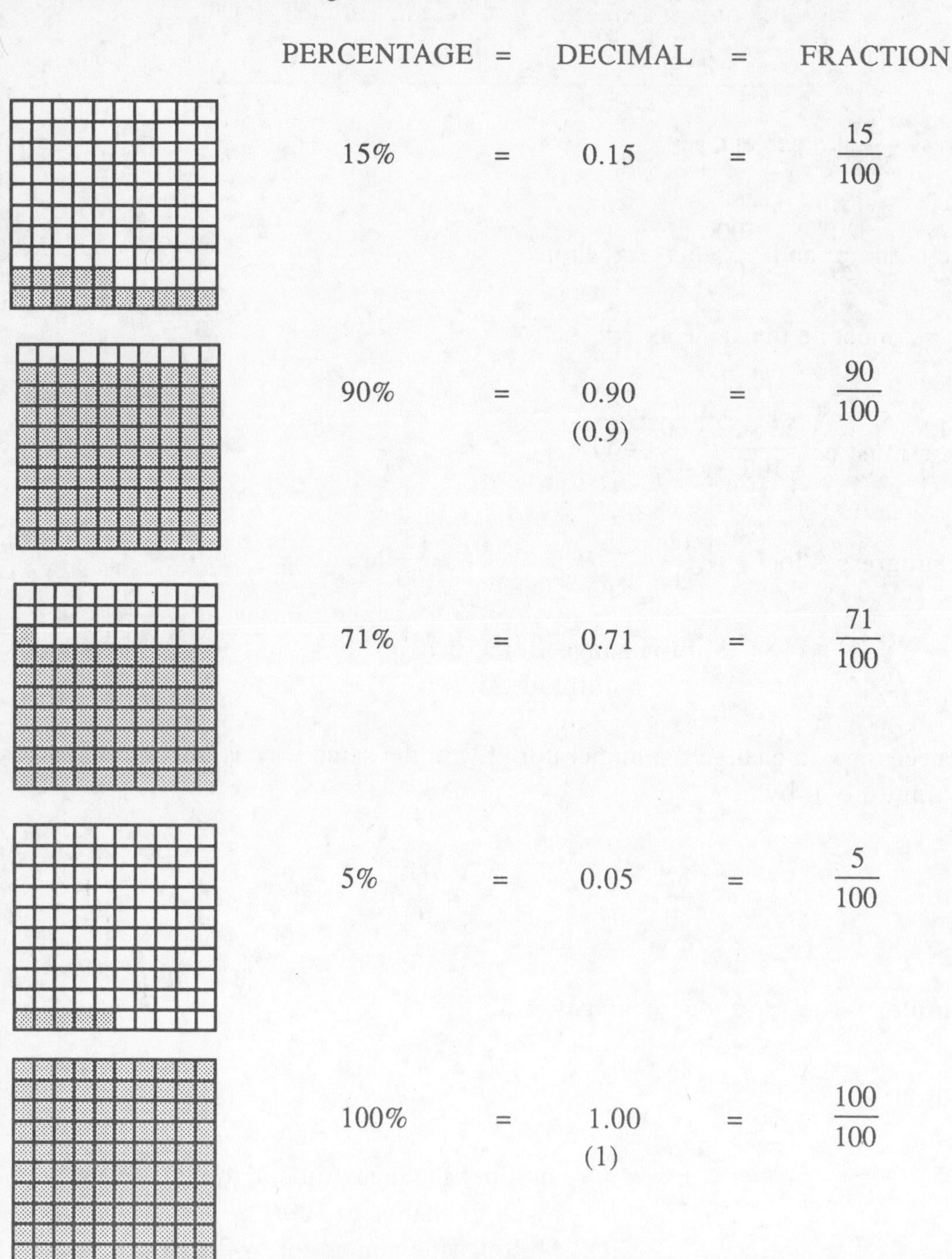

PERCENTAGE	=	DECIMAL	=	FRACTION
15%	=	0.15	=	$\frac{15}{100}$
90%	=	0.90 (0.9)	=	$\frac{90}{100}$
71%	=	0.71	=	$\frac{71}{100}$
5%	=	0.05	=	$\frac{5}{100}$
100%	=	1.00 (1)	=	$\frac{100}{100}$

NOTE: In the last diagram, all the squares have been shaded. Therefore 100% or '1 whole square' has been shaded.One whole unit can be written as l or l.0 or 1.00.

As can be seen on the previous page, percentages can be written in their equivalent decimal or fraction form. Some of these occur so regularly in everyday living (as well as in tests!), that they should be memorised. The most important conversions are listed below.

PERCENTAGE	DECIMAL	FRACTION	SIMPLIFIED FRACTION	
25%	0.25	$\frac{25}{100}$	$\frac{1}{4}$	Essential to know
50%	0.50	$\frac{50}{100}$	$\frac{1}{2}$	
75%	0.75	$\frac{75}{100}$	$\frac{3}{4}$	
100%	1.00	$\frac{100}{100}$	1	
20%	0.2	$\frac{20}{100}$	$\frac{1}{5}$	
40%	0.4	$\frac{40}{100}$	$\frac{2}{5}$	
60%	0.6	$\frac{60}{100}$	$\frac{3}{5}$	
80%	0.8	$\frac{80}{100}$	$\frac{4}{5}$	
$33\frac{1}{3}$%	$0.\dot{3}$	$\frac{33\frac{1}{3}}{100}$	$\frac{1}{3}$	Useful to know
$66\frac{2}{3}$%	$0.\dot{6}$	$\frac{66\frac{1}{3}}{100}$	$\frac{2}{3}$	
$12\frac{1}{2}$%	0.125	$\frac{125}{1000}$	$\frac{1}{8}$	
$37\frac{1}{2}$%	0.375	$\frac{375}{1000}$	$\frac{3}{8}$	
$62\frac{1}{2}$%	0.625	$\frac{625}{1000}$	$\frac{5}{8}$	
$87\frac{1}{2}$%	0.875	$\frac{875}{1000}$	$\frac{7}{8}$	

NOTE: (i) The first two groups above are essential to know. The second two groups would certainly be useful to know, but they have been included only as extension work for the more advanced students.

(ii) $0.\dot{3}$ means 0.33333 . . .

$0.\dot{6}$ means 0.66666 . . .

EQUIVALENT FRACTIONS

1. 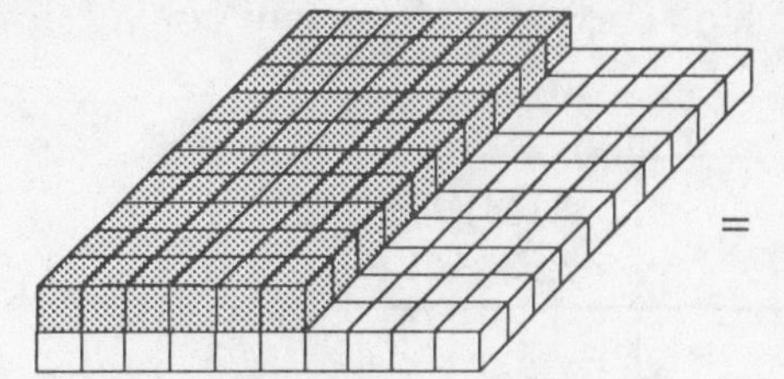 = 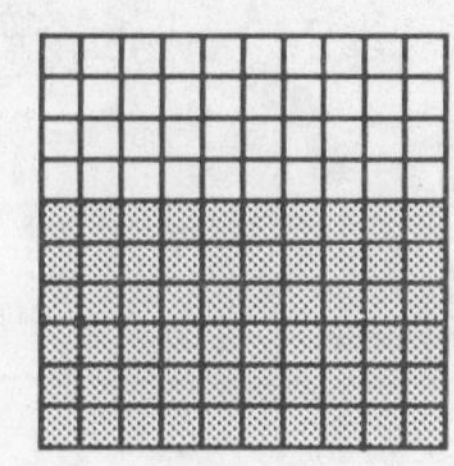 $= \frac{60}{100} = \frac{6}{10} = 0.6 = 60\%$

These decimal and common fractions all mean the same as what has been modelled in Base 10 materials and shown on the grid paper. They are **equal** or **equivalent.**

2. In the following examples it can be clearly seen that the shaded area in each of the circles is exactly the same.

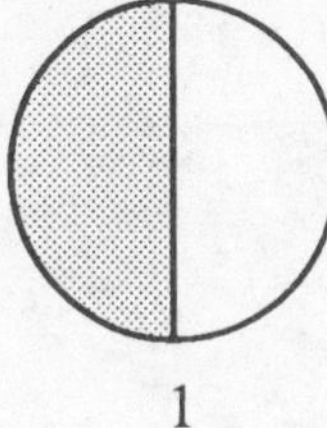 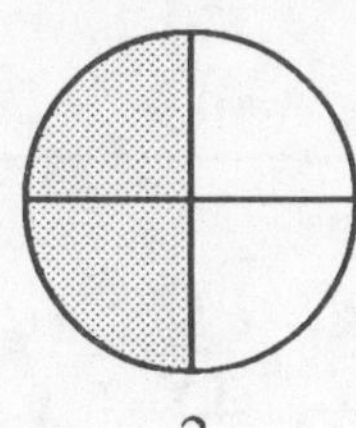 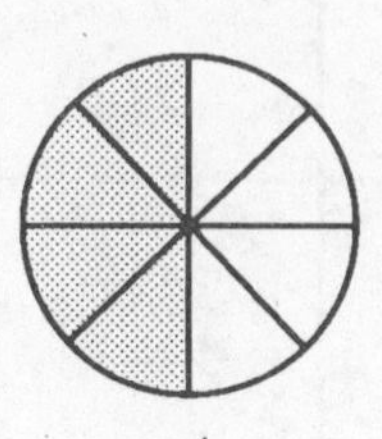

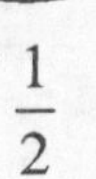 $\frac{2}{4}$ $\frac{4}{8}$

It must follow that $\frac{1}{2} = \frac{2}{4} = \frac{4}{8}$

They are EQUAL or EQUIVALENT fractions even though they have different numerators and denominators.

> Equivalent fractions are obtained by multiplying or dividing both the numerator and denominator by the same number.

Example (i): $\frac{3}{4} = \frac{\square}{20}$

The denominator 4 must be multiplied by 5 to get 20. To obtain an equivalent fraction, the numerator 3 must also be multiplied by 5 to get 15.

Therefore $\frac{3}{4} = \frac{15}{20}$

Example (ii): $\frac{30}{50} = \frac{\square}{5}$

The denominator 50 must be divided by 10 to get 5. To obtain an equivalent fraction, the numerator 30 must also be divided by 10 to obtain 3.

Therefore $\frac{30}{50} = \frac{3}{5}$.

SIGNIFICANT AND NON-SIGNIFICANT ZEROS

The concept of significant and non-significant zeros often takes some considerable time to understand. Although the terms can be used, it is more important that students understand what they mean rather than knowing the terms themselves.

SIGNIFICANT ZEROS are zeros used as place holders and affect the value of the number. NON- SIGNIFICANT ZEROS do not affect the value of the number.

For example:

1 7 9	means one hundred and seventy-nine.
0 1 7 9	means one hundred and seventy-nine
0 0 1 7 9	means one hundred and seventy-nine
0 0 0 1 7 9	means one hundred and seventy-nine

The zeros have no function, they are serving no purpose, they are non-significant.

Example:

'109 is read 'one hundred and nine'.

This means one hundred, no tens and nine ones or units.

The zero is holding the tens place. Without it, the number would be written 1 9 and could be read as nineteen which is not the intended value. The zero is significant.

1 . 3 5	means 1 whole, 3 tenths and 5 hundredths.
1 . 3 5 0	means 1 whole, 3 tenths and 5 hundredths.
1 . 3 5 0 0	means 1 whole, 3 tenths and 5 hundredths.
1 . 3 5 0 0 0	means 1 whole, 3 tenths and 5 hundredths.

The zeros are not changing the value of the decimal fraction.

The zeros are non-significant.

However, when writing decimal fractions like 0.19, a non-significant zero must be written in the units place. This emphasises that there are no units and ensures the decimal point is not overlooked. The zero does not change the value of the decimal fraction and so is non-significant.

Similarly:

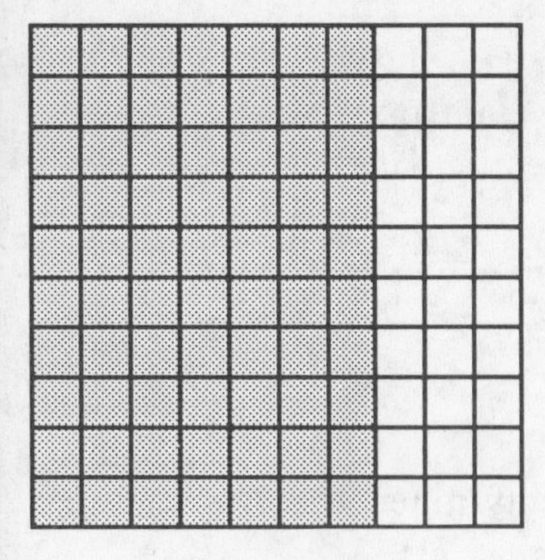

=

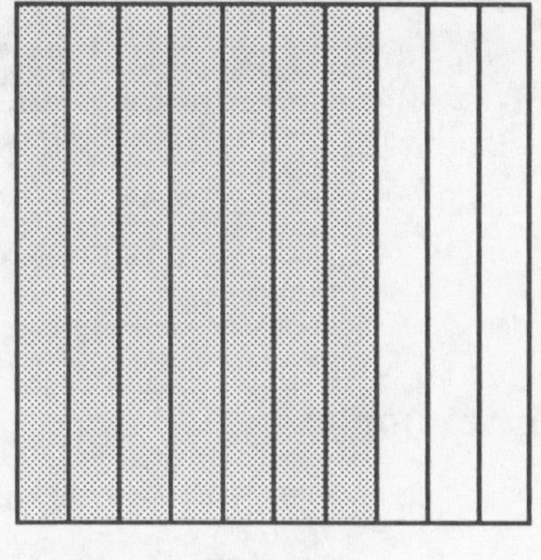

70 hundredths is the same as 7 tenths

Since $\frac{70}{100}$ is the same as $\frac{7}{10}$

Then $\frac{70}{100} = 0.70 = \frac{7}{10} = 0.7$

$\frac{70}{100}$ may be written as 0.7 leaving out the non-significant zero.

The final zero does not change the essential meaning.

However, when recording money in decimal currency, the cents are always recorded as hundredths.

$1.50 = $1 and 50c.

e.g. it would be incorrect to write $1.5

ADDITION AND SUBTRACTION OF TENTHS AND HUNDREDTHS IN DECIMAL FORM

Use real life situations as the basis for addition and subtraction problems. Addition and subtraction of decimal fractions follow the same rules as for whole numbers. It is very important to keep the different columns very straight and neat. Tenths go directly under tenths, hundredths under hundredths, etc. The point doesn't belong in a column—it's always between the units and tenths.

Place the points under the points

```
   1  2
   8 . 3 2
 2
 1 5 . 4 9
   6 . 0 7
 2 7 . 3 6
 ---------
 5 7 . 2 4
 ---------
```

Example (i):

4B collected $7.35, 4H collected $8.00 and 4K collected $16.95 for Guide Dogs For The Blind. $0.35 had been unclaimed in Lost Property for two terms. It was added to the collection. What was the total amount sent to Guide Dogs For the Blind? (Estimate.)

MAKE SURE THE AMOUNTS ARE WRITTEN IN THE CORRECT COLUMNS.

```
              1  1
Solution: $   7 . 3 5
            2 8 . 0 0
            1 6 . 9 5
              0 . 3 5
          -----------
          $ 3 2 . 65    $32.65 was sent to the Guide Dogs for the Blind.
          -----------
```

Example (ii):

Mum had $82.75 in her bank account. She wrote a cheque for $63.49 to pay for the groceries. How much was left in her account? Estimate.

Solution:

It is necessary to trade tenths for hundredths of a dollar and tens for ones.

```
  7 1   6 1
 $8̸ 2 . 7̸ 5
   6 3 . 4 9
 -----------
 $ 1 9 . 2 6   Mum had $19.26 left in her account.
 -----------
```

MULTIPLYING TENTHS AND HUNDREDTHS BY WHOLE NUMBERS UP TO 10

Mutiplication follows the same rules as for whole numbers but care should be taken with the position of the decimal point.

Example (i):
What is the perimeter of the school sick room if each of the 4 walls measures 3.7m?

$^{2}3.7$	This algorithm says 4 times 3.7
$\times\ 4$	$4 \times .7$ tenths = 2.8 tenths
14.8	28 tenths = 2 units + 8 tenths
	Put 8 in the tenths answer place
	The 2 units are transferred to the units column
	$4 \times 3 + 2$ (made by 20 tenths) = 14
	The perimeter is 14.8 metres

Example (ii):
Three curtains were needed at the back of the stage for the school play. Each curtain needed 5.62 metres of cloth. How much cloth was needed altogether? (Estimate.)

$^{1}5.62$	This algorithm says 3 times 5.62
$\times\ 3$	3×2 hundredths (0.02) = 6 hundredths (0.06)
16.86	3×6 tenths (0.6) = 1.8
	Put 8 into the tenths column
	3 x 5 + 1 (made from 10 tenths)
	16.86 metres of cloth were needed.

CHECK ANSWERS WITH A CALCULATOR

MULTIPLYING BY 10

When multiplying by 10, all digits become 10 times larger: hundredths become tenths, tenths become ones, ones become tens, tens become hundreds, etc.

Therefore, the decimal point stays still and all the digits move one place to the left.

Example: 76.32×10

Move all the digits one place to the left.

= 763.2.

DIVIDING TENTHS AND HUNDREDTHS BY WHOLE NUMBERS UP TO 10

Dividing decimal fractions by whole numbers up to 10 follows the same rules as for division of whole numbers.

Example (i):

$$5\overline{)21.5} = 04.3$$

```
   04.3
5)21.5
  20↓
   15
   15
    0
```

Place decimal point in answer above the point in the dividend.

Steps:
(i) 2 ÷ 5 can't be done. The non-significant zero in the answer ensures the next digit goes over the 1, in its correct place.
(ii) 21 ÷ 5 = 4. Write 4 above the 1.
(iii) 4 × 5 = 20 Subtract 20 from 21. 1 remains.
(iv) 1 unit and 5 tenths = 15 tenths.
(v) 15 ÷ 5 = 3. Write 3 above the 5.
(vi) 3 × 5 = 15 so no remainder.
After a little practice, students will become accurate in their placing of the answers. Then the non-significant zeros can be omitted.

Example (ii): Share $17.40 between 3 people.

```
    5.80
3)17.40
  15↓ |
   24 ↓
   24
    00
```

or

```
    5 . 8 0
3)1 7 . ²8 0
```

Each person will receive $5.80

DIVIDING BY 10

When dividing by 10, all digits become 10 times smaller: hundreds become tens, tens become ones, ones become tenths, tenths become hundredths, etc.

Therefore, the decimal point stays still and all the digits move one place to the right.

Example: Find 67.3 ÷ 10

Move all the digits one place to the right.

= 6.73

DECIMAL FRACTION ALGORITHMS— FURTHER EXAMPLES

Example (i):
Jason went to the supermarket and bought toothpaste for $2.35, soap for $1.49, hair shampoo for $3.92 and a comb for 79 cents. How much change will Jason get from $20.00.

Solution:
Add up all the items to find the total, and then subtract this total from $20.00.

```
  2 2              1 9 9 1
  2.35            -20.00-
  1.49          – ¹8.55
  3.92            ------
  0.79             11.45
  ----            ------
  8.55
  ----
```

Jason will get $11.45 change.

Example (ii):
One kilogram of lamb chops costs $7.45. How much would 3 kilograms cost?

Solution:

```
     1 1
  $  7.4 5
       × 3
  --------
   2 2.3 5
  --------
```

3 kilograms will cost $22.35

Example (iii):
Prize money of $2 356.90 has to be shared equally between 5 people. How much will each person receive?

Solution:

```
     4 7 1 . 3 8
  5)2 3 5 6 . 9 0
    2 0↓
      3 5
      3 5↓
        0 6
          5↓
          1 9
          1 5↓
            4 0
            4 0
              0
```

'Sharing equally' is another way of saying divide $2 356.90 by 5.

Each person will get $471.38

or

```
     4 7 1 . 3 8
  5)2 3³5 6 .¹9⁴0
```

FINDING A FRACTION OF A QUANTITY

Example (i): What is a quarter of $3.00?

Solution: Change the $3.00 to cents—300 cents.

$$\frac{1}{4} \text{ of } 300 = 4\overline{)300}^{\,75}$$

$$= 75.$$

A quarter of $3.00 is 75 cents or $0.75.

Example (ii):

Find $\frac{3}{5}$ of 20 apples

Solution: First find one fifth.

$$\frac{1}{5} \text{ of } 20 = 20 \div 5 = 4$$

Then $\frac{3}{5}$ of $20 = 3 \times 4 = 12$

$\frac{3}{5}$ of 20 apples is 12 apples.

Example (iii): Find $\frac{2}{3}$ of 18.

Solution:

$$\frac{1}{3} \text{ of } 18 = 6$$

$$\frac{2}{3} \text{ of } 18 = 12.$$

FRACTIONS AND DECIMALS ASSESSMENT

Students should understand the following ideas:

Recording as decimals

- understand that zero is used as a place holder
- understand that whole numbers are written to the left of the decimal point
- trade hundredths (shorts) for tenths (longs)
- model whole numbers, tenths and hundredths
- use decimal place value chart for recording these models
- write the name for these models
- read the name for these models
- read and record lengths in decimal form
- read and record amounts of money in decimal form
- compare and order decimal fractions

Common fractions

- describe into how many equal parts the whole has been divided
- describe how many equal parts have been shaded and how many unshaded
- read models of common fractions
- record models of fractions in writing

Percentages

- understand that percentage means 'out of a hundred'
- model hundredths and name them in as many ways as possible
- identify percentages in the environment
- demonstrate understanding that one whole is 100%
- write percentages as fractions
- write percentages as decimals
- change simple fractions to decimals
- describe the link between percentages, decimals and fractions

FRACTIONS AND DECIMALS ASSESSMENT

Equivalent fractions

- demonstrate understanding of equivalent decimal fractions
- demonstrate understanding of equivalent common fractions
- demonstrate understanding of significant and non-significant zeros

Addition and subtraction of decimal fractions

- demonstrate estimation and rounding off before solving
- using real-life situations, add decimal fractions involving tenths and hundredths
- using real-life situations, subtract decimal fractions involving tenths and hundredths

Multiplication and division of decimal fractions

- use a calculator to solve real-life multiplication problems involving tenths and hundredths multiplied by whole numbers up to 10
- estimate then solve real-life multiplication problems using pencil and paper; check answer with a calculator
- show understanding of the position of the decimal point when a decimal fraction is multiplied by 10
- use a calculator to solve real-life division problems involving tenths and hundredths divided by whole numbers up to 10
- estimate then solve real-live division problems using pencil and paper; check answer with a calculator
- show understanding of the position of the decimal point when a decimal fraction is divided by 10

Fractions of quantities

- Explain the process needed to solve problems involving finding a fraction of a quantity
- solve problems involving finding a fraction of a quantity

LEVEL 1 FRACTIONS

EASIER QUESTIONS

Q1. Write the shaded area as a decimal.

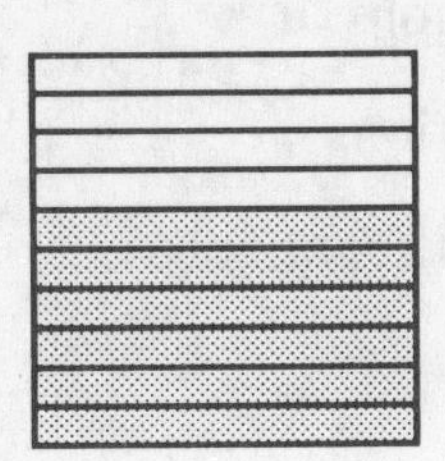

Q2. What is the place value of 7 in the following?

(a) 53.72 (b) 631.07 (c) 73.5

Q3. Order the following numbers from greatest to least:

(a) 5.69, 5.7, 5.71 (b) 3.47, 3.45, 3.54

Q4. Name the shaded parts of each figure.

(a)

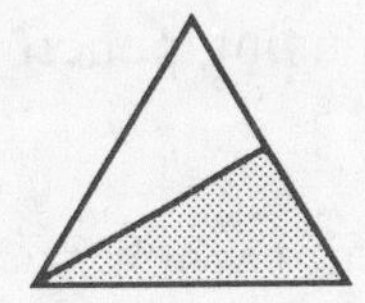

(b)

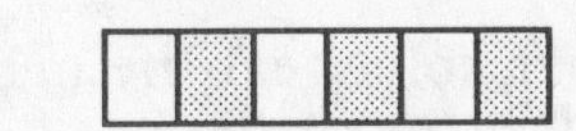

Q5. Shade in:

(a) $\frac{3}{4}$

(b) $\frac{5}{8}$

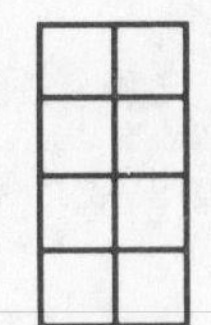

Q6. What percentage has been shaded?

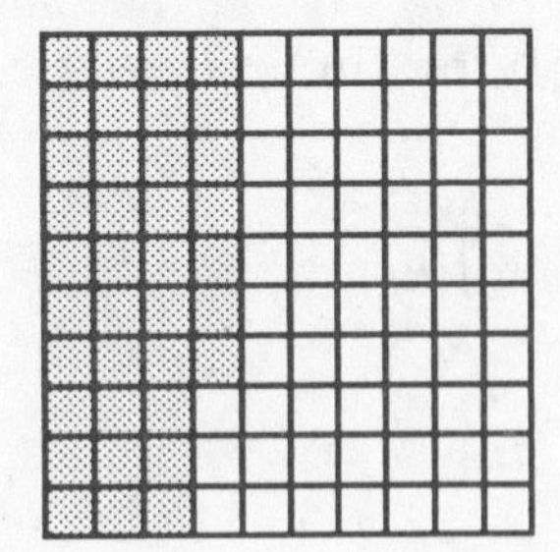

Q7. Shade in the percentage given

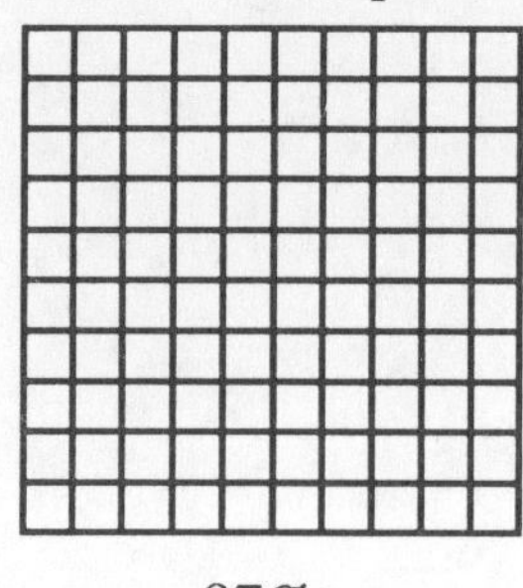

87%

Q8. Change the following percentages to fractions:

(a) 31% (b) 49% (c) 7% (d) 19%

Q9. Change the following fractions to percentages:

(a) $\frac{17}{100}$ (b) $\frac{45}{100}$ (c) $\frac{1}{2}$ (d) $\frac{1}{4}$

Q10. Change the following to equivalent fractions:

(a) $\frac{1}{2} = \frac{\square}{16}$ (b) $\frac{1}{3} = \frac{\square}{6}$ (c) $\frac{3}{5} = \frac{\square}{10}$

Q11. (a) $\begin{array}{r} 4.92 \\ +\ 1.35 \\ \hline \end{array}$ (b) $\begin{array}{r} 8.4 \\ -\ 3.6 \\ \hline \end{array}$ (c) $\begin{array}{r} 3.8 \\ \times\ 5 \\ \hline \end{array}$ (d) $5\overline{)7.5}$

Q12. (a) How many quarters in 2 wholes?
(b) How many halves in $2\frac{1}{2}$

Q.13 Write the following amounts of money as a decimal:

(a) 8 dollars and 14 cents
(b) 93 dollars and 5 cents

Q.14 Find the percentages of the quantities shown: (Hint: you can change the percentages to fractions if you find that easier.)

(a) 10% of $30 (b) 50% of 20 apples
(c) 25% of 40 students (d) 20% of 10 lollies

LEVEL 2 FRACTIONS

AVERAGE QUESTIONS

Q1. Write the shaded area as a decimal.

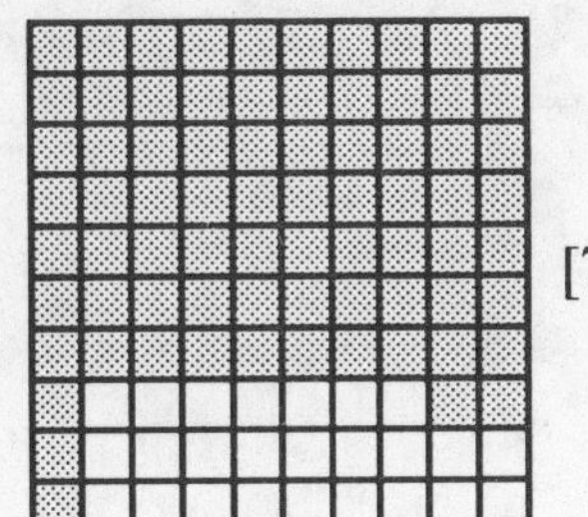

[75%]

Q2. What is the place value of 3 in the following?

(a) 4.03 (b) 17.3

Q3. Order the following numbers from least to greatest:

4.7, 4.07, 4.72, 4.27

Q4. Name the shaded parts of each figure as a fraction.

(a)

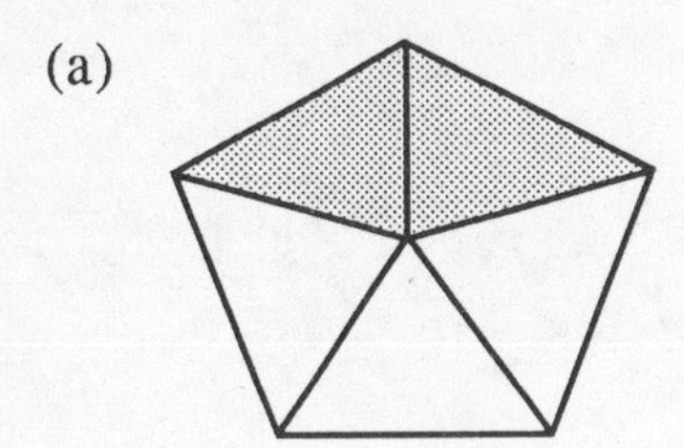

(b)

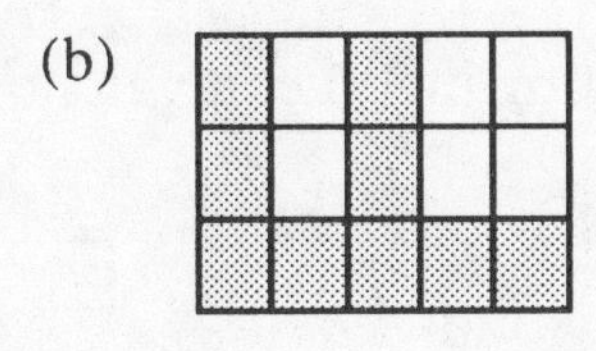

Q5. Shade in:

(a) $\frac{1}{3}$

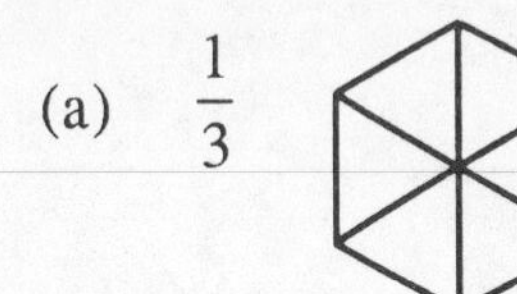

(b) $\frac{3}{4}$

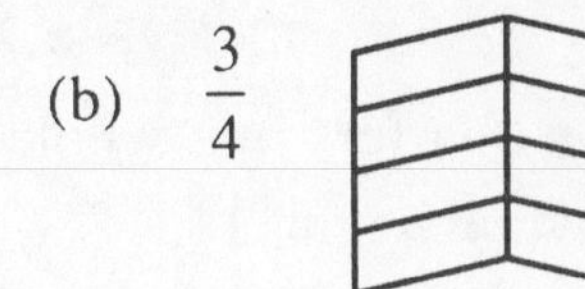

Q6. What percentage has been shaded?

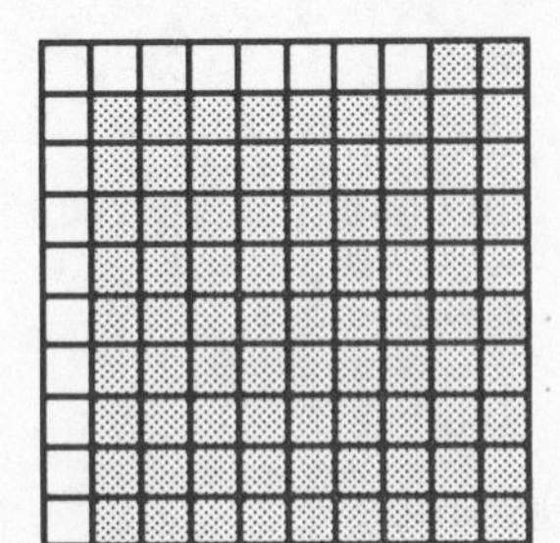

LEVEL 2 FRACTIONS **Continued**

Q7. Shade in the percentage given.

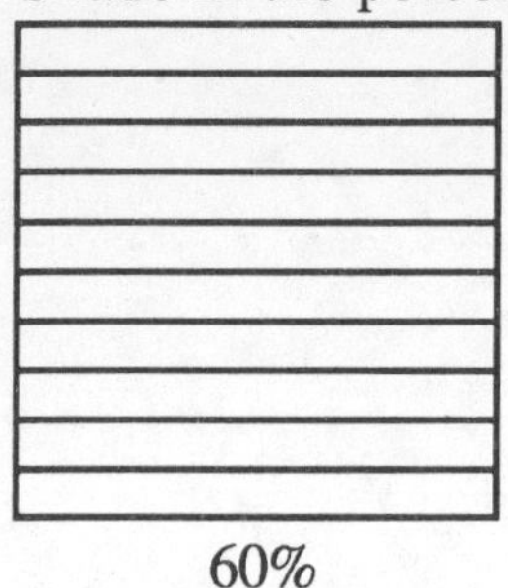

60%

Q8. Change the following fractions to percentages:

(a) $\frac{63}{100}$ (b) $\frac{8}{10}$ (c) $\frac{12}{20}$ (d) $\frac{20}{25}$

Q9. Change the following percentages to decimals:

(a) 16% (b) 9% (c) 32% (d) 100%

Q10. Change the following to equivalent fractions:

(a) $\frac{2}{3} = \frac{\square}{9}$ (b) $\frac{3}{4} = \frac{\square}{8}$ (c) $\frac{4}{5} = \frac{\square}{15}$

Q11. (a)
```
   16.73
   53.21
 +  8.97
 -------
```
(b)
```
   68.35
 - 14.93
 -------
```
(c)
```
   12.5
 ×    7
 ------
```
(d) $6\overline{)13.8}$

Q12. (a) What fraction is 15 minutes of 1 hour?
(b) What fraction is 4 days of 1 week?
(c) What fraction is 3 millimetres of 1 centimetre?

Q.13 (a) \$132 + \$76.08 + 72 cents + \$15.94
(b) \$100 – \$16.72
(c) \$7.42 × 10
(d) \$13.50 ÷ 10

Q.14 Find the percentages of the quantities shown.

(a) 10% of 1 kilogram (b) 25% of 1 litre
(c) 60% of \$2.00 (d) 75% of 2 metres

LEVEL 3 DIVISION

DIFFICULT QUESTIONS

Q1. Write the shaded area as a decimal.

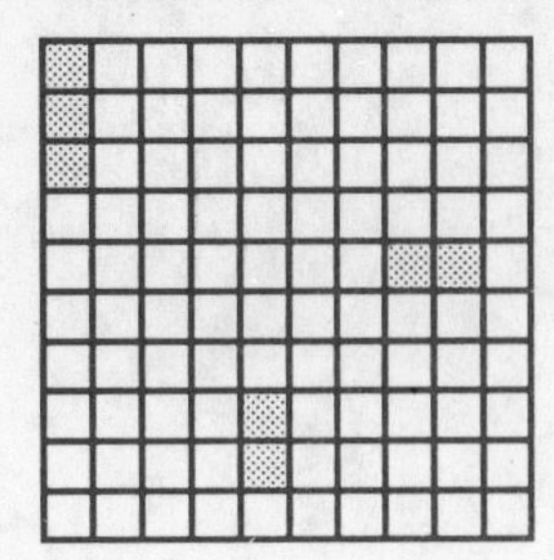

Q2. What is the place value of 7 in the following?

(a) 137.02 (b) 18.67

Q3. Order the following numbers from greatest to least:

1.34, 1.04, 1.4, 1.3, 1.43

Q4. Name the shaded parts of each figure.

(a)

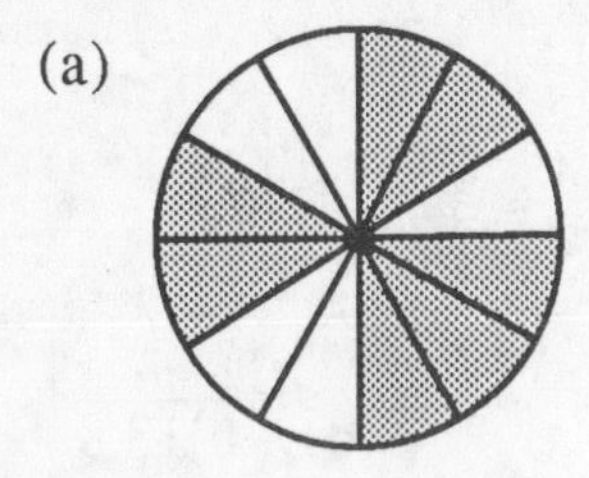

(b)

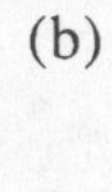

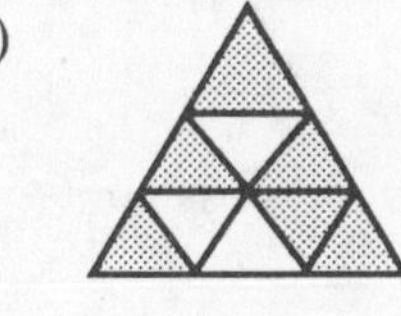

Q5. Shade in:

(a) $\frac{1}{3}$

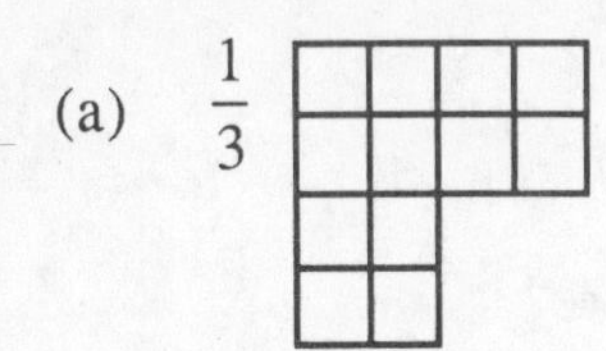

(b) $\frac{5}{8}$

Q6. What percentage has been shaded?

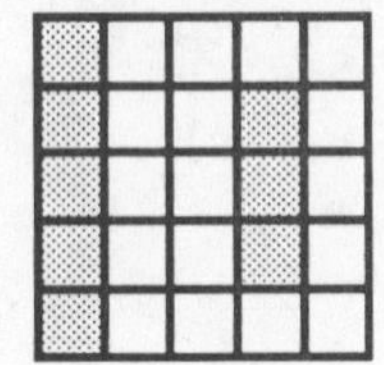

LEVEL 3 FRACTIONS Continued

Q7. Shade in the percentage given.

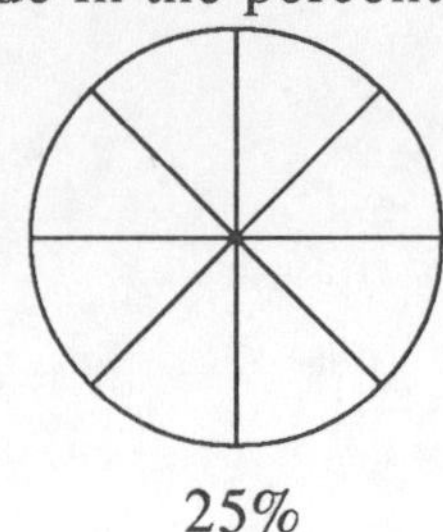

25%

Q8. Change the following fractions to percentages:

(a) $\frac{4}{25}$ (b) $\frac{160}{500}$ (c) $\frac{31}{50}$ (d) $\frac{3}{5}$

Q9. Change the following decimals to percentages:

(a) 0.25 (b) 0.82 (c) 0.09 (d) 0.6

Q10. Change the following to equivalent fractions:

(a) $\frac{3}{5} = \frac{\square}{20}$ (b) $\frac{3}{4} = \frac{\square}{20}$ (c) $\frac{2}{7} = \frac{\square}{21}$

Q11. (a) \$8.60 + \$4.98 + \$128.37 + \$0.70
(b) \$9.63 × 27
(c) \$33.04 ÷ 7
(d) 8.1 – 3.95 ÷ 5 + 6.4

Q12. (a) What fraction is 150 mL of 1 litre?
(b) What fraction is 80 cents of \$4.00?
(c) What fraction is 125 grams of 1 kilogram?

Q.13 (a) Decrease 13.72 by 5.8.
(b) Find the product of 8.75 and 5.
(c) Find the difference between 18.01 and 3.94.
(d) Find the quotient of 8.75 and 5.

Q.14 What percentage is the first quanity of the second quantity?

(a) 15 seconds, 1 minute
(b) 18 hours, 1 day
(c) 48 cm, 1 metre

Extra page for your own additional notes

MONEY

Money is used by everyone. It is, therefore, important that students become familiar with their currency.

During the final two primary years, students are given further opportunity to investigate the $5, $10, $20, $50 and $100 notes and also the development of currency and the monetary system.

VOCABULARY

Bank, banking, barter, bill, bought, borrow, buy, cash, calculator, catalogue, charge, cheap, coins, cost, costs, counterfeit, credit, currency, customer, delivery, denomination, design, display, docket, dollar, earn, exchange, expensive, free, goods, interest, invoice, less, lend, loss, match, measure, menu, metallic thread, money, more, note, owe, pattern, pay, picture, price, price tag, profit, register, retail, sale, salary, save, sell, sequence, serial number, share, shop assistant, shopkeeper, sold, spend, stock, swap, tendered, total, trade, value, water-mark, wholesale, worth.

CONTENTS

AUSTRALIAN BANK NOTES

Students should by now be familiar with the Australian coins and have had experience shopping and giving change up to $2. The Australian bank notes which are made of plastic and represent larger amounts of money may have been introduced but will need to be investigated further.

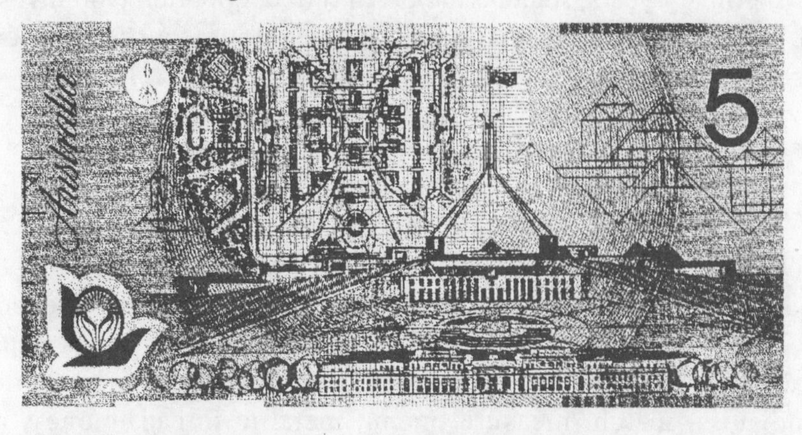

(a) Students should be able to recognise the notes by their colour and the pictures printed on them.
(b) Order the notes from smallest to largest in value and size.
(c) How many e.g. $10 notes could be exchanged for a $50 note?

Students require many opportunities to go 'shopping' so that they become familiar with the Australian currency and can tender amounts and give change with ease.

ACTIVITIES:

1. If a man needed to exchange a $100 note for smaller notes, what are all the possible combinations of notes he could receive? (2 × $50, 5 × $20, $50 + 2 × $20 + $10, 4 × $20 + 2 × $10, etc.)

2. What combination of notes could be used to pay $195?

   ($100 + $50 + 2 × $20 + $5, etc.)

3. A shirt was bought for $55, a pair of pants for $75 and a tie for $23.

   How much was spent?
   If a $100 note, $50 note and a $20 note were tendered how much change would be given?

   ($153 was spent. $17 was given in change.)

4. How many ways can you make $25 with notes.?

   (5 × $5, 2 × $10 + $5, $10 + 3 × $5)

5. Shopping should now involve more items and include items priced in dollars and cents. They should involve problems which compare prices and require judgement of the best value.

5. Opportunities should be given to reinforce addition, subtraction, multiplication and division (sharing) of money using amounts to $2, through larger amounts of whole dollars to larger amounts of dollars and cents.

WHY MONEY?

It is important that students research why money is used and the many ways it is used in everyday life and in commerce. These topics provide excellent opportunities for individual or group investigations. A few suitable focus questions are listed below but there are many more.

ACTIVITIES:

1. What was bartering and why was it used in some communities? Is it still used?
2. Early transactions involved buying items with tokens. What sort of tokens were used, why were they used and where were they used?
3. When and where did coins and money made from paper first appear? Coins have been made from what materials? From what are they made now?
4. Why is money needed and how do people earn it?
5. Research the development of currency throughout Australia's history pre- and post-1788.
6. Where is money made? How is it made? What measures are taken to prevent people making their own copies of paper money?
7. What are banks and credit unions and how do they work?
8. What do the terms profit and loss mean?
9. What is interest and how does it work?
10. Why do people save? Why do people borrow?
11. Why do people use cheques? What is a credit card and how does it work?
12. How can shopkeepers sell their goods so much more cheaply at sale time?
13. What part do advertisements play in e.g. promoting sales or the services offered by a bank?

MONEY ASSESSMENT

Students should understand the following ideas:

Bank notes

- recognise and describe Australian bank notes by colour and their design
- sort notes into the various denominations
- find the total amount of a selection of different bank notes
- trade lesser value notes for those with greater value and vice versa
- tender the correct bank notes for a given amount
- tender a suitable greater valued note to pay for an object of specified cost
- tender the correct change

The concept of currency

- describe bartering
- understand why notes and coins were introduced
- run a shop in class or at home
- explain how money is earned
- understand the basic principles of saving, interest, banks, building societies, credit cards, etc.

LEVEL 1 MONEY

EASIER QUESTIONS

Q1. (a) $\begin{array}{r}\$17.35\\ +\ \ 8.72\\ \hline \\ \hline\end{array}$ (b) $\begin{array}{r}\$183.47\\ -\ \ 63.15\\ \hline \\ \hline\end{array}$ (c) $\begin{array}{r}\$3.47\\ \times\ \ \ 5\\ \hline \\ \hline\end{array}$

(d) $5\overline{)\$6.25}$ (e) $\begin{array}{r}\$19.53\\ 5.41\\ +\ 0.39\\ \hline \\ \hline\end{array}$

Q2. On a certain day Bill spends $18.59 on taxi fares, $8.49 on lunch and $4.38 on dry cleaning. How much does he spend altogether?

Q3. Patricia spends $1.68 on sweets, $3.45 on a hamburger and 70 cents on bus fares.

(a) How much does she spend in total?

(b) How much change does she have left from $20?

Q4. Conrad has $100 in a savings account which pays 10% interest per year (i.e. per annum). How much interest will Conrad earn in one year? If he adds this interest to his savings account, how much interest will he earn in his second year?

Q5. Anne has saved $150. She spends 10% of her savings on a T-shirt. How much did the T-shirt cost?

Q6. Yolanda spent 25% of her pocket money on magazines costing $5. How much money did she have to begin with?

Q7. Find the total cost of $2\frac{1}{2}$ kg of prawns at $12.50 per kg and $1\frac{1}{2}$ kg of mussells at $3.50 per kg.

AVERAGE QUESTIONS

Q1. (a) \$369.14 + \$70.32 + \$0.15

(b) \$793.58 + 16 cents + \$205.07 + \$48.35

(c) \$72.35 – \$16.47

(d) \$49.53 – \$6.41 – \$12.85

Q2. A butcher charges \$8.40 per kilogram of steak. How much would it cost to buy 2.5 kilograms of steak?

Q3. Dress material costs \$4.90 per metre. How much will it cost Mrs. Roberts to buy 0.6 metres?

Q4. Damien buys a new car for \$15 500. After one year the car has lost 15% of its original value. What is the value of Damien's car after 1 year?

Q5. What is the interest earned on \$600 at 15% p.a. in 1 year. Each year the interest is given to charity. How much interest will have been given away to charity after 4 years?

Q6. Jemima puts \$500 into a savings account for 1 year and earns \$25 interest. What is the interest rate per year on the account?

Q7. Joe gets paid \$620 for working a 40-hour week. How much does he get paid per hour?

Q8. At the first stall, Peter bought 6 mangoes and 5 oranges. Each orange cost 40 cents less than each mango. He paid \$15.60 altogether. How much did a mango cost and how much did an orange cost?

DIFFICULT QUESTIONS

Q1. (a) $8.16 × 12 (b) $51.03 ÷ 9 (c) 0.6 of $1.50

Q2. Gretchen gets paid $12.08 per hour. How much does she get paid for working 38 hours?

Q3. Mr. O'Brien has to pay 36 cents tax for every $1 he earns. How much tax will he have to pay if he earns $450?

Q4. Find the interest earned on $3 000 at 12% p.a. for half a year (i.e. 6 months).

Q5. Decrease (make smaller) the following amounts by 10%:

(a) $60 (b) $84 (c) $135

Q6. Increase (make larger) the following amounts by 10%:

(a) $80 (b) $210 (c) $350

Q7. Last year a new car cost $27 800. This year the price has risen by 8%. What is the price of the car this year?

Q8. Darlene bought a second-hand bicycle for $80, and after repainting it she sold it for $110.00.

(a) What is her profit?

(b) What is the profit as a percentage of the cost price?

Q9. Mrs Nutbeam bought some material for $41.60 @ $5.20 per metre. She made 6 identical tops for the school play and had 0.5 m left over. How much material was used in each top?

CHANCE AND DATA

page

INTRODUCTION

Chance or probability, is the likelihood of an even occurring.

Chance plays a quite significant role in everyday life, influencing many of the decisions we make. Weather predictions, many games and competitions, etc. involve an element of chance. We can assess the possible result but cannot be absolutely certain.

It is important that people have the ability to understand and interpret the vast amount of information with which they must deal every day.

To develop skills needed to help in the assessment of chance and also the interpretation of information, a student needs to conduct probability experiments, sort the information collected, record this information and then be able to interpret the findings. Such activities help to reinforce the fact that there are many situations where there is no one 'right' answer but many possible solutions.

Following on from previous experiences, in Years 5 and 6, the experiments are now more complex and the discussion, explanations and comparisons more in depth. Data should be organised in different ways to solve different problems, and recorded in appropriate ways, e.g. bar graphs, tables, etc. By interpreting data, students should be able to order situations from least likely to most likely.

Students should develop an awareness of the limitations of statistical data. They should also be questioning whether assumptions made from given data are reasonable.

Experience with probability and data allows students to develop the skills whereby they can make reasoned judgements, form reasonable opinions and reach reasonable conclusions.

Whilst chance and data are treated as a separate strand in this book, they are in fact closely interlinked with all the other mathematics strands and also with all areas of the curriculum.

VOCABULARY

Always, average, biased, calculators, certain, chance, collect, common, data, deduce, difference, equal, estimate, even, fair, fifty-fifty, gather, graph, impossible, interpret, least likely, less, line graph, lucky, might, more, most, never, often, organise, outcomes, patterns, pictogram, predict, possible, probability, probably, random, record, sample, sort, survey, systematic, table, tally, total, typical, uncertain, unlikely.

DATA COLLECTION

Data collection can be fun as students enjoy observing and then tallying, graphing and interpreting their observations. For example, they may wish to know the most frequently seen colour of car passing the school. This can only be achieved by observing, tallying and totalling. It is important, and enjoyable, to predict the colour first. The data must be analysed and a conclusion drawn:

> "The most frequently seen colour of car passing school was blue because the blue car column on our graph is the longest'.
>
> 'The pink car column is shortest, so it was seen the least.'

This may lead the children to make more predictions:

> 'It is more likely to be a blue car which will pass by than a pink car.'

This encourages them to use their data to make predictions and talk in terms of 'chance' or 'data'.

ACTIVITIES:

1. (a) Make a list of things that always happen.

   (b) Make a list of things that sometimes happen.

   (c) Make a list of things that will never happen.

   (d) Re-sort the lists under the following headings

certain	very likely	equal chance	unlikely	impossible

2. (a) Predict how many different shoe sizes are worn by the students in the class. Give reasons for the predictions. Are the predictions reasonable?

   (b) Collect and record the shoe size data in appropriate ways with tallying and graphs (see Graphs substrand). Were the predictions accurate?

   (c) Discuss the data. Can any conclusions be drawn?

   (d) Were the methods of collecting and organising the data appropriate? Was the correct interpretation made?

   (e) Using the data collected, what other questions could be posed?

CHANCE/PROBABILITY

Some occurrences have a more simple mathematical basis and it is possible to predict the chances or probability of some events occurring.

Coin tossing
Since a coin can land 2 ways—'heads' or 'tails', clearly there is a 1 in 2 chance of it landing 'heads'.

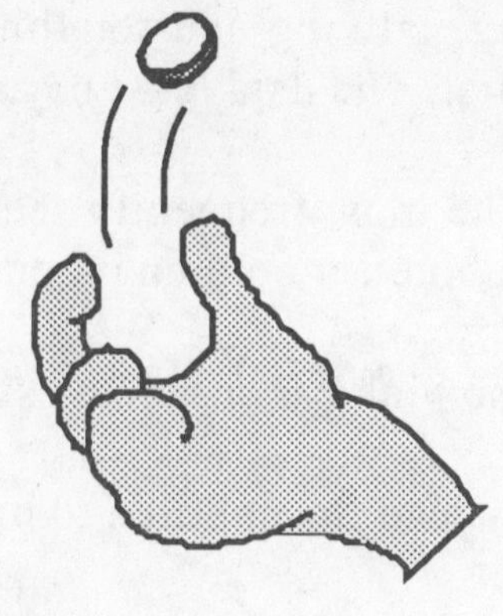

Rolling a die
However, a six-faced die only has:

a 1 in 6 chance of showing a 3

or a 1 in 6 chance of showing a 5.

Birthdays
There is a 1 in 12 chance of being born in August, a 1 in 7 chance of being born on a Tuesday and a 1 in 365 (or 366) chance of being born on Christmas Day.

These probabilities are worked out by first establishing the total number of possibilities.

When 2 coins are tossd, they can land **H**(ead) **H**(ead), **H**(ead) **T**(ail), **TH**, **TT**. There are 4 possibilities. **HH** has a 1 in 4 chance of being tossed, as does **TT**.

A mixture of faces **HT** or **TH** has 2 in 4 chances of being tossed, i.e. 1 in 2. Therefore, a mixture of faces is twice as likely to be tossed as **HH** or **T T**.

This mathematical approach should be encouraged because students too readily allow their heart to rule their head. For example, most students when asked the probability of cutting an ace from a pack of cards would say the chances were poorer than of cutting the ace from the diamonds suit alone. In fact, the chances are the same—1 in 13.

By expressing results in terms of chances it is possible to compare the probability of one event occurring as compared with another.

A 1 in 2 chance of 2 coins showing a mixture of faces gives a greater probability than a 1 in 4 chance of a pair of 'heads' or a pair of 'tails'.

Example:
There are 5 black marbles, 3 blue marbles and 2 red marbles in a bag.

(a) If one marble is drawn out, what is the chance that it is blue?

(b) What is the chance that it is black or red?

Solution:
(a) Altogether there is a total of $5 + 3 + 2 = 10$ marbles in the bag.
3 of these marbles are blue out of the total of 10.

Therefore my chance of picking a blue one is 3 out of 10 or $\frac{3}{10}$

(b) Once again, there is still a total of 10 marbles in the bag.
8 of these are either black or red.

Therefore my chance of picking a black or red marble is 8 out of 10 or $\frac{8}{10}$

NOTE:
We normally leave the answer as a fraction. However, we could have written the answers to the last example in 4 ways:

$\frac{8}{10}$ **(fraction form)** **0.8 (decimal form)** **80% (percentage)**

$\frac{4}{5}$ **(simplified fraction form)**

THE OUTCOMES OF THROWING 2 DICE

It is important to understand this idea because so many board games (monopoly, backgammon, etc.) involve chances relating to dice. Imagine one red and one blue die. If we rolled the dice, there are many different possibilities or outcomes that could occur. Always keep in mind that a 4 on the red die and a 2 on the blue die is a different outcome to a 2 on the red die and a 4 on the blue die.

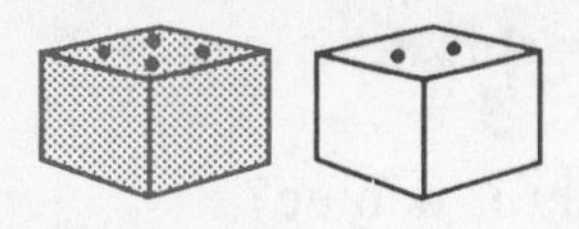

is a different outcome to

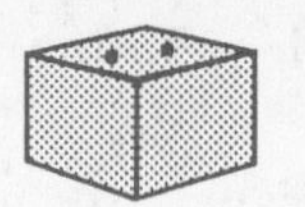

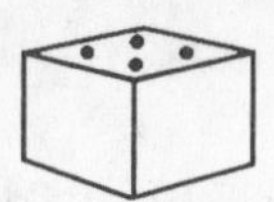

There are 36 different possibilities or outcomes:

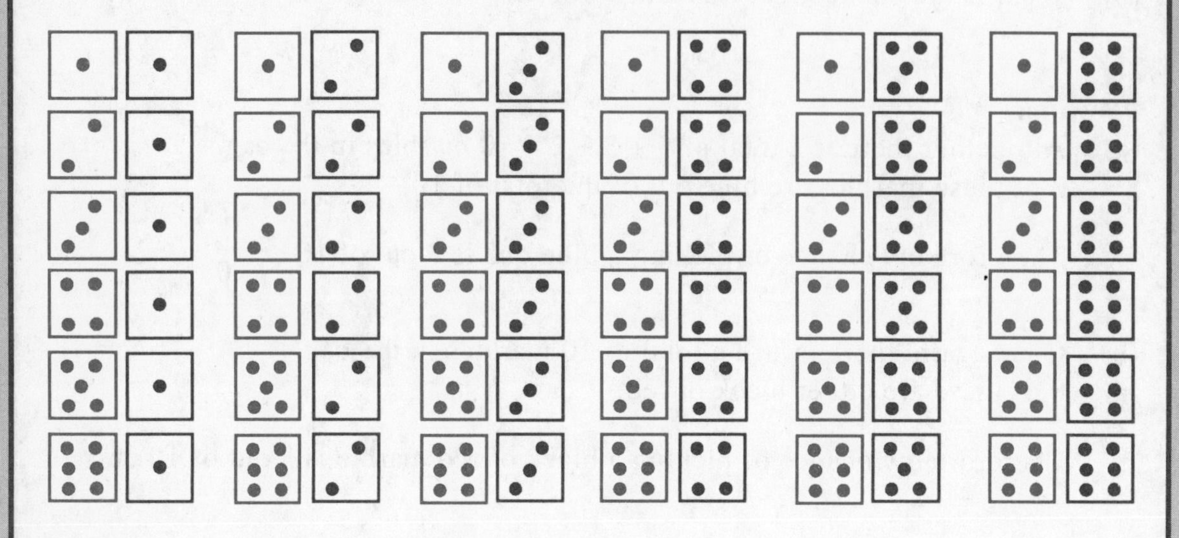

Questions:

(a) How many ways are there of getting a total of 4?
What is the chance of getting a total of 4?

(b) How many ways are there of getting a total of 5?
What is the chance of getting a total of 5?

(c) If you threw the 2 dice a large amount of times which total would you expect to turn up most times?

Solutions:

(a) There are 3 ways of getting a total of 4.

The chance is 3 out of 36 or $\frac{3}{36}$.

(b) There are 4 ways of getting a total of 5.

The chance is 4 out of 36 or $\frac{4}{36}$.

(c) There are more ways of getting a total of 7 than any other total. Therefore the total of 7 should accur most times.

ACTIVITIES:

1. (i) Make a list of things which are judged to have an equal or fifty-fifty chance of happening,
   (ii) Make a list of everyday happenings and place them in order from those which are most likely to happen through to those which are least likely to happen. Give reasons for their position in the ranking.

2. Make predictions about the favourite food of members of the group.
   (i) What information would be needed to find out which food was the favourite? Does this refer to snack food, breakfast food, fruit, etc.?
   (ii) What question(s) would be needed to find the answer?
   (iii) Decide on how to classify the data.
   (iv) Record the data in an appropriate form, firstly by summarising with tallying and then by representing the data (in column, line, bar or pictographs, tables or diagrams).
   (v) Describe the frequency of each of the foods as represented. Were the predictions accurate? What other comments can be made about the results?
   (vi) Could this data be used to answer other questions?

3. Read, analyse and describe information from column, line, bar or pictographs, tables or diagrams found in newspapers, magazines, etc.

4. Make or purchase some raffle tickets.
   (i) Give out one raffle ticket to each member of the group.
   (ii) If there is one prize, what are the chances of winning? Give reasons for this result
   (iii) If there are two prizes, what are the chances of winning? Give reasons for this result
   (iv If there is one prize and each person has two tickets, what are the chances of winning? Give reasons for this result.
   (v) What other questions could be asked about raffles?

5. (i) Pose questions relating to the amount of pocket money received by children.
   (ii) Select an appropriate, fair sample of people and then collect the necessary data.
   (iii) Organise and represent the data in an appropriate form.
   (iv) Prepare a report on the findings.
   (v) Evaluate the validity of the data collected, the way that it was presented and whether inferences were correctly made

CHANCE AND DATA ASSESSMENT

Students should understand the following ideas:

- demonstrates an understanding of the terms 'chance' and 'probability'
- differentiate between certain and uncertain
- predict the likelihood of an everyday happening using the appropriate terminology from 'unlikely' through 'fifty-fifty' to 'likely'
- pose questions individually and in discussion with others to help solve a problem
- systematically list possible results (outcomes)
- classify and sequence data, varying the classification according to the problem
- record data from investigations in appropriate ways graphs, tables, charts
- predict the order of probability of the outcomes
- conduct experiments to compare the predictions with the results
- predict then conduct experiments to solve problems in situations which require testing to find the results
- represent, analyse and discuss data in response to questions formulated by self or others
- show understanding of samples
- select appropriate samples for specific investigations and draw conclusions from the data collected
- judge the validity of assumptions made about given data

LEVEL 1—CHANCE AND DATA

EASIER QUESTIONS

Q1. A coin is tossed once. What are the chances of tossing:

(a) a head? (b) a tail?

Q2. 3 marbles: 1 red, 1 blue and 1 green, are put in a bag. If one marble is drawn out of the bag, what is the chance that it is:

(a) green? (b) red? (c) blue?

Q3. 2 white balls and 1 black ball are put in a bag. 1 ball is drawn out. What is the chance that the ball is:

(a) black? (b) white?

Q4. Take 4 cards and draw a different picture on each one. Place the cards in a bag.

Draw out one card, record the picture and then replace the card in the bag. Repeat the process 50 times.

Collect the data on a frequency chart and prepare a column graph.

(a) What are the chances of picking out each picture?
(b) Looking at the graph, which card was picked:

(i) most often? (ii) least often?

(c) Repeat the experiment having predicted if the results are likely to be the same, similar or different.

Q5. Are winning LOTTO numbers more likely to be ODD or EVEN or are the chances equal?

Q6. What are the chances of being born (a) in January (b) on a Monday?

Q7. By looking at page 106 you will see that there are 36 different ways that 2 dice can be thrown.

(a) How many ways are there of getting a total of 10?
(b) What are the chances of getting a total of 10?
(c) What are the chances of throwing a double six?
(d) What are the chances of throwing any double?

LEVEL 2—CHANCE AND DATA

AVERAGE QUESTIONS

Q1. Two coins are tossed at the same time.

(a) How many different ways could the coins land?
(b) What is the chance of the coins showing 2 tails?
(c) What is the chance of the coins showing 1 head and 1 tail?

Q2. A bag contains 3 red lollies, 2 yellow lollies and 1 blue lolly. If I draw 1 lolly out of the bag, what is the chance of the lolly being:

(a) yellow? (b) blue? (c) red?

Q3. Make up 16 cards of the same size. Draw circles on 4 of the cards, squares on 4, triangles on 4 and crosses on the last 4.

Place the cards in a bag.

Draw out 4 cards at a time, and record the number of squares drawn, then place the cards back in the bag.

Repeat for 20 draws, recording the number of squares each time (i.e. each time either no squares, 1, 2, 3 or 4 squares can be drawn out).

Collect the data on a frequency chart and prepare a column graph.

(a) Each time, what is the chance of drawing out a card with a square?
(b) Analyse the graph to discover which number of cards with squares was drawn:

(i) most frequently? (ii) least frequently?

(c) Repeat the experiment having predicted if results are likely to be the same, similar or different.

Q4. Investigate a pack of 52 playing cards:
How many are red and how many are black?
There are 13 of each of the 4 suits.
2 suits are red—hearts and diamonds, and 2 suits are black—spades and clubs.
What are the chances of cutting:
(a) a black card?
(b) a spade?
(c) a heart?
(d) a six?
(e) a picture (Jack, Queen or King)?

LEVEL 3—CHANCE AND DATA

DIFFICULT QUESTIONS

Q1. Three coins are tossed at the same time.

(a) How many different ways can the 3 coins land?
(b) What is the chance of the coins showing 3 heads?
(c) What is the chance of the coins showing 2 tails and 1 head?

Q2. A bag contains 3 white balls and 4 black balls.

(a) If a ball is drawn out, what is the chance that it is:

(i) white? (ii) black?

(b) Lets say the first ball drawn out (in (a)) was black, and it was not put back in the bag. If a second ball is now drawn out of the bag, what is the chance that it is:

(i) white? (ii) black?

Q3. Make up 8 cards—4 of different colours (e.g. red, yellow, green, blue) and 4 with the numbers 1 to 4 written on them.

Place the coloured cards in one bag, and the number cards in another bag.

Predict how many different combinations can be made.

Draw out one card from each bag, record the combination drawn out, and return the cards to their respective bag.

Repeat the experiment for 50 draws.
Collect the data on a frequency chart and prepare a column graph.

Analyse the graph to discover which combination was drawn:

(a) most frequently. (b) least frequently.

Repeat the experiment having predicted if results are likely to be the same, similar or different.

Q4. A target has scores from 1 to 20 arranged randomly on it, each number in a different square on the checkerboard pattern. A dart is thrown at the board without aiming. What are the chances of scoring:

(a) an even score?
(b) a 2?
(c) more than 15?
(d) less than 3?
(e) a multiple of 5?

Extra page for your own additional notes

SPACE STRAND

page

'in doing we learn'

INTRODUCTION

By the time students begin school they will already have learned a lot about themselves in their surroundings through play and interaction with other people and with objects.

This course is designed to build on that knowledge, developing spatial awareness and geometrical understanding so that the student will have the ability to follow directions, read maps, pack or stack objects, order with confidence floor coverings, curtains or furniture that will fit into a particular room, etc.

The four spatial sub-strands are essentially practical. It is only through many hands-on experiences that a student truly understands how to take advantage of the properties of different 2 dimensional and 3 dimensional shapes, how to interpret statistical information represented by diagrams, etc.

The aim is to develop an understanding of space in its broadest sense rather than simply the acquisition of rote learned facts and figures about e.g. length or mass.

CONCRETE MATERIALS

Storage

Bowls, boxes, cartons, containers, jars, shoeboxes.

Materials

adhesive tape, atlases, balloons, balls, board games, boxes, building blocks, cans, cardboard, ceramic tiles, chalk, clay, coloured paper-sheets, circles, squares and rectangles, compasses, containers, cord, crayons, cylinders, dot-to-dot puzzles, Duplo bricks, egg cartons, elastic, fabric, fishing line, foil, fruit, geo-board, geometric shapes, geometric models of prisms, geostrips, glue, graph paper, grid paper, hole punch, hundred square grid paper, hexagonal bricks, isometric dot paper, leaves, Lego bricks, lids, LOGO computer program, magazines, maps, marbles, masking tape, Meccano, Mira mirrors, newspapers, overhead projector, packets, paint, paper fasteners, pattern blocks, pencils, photographs, pipecleaners, plastic blocks, plasticine, playdough, protractors, pyramids, ribbon, rope, rubber bands, scissors, screen, set square, shape templates, soft wire, spirit level, sticks, stickers, street directories, square bricks, straws, string, tangram puzzles, textas, toothpicks, torches, triangular bricks, Unifix, vegetables, wooden blocks, wood off cuts, wool, wrapping paper.

SPACE 3D

It is important that the skills outlined in the first volume of this series are mastered before progressing.

The properties of pyramids, cones and spheres, together with topology and knots, are investigated during Years 5 and 6.

VOCABULARY

arrangements, base, bottom view, circle, circular, clove hitch, cone, corner cross-section, curved, cylinder, double knot, edge, enlarge, enlarger, enlargement. equivalent, face, figure of eight knot, from the front, front view, granny's knot, height, hexagonal, horizontal, knot, looking up (down), microscope, Moebius Strip, pentagonal, prism(s), rectangle, rectangular, reduce, reduction, representation, round turn and two half hitches, scale, side view, sphere, square, surface, telescope, tetrahedron, thumb knot, tie, top view, tighten, tighter, triangle, triangular, untie, vertical, viewpoint, weaver's knot.

CONTENTS

Page

3D REPRESENTED IN 2D

Ensure that all the activities suggested in the previous volumes have been completed before continuing.

An important link is made here with investigations into perspective in the 2D sub-strand.

Students should be developing the ability to recognise 3D objects as they are represented in 2D. This is an understanding of perspective.

Students should be given opportunities to develop their skills in representing 3D objects in 2D.

ACTIVITIES:

1. Study different objects from different sides, the top and the bottom, and draw representations of them, e.g. a saucepan, an aeroplane, a cup. Skill levels increase with practised observation.

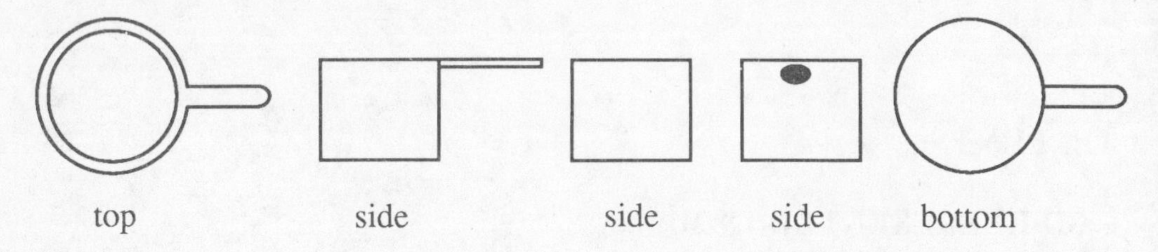

top side side side bottom

2. Make 3D models of objects in pictures or photographs for others to identify.

3. From memory or imagination, draw an object from a specified point of view, e.g. looking down on it.

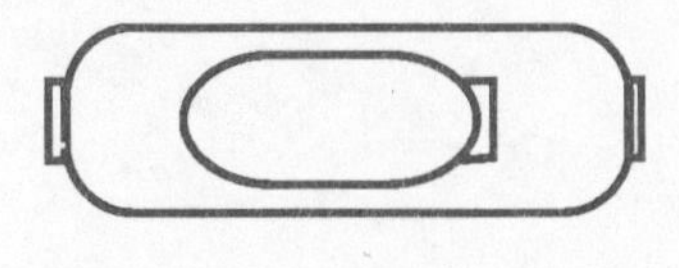

a car

CUBE MODELS AND ISOMETRIC DRAWINGS

ACTIVITIES:

1. Students should make models from inter-locking cubes which are then represented on isometric dot paper. They should also construct models from drawings on isometric dot paper.

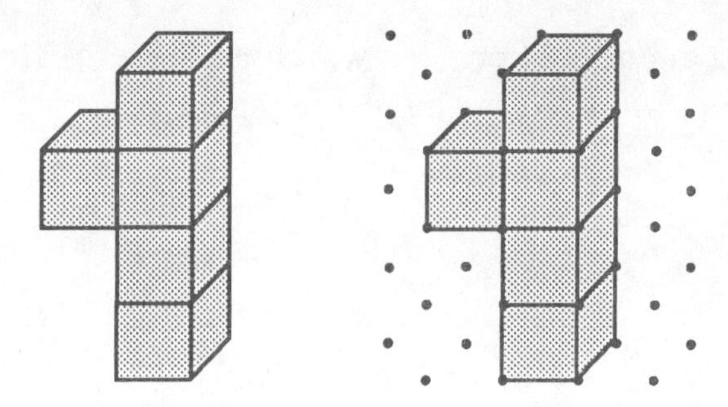

2. (a) Explore the dlfferent possible combinations of 2, 3, 4, etc., interlocking cubes. Represent on isometric paper.

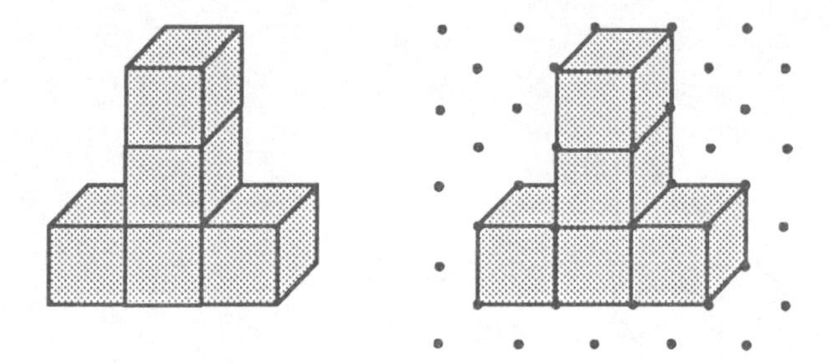

   (b) Draw what a model would look like from the front, side or top. This kind of activity shows how much a student can visualise and manipulate 3D images.

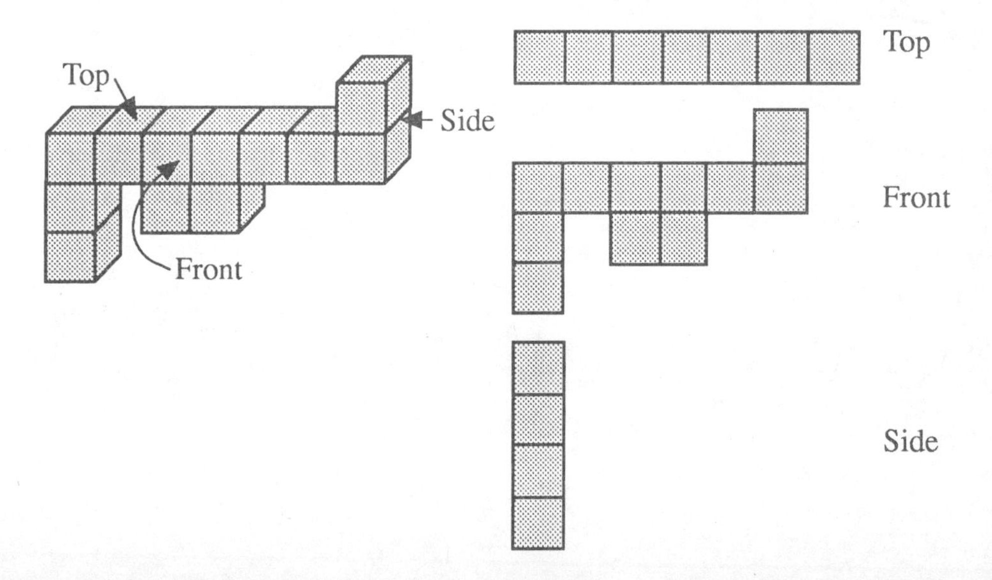

CONES, CYLINDERS AND SPHERES

In the same way that a cylinder could be seen as a 'circular prism', a cone could be seen as a 'circular pyramid'.

A sphere is ball shaped.

All of these solids have curved surfaces which are very difficult to represent in 2D. Shading techniques are used to suggest perspective.

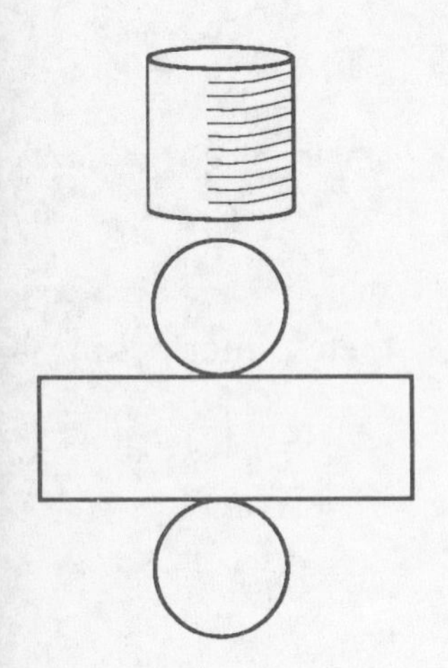

A cylinder has 2 circular faces and 1 curved surface. When opened out and flattened to make a net, the cylinder becomes a rectangle with two circles attached to opposite sides of the rectangle.

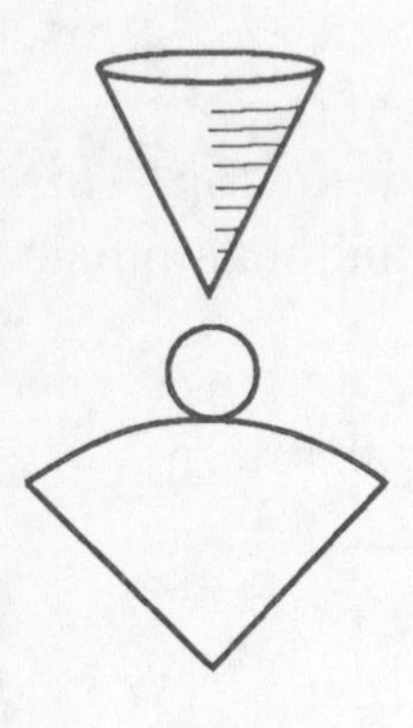

A cone has one circular face. It has a curved surface which tapers away from the circular face to a point (apex). When the cone has been opened and flattened it becomes a circle attached to the sector of a circle.

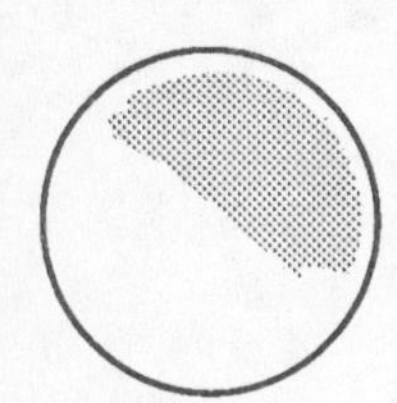

A sphere has one curved surface. Nets cannot be made.

ACTIVITIES:

1. (a) Collect items which are cones, cylinders or spheres. Investigate their edges, surfaces or faces (flat) and corners (vertices). A volcano is cone shaped, a sharpened pencil is a cylinder with a cone attached, a coin is a cylinder.

   Add items to the collection or collect pictures of objects with these shapes

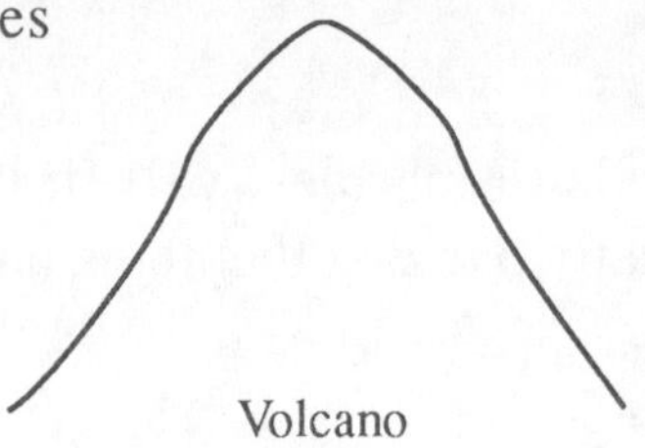

   (b) Explore whether these shapes will roll and/or stack.
   Discuss differences in the way these shapes roll and why.
   How easily does each stack? Which shapes are most popular for packaging and why?
   How would each of these shapes be wrapped?

   (c) Make prints with paint using models of 3D shapes.

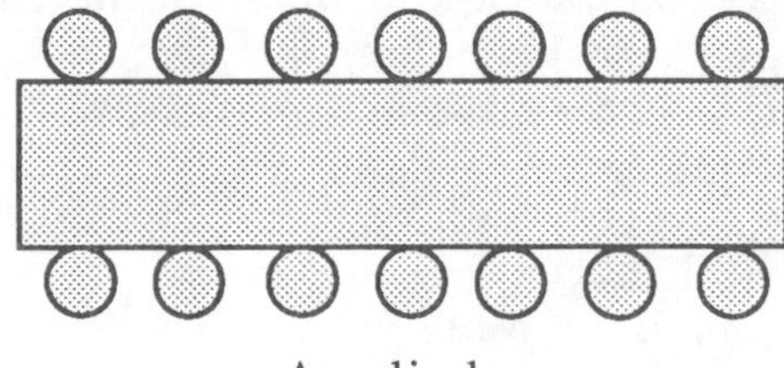

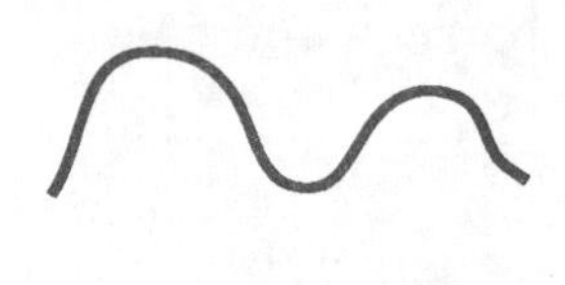

A cylinder   A ball

2. Draw conical, cylindrical and spherical objects from different viewpoints, that is, draw different elevations—from the top, front and sides.

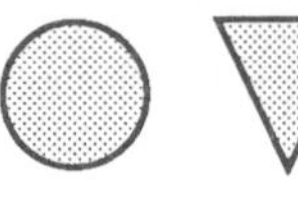
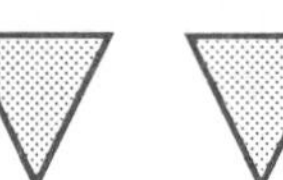

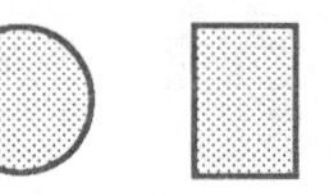
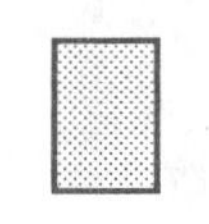
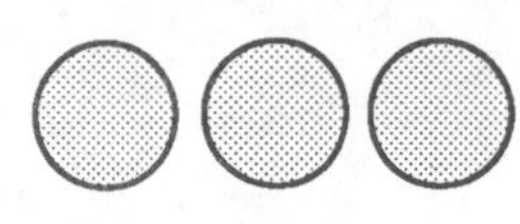

3. Make skeletons of the 3D shapes with e.g. match sticks and plasticine or pipe cleaners where possible, or use clay or plasticine. Investigate their cross-sections.
   Open out conical or cylindrical packaging and design nets.

4. Make models of cones and cylinders from nets.

3D OBJECTS—PACKING PROPERTIES

ACTIVITIES:

1. Explore why various objects are particular shapes.
   e.g. Cylindrical objects and triangular prisms are strong.
   Rectangular prisms pack with no spaces.
   Circular items will roll, etc.
   etc.

2. Estimate how many items, e.g. pencils or marbles, will fit into a particular container. Check the estimate by actually packing the items into the container. How close was the estimate?

3. Create testing procedures to test various shapes for strength and rigidity. Experiment with the tests and discuss the results and their significance.

4. Students produce isometric drawings of stacks of cubes. Partners calculate how many are in the stack, how many have one, two, three or more faces showing and how many cubes cannot be seen from this viewpoint

   Make models from the drawings. Now, calculate again to answer the above questions but this time looking all around the stack rather than from one viewpoint. Will the answers be the same? Colour or mark the faces which can be seen and check the answers.

Examples:

(a) How many cubes are in the stack?
(b) How many cannot be seen from this viewpoint?
(c) How many have one face showing from this viewpoint?
(d) How many have 2, 3, and 4 faces showing from this viewpoint?
(e) How many cannot be seen at all from any viewpoint?
(f) How many have 1, 2, 3 or 4 faces showing when the stack is viewed from all directions?

Solutions:

(a) 27 cubes
(b) 6 cubes
(c) 1 face — 11 cubes
(d) 2 faces—8 cubes; 3 faces—2 cubes.
(e) All cubes can be seen.
(f) 1 face—3 cubes; 2 faces—10 cubes; 3 faces—12 cubes; 4 faces—2 cubes.

POLYHEDRA

Solids with polygons for surfaces are known as polyhedra.

The surfaces of a polyhedron are flat and the edges are straight. Cones, spheres and cylinders are not polyhedra.

A particular group of polyhedra are the **platonic solids**.

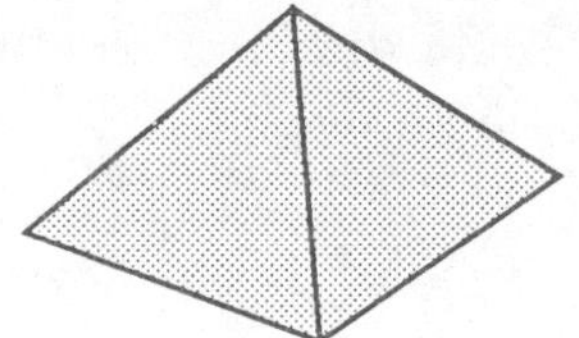

The tetrahedron — 4 equilaterial triangles as faces

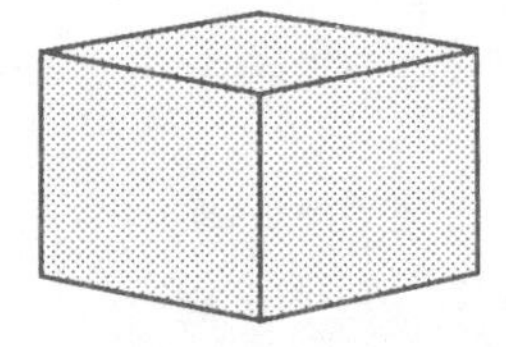

The cube — 6 squares as faces

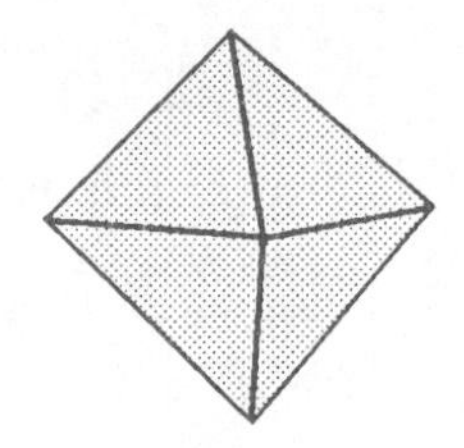

The octahedron — 8 equilateral triangles as faces

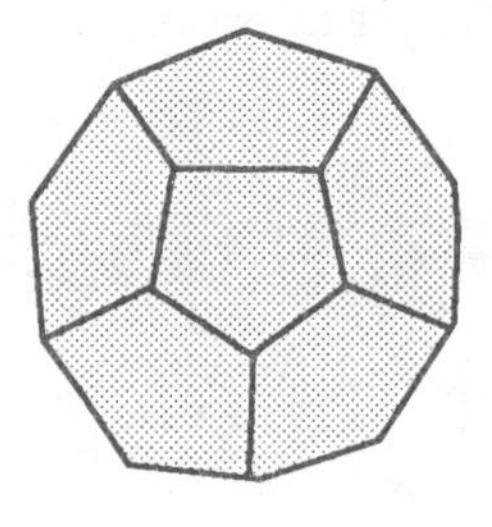

The dodecahedron — 12 regular pentagons as faces

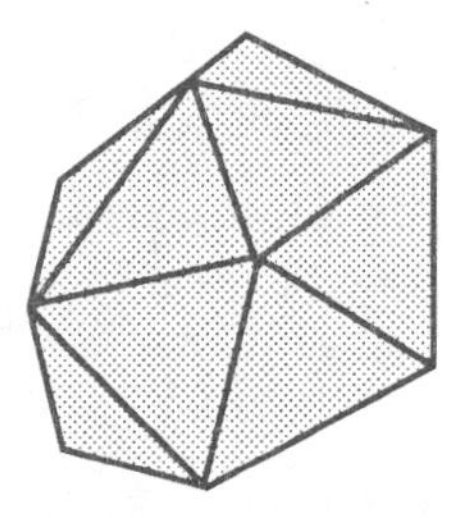

The icosahedron — 20 equilateral triangles as faces

ACTIVITIES:

1. Explore the faces, edges and corners (vertices) of various polyhedra. Record the results of the investigations in a table. Discuss. Is there a pattern?
2. Construct the platonic solids with e.g. straws and plasticine or pipe cleaners. Examine and explain why they are special.

SCALE

Scale is a means of proportionally reducing or enlarging the size of an object so that it can be represented on paper with a scale drawing.

Scale enables large tracts of land to be scaled down and represented as maps or plans on paper, or life size, e.g. yachts to be built from prototype models and plans by scaling up.

Reduction: Reduction produces a scale drawing smaller than the object. The size of the object is 'scaled down'.

e.g. A ratio of 1:10 means the drawing is ten times shorter than the actual object (not 10 times smaller).

1 centimetre on the drawing represents 10 centimetres on the object.

Enlargement: An enlargement is a scale drawing larger than the actual object. The size of the object is 'scaled up'.

e.g. A Ratio of 10:1 means that the drawing is 10 times longer than the object.

10 cm on the scaled drawing represents 1 cm on the actual object.

Scale is expressed in three ways.

(a) as a statement. 1 cm represents 50 cm

(b) as a diagram.

0 50 100
centimetres

(c) as a ratio. 1:50

All of these ways mean that 1 cm on the plan or map represents 50 cm on the ground.

NOTE: When a tracing is made its ratio is 1:1.

ACTIVITIES:

1. Link with Area and Volume sub-strands.

   (a) Begin by drawing a simple shape on grid paper and calculating its area. Draw an enlargement by doubling the length of the sides. Estimate the area of the enlargement before calculating. Explain the result. Continue with more complex drawings.

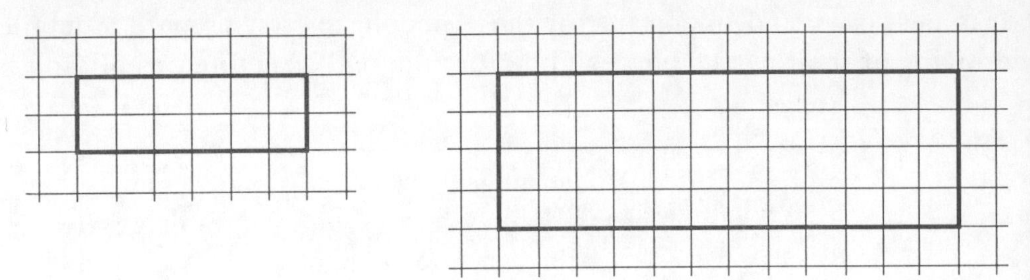

   (b) Draw a representation of a small rectangular prism on isometric paper. Calculate the volume. Double the length of all the dimensions. Estimate, then calculate, the volume of the enlargement. Explain the result. Continue with more complex drawings.

2. Use centicubes to make a simple model. Build a new, but similar, model by enlarging the scale. Repeat but reduce the scale from the original.

   Build models to a specified enlargement or reduction, e.g. twice as big or half as big. Estimate, then calculate, how many cubes will be used in the different models.

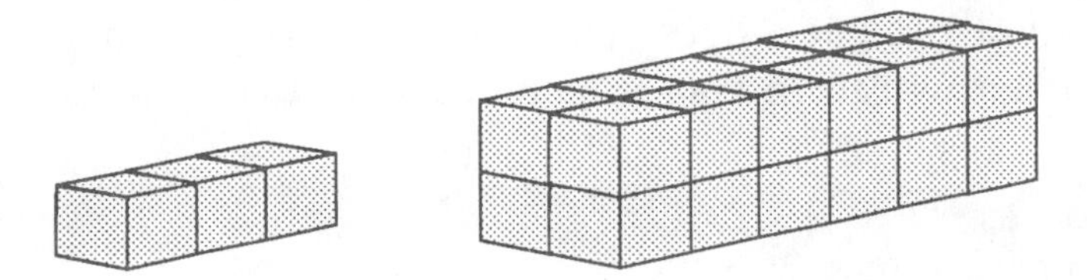

3. Look at photographs and pictures and discuss why they are or are not life-size.

4. Examine plans of buildings or sites, and maps in street directories or atlases. Look at the scales used. Which are used most frequently? Using these scales, calculate distances following certain routes or between given places.

SCALE DRAWINGS

Scale drawings are used a great deal by many professions including: Architects, Draftsmen, Engineers, Town planners, Builders, Designers of cars, aeroplanes, boats, etc.

It is necessary and important for these people to first prepare a detailed scaled drawing of their particular design before the real structure or building is built.

> A scaled drawing has exactly the same shape of the object they represent, but a different size (usually very much smaller).

Example (i): Look at a typical map scale and answer the following:

METRES

0 200 400 600 800 1000

(a) How many metres do 3 cm represent?

(b) How many metres does 1 mm represent?

(c) How many metres do 4.6 cm represent?

(d) If the actual distance between the Post Office and the Town Hall is 1640 m, what will the distance be on the map?

Solutions:

(a) 1 cm represents 200 m

$\therefore$ 3 cm represents 600 m

(b) 1 cm represents 200 m

$\therefore$ 1 mm = $\frac{1}{10}$ cm represents 20 m

(c) 1 cm represents 200 m

$\therefore$ 4.6 mm represents $4 \times 200 + 6 \times 20 = 920$ m

(d) 200 m is represented by 1 cm

$\therefore$ 1600 m is represented by 8 cm

20 m is represented by 1 mm = 0.1 cm

$\therefore$ 40 m is represented by 2 mm = 0.2 cm

$\therefore$ 1640 m is represented on the map by 8.2 cm.

Example (ii):
An architect has to design a new upstairs extension to an existing house. His design plans are shown below using a scale of 1 cm to 1 m.

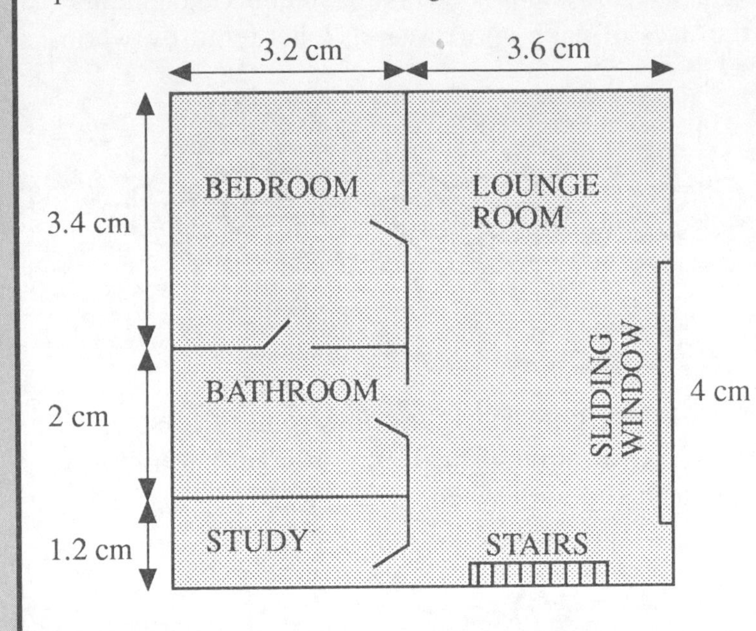

(a) What is the real size of the bedroom?

(b) What is the real width of the study?

(c) What is the real length of the lounge room?

(d) How wide are the sliding windows?

Solutions: Scale is 1 cm to 100 cm or 1:100.

(a) Scaled length and breadth of bedroom is 3.2 cm long and 3.4 cm wide.
Real length is $3.2 \times 100 = 320$ cm = 3.2 m long.
Real width is $3.4 \times 100 = 340$ cm = 3.4 m wide.

(b) Scaled width of study is 1.2 cm wide.
Real width of study is $1.2 \times 100 = 120$ cm = 1.2 m wide.

(c) Scaled length of lounge room is $3.4 + 2.0 + 1.2 = 6.6$ cm long.
Real length of lounge room is $6.6 \times 100 = 660$ cm = 6.6 m long.

(d) Scaled width of window is 4 cm.
Real width of window is 4 cm $\times$ 100 = 400 cm = 4 m wide.

Example (iii):
An aeroplane designer first builds a scaled model of the plane on a scale 1 cm to 68 cm. If the wingspan of the model is 32 cm, what will the wingspan of the real plane be?

Solution:
Scale is 1 cm to 68 cm or 1:68

$\therefore$ 1 cm on model = 68 cm on real plane
$\therefore$ 32 cm on model = 32×68 cm
= 2176 cm = 21.76 m.

KNOTS

Students should use thin cord to investigate and practice tying and untying a number of knots. They should learn the uses of each and research where and by whom each would be used.

thumb (or overhand) knot figure of eight knot

The thumb, or overhand knot, and the figure of eight knot are used to stop the rope or cord pulling through a hole. A variation of the figure of eight knot, known as the packer's knot, can be used as a slip knot when tying parcels.

double thumb knot

The double thumb knot, or fisherman's knot, is often used to join two fishing lines together

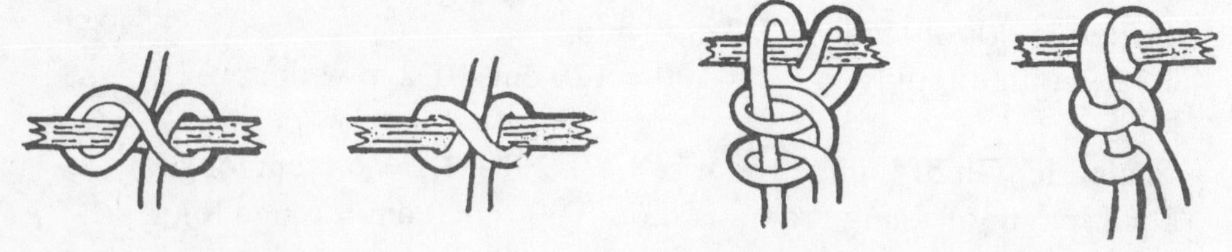

clove hitch round turn and two half hitches

The clove hitch and the round turn and two half hitches are used to fasten rope to a pole or through a loop. They don't slip and are difficult to untie.

reef (or square) knot weavers knot (or sheet bend)

The reef, or square, knot and the weaver's knot, or sheet bend, are useful for joining 2 pieces of rope. When joining one thick and one thin use the weaver's knot.

THE MOEBIUS STRIP

1. (a) Cut 3 strips of paper 30 cm by 2 cm. On each strip draw a coloured line down the centre of one side.

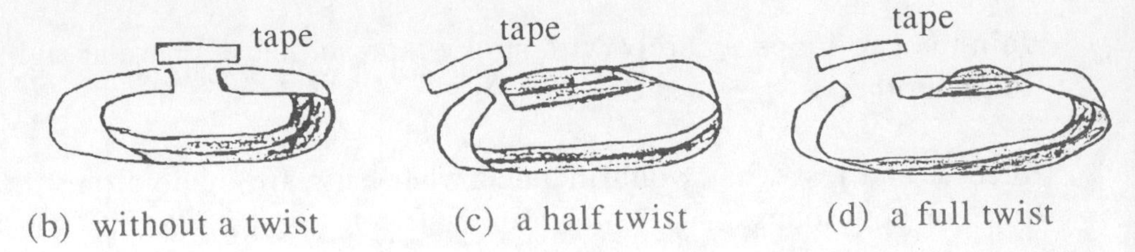

(b) without a twist (c) a half twist (d) a full twist

(b) Join the ends of one strip to make a loop without any twists. Investigate the loop and discuss with a partner how many edges and faces it has.

Predict and then discover what would happen when one partner cut along the line drawn down the centre of the loop.

(c) Join the ends of the second strip giving a half twist before sticking. Investigate the loop. How many edges and faces does it have? Check by drawing a pencil line down the centre of the loop. Also draw a line very close to the edge to check the number of edges. What fascinating discoveries are made?

Predict and test what will happen when a cut is made all along the coloured centre line.

This loop with a half twist is known as a Moebius Strip.

(d) Join the ends of the third loop giving a full twist before sticking. How many faces and edges does it have? Careful! Investigate the loop and discuss with a partner. Draw a pencil line down the centre of the length to check the number of faces.

Predict and test what will happen if a cut is made down the length of the coloured centre line.

No solutions—Try it!

2. Research where and why Moebius strips are used.

PAPER RINGS

ACTIVITIES:

1. Cut two 30 cm by 2 cm strips of paper. Make each into a simple loop.

   Join the two loops securely with sticky tape so that they are at right angles to each other.

   Predict and test what would happen when cuts are made along the centre lines of both loops.

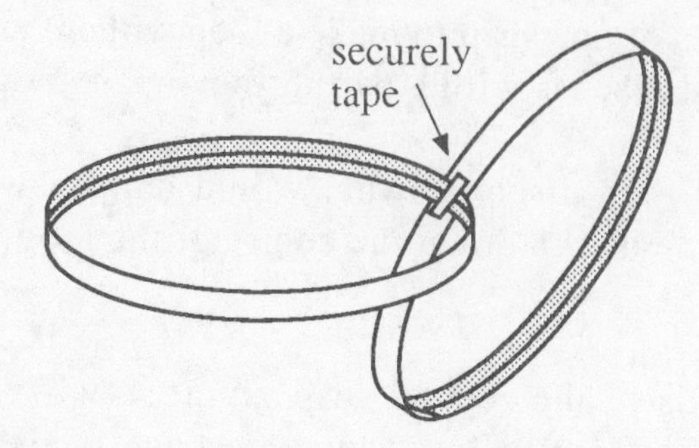

2. Cut three 30 cm by 2 cm strips of paper. Make each into a simple loop.

   Join the three loops securely with sticky tape so that they are at right angles to each other.

   Predict and test what would happen when cuts are made along the centre lines of the three loops.

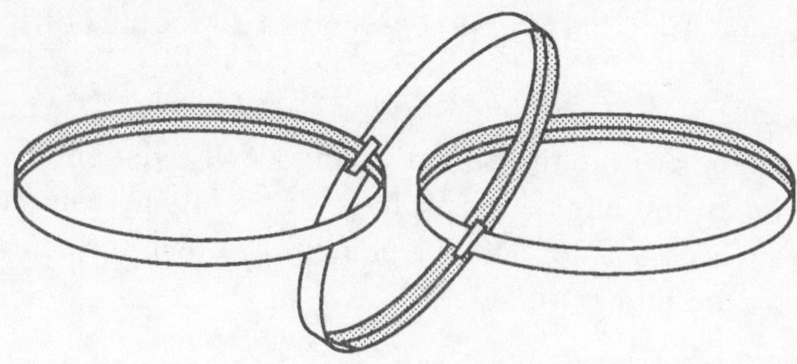

3. Experiment with more than three joined loops. Always predict the outcome before cutting along the centre lines.

3D ASSESSMENT

Students should understand the following ideas:

3D represented in 2D

- describe and draw objects from various viewpoints
- make models from photographs or pictures
- from memory, draw objects from various viewpoints

Cube models and isometric drawings

- build different arrangements of a given number of interlocking cubes
- represent these models on isometric paper
- build models from representations on isometric paper

Cones, cylinders and spheres

- describe the properties of a cone
- discuss the faces, edges and corners of a cone
- model various cones
- identify cones in the environment
- construct models of cones from nets
- identify the nets of various cones
- name and label various cones
- describe the cross-sections of cones
- describe the properties of a cylinder
- discuss the faces and edges of a cylinder
- model various cylinders
- identify cylinders in the environment
- construct models of cylinders from nets
- identify the nets of various cylinders
- name and label various cylinders
- describe the cross-sections of cones
- describe the properties of a sphere
- model a sphere
- identify spheres in the environment
- describe the cross-sections of a sphere

3D objects—packing properties

- discuss reasons for the shape of packaging
- describe which shapes pack without leaving spaces
- estimate and test how many items will fit into a given container
- estimate the number of interlocking cubes in a given model

Polyhedra

- describe the properties of polyhedra and platonic solids
- discuss the faces, edges and corners of polyhedra and platonic solids
- model various polyhedra and platonic solids

Scale

- describe reduction and enlargement and their uses
- recognise the different ways that scale is expressed
- enlarge and reduce simple shapes on grid paper
- draw a simple plan on grid paper and enlarge or reduce it
- enlarge or reduce simple models made with interlocking cubes
- discuss and interpret the scale of a variety of scale drawings, plans and maps
- using interlocking cubes, construct a model from a simple plan which has been drawn to scale
- make an exact scale model to represent a 3D object in a picture or photograph

Topology

- tie the most commonly used knots and know their uses
- construct a Moebius Strip and explain its uses

LEVEL 1 — 3D

EASIER QUESTIONS

Q1. Draw the model from the front, side and top.

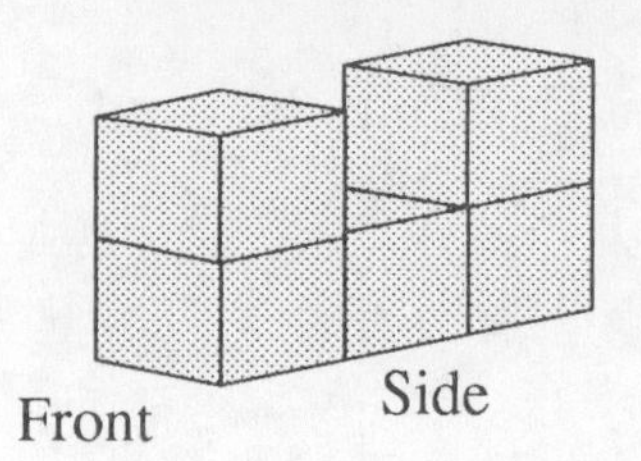

Q2. What solids are formed by the nets below?

(a)

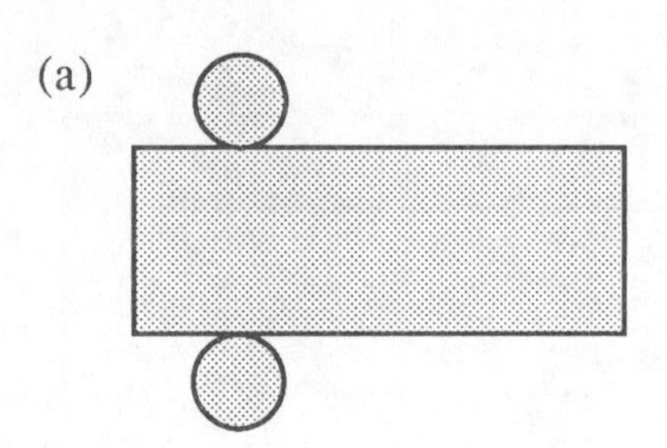

(b)

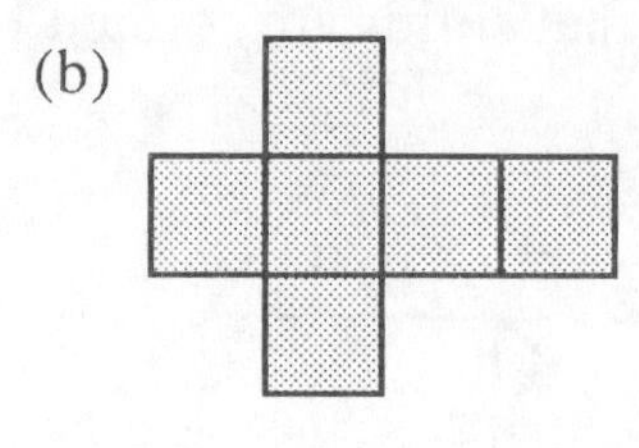

Q3. Which polyhedra has 4 faces, all of which are equilateral triangles?

Q4. How many faces, vertices and edges does a rectangular prism have?

Q5. The model is made up of 6 interlocking cubes. When viewed from all sides, how many cubes have:

(a) 4 faces showing?
(b) 3 faces showing?

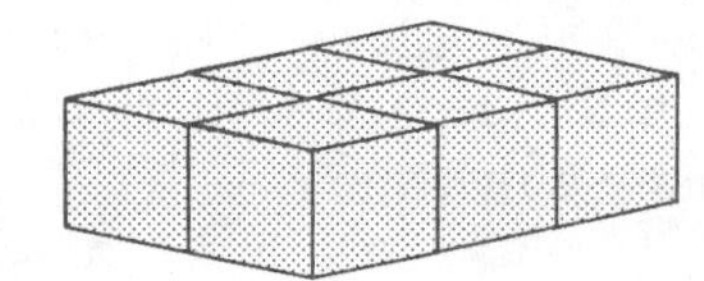

Q6. The scale on a map is as follows:

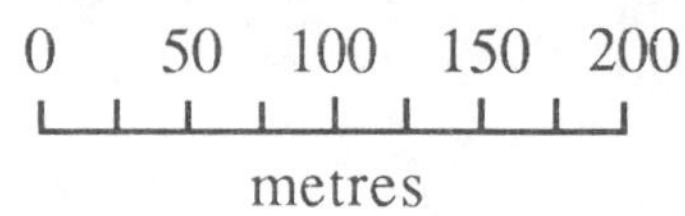

(a) How many metres does 1 cm represent?

(b) How many metres does 1.5 cm represent?

(c) How many metres does 1 mm represent?

LEVEL 2 — 3D

AVERAGE QUESTIONS

Q1. Draw the model from the front, side and top.

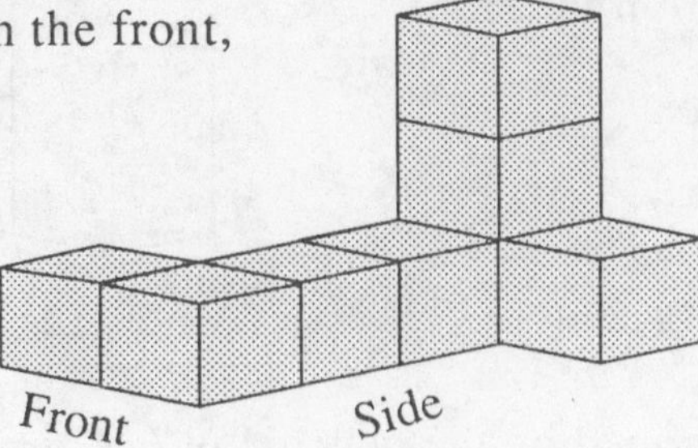

Q2. What solids are formed by the nets below?

(a)

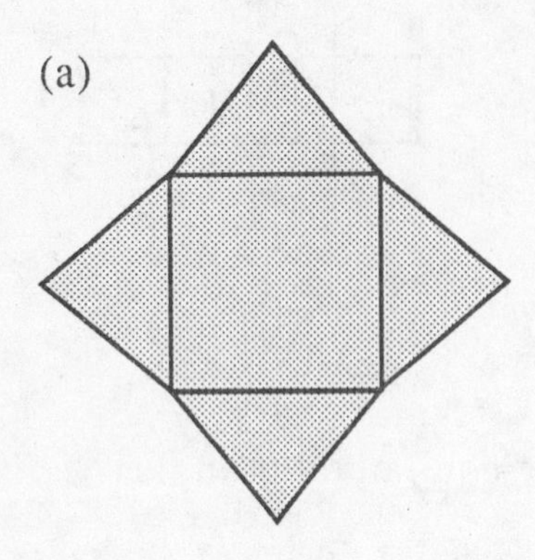

(b)

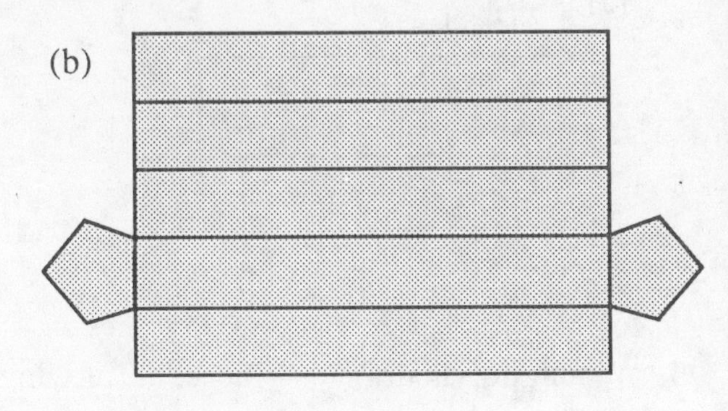

Q3. How many faces, edges and vertices has a square pyramid?

Q4. Which polyhedra has 12 regular pentagons as faces?

Q5. The model is made up of 24 interlocking cubes. When viewed from all the sides, how many cubes have:

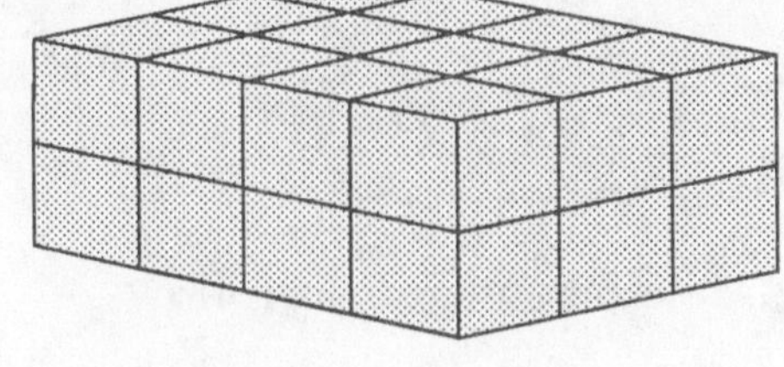

(a) 1 face showing?
(b) 2 faces showing?
(c) 3 faces showing?

Q6.

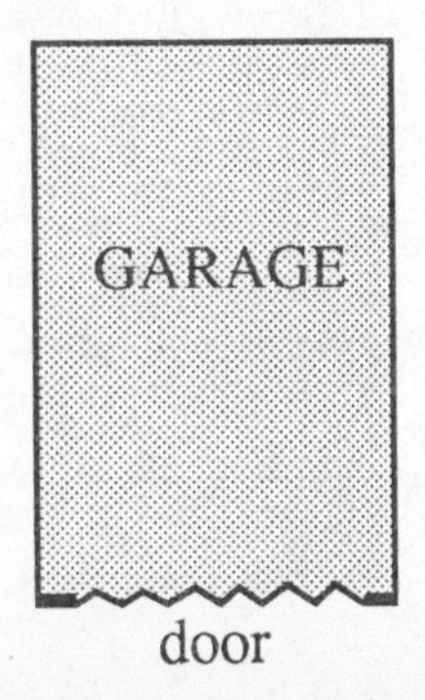

A garage has been drawn on the left using a scale where 1 cm represents 2 m.

(a) What is the actual width of the garage?

(b) What is the actual length?

(c) How wide is the garage door?

LEVEL 3 — 3D

DIFFICULT QUESTIONS

Q1. Draw the model from the front, side and top.

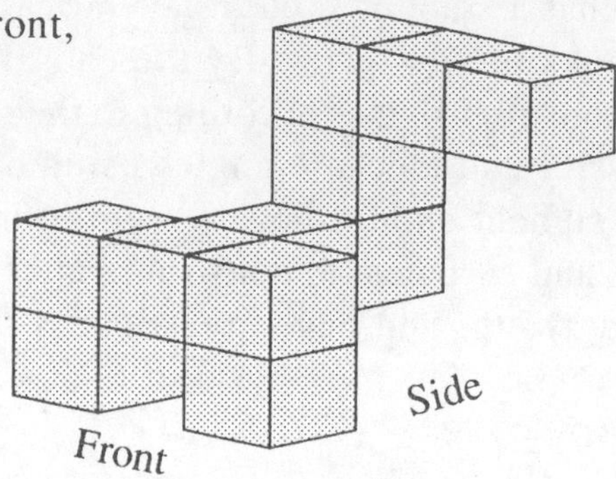

Q2. How many faces, edges and vertices has an octahedron?

Q3. Which polyhedra has 20 equilateral triangles as faces?

Q4.

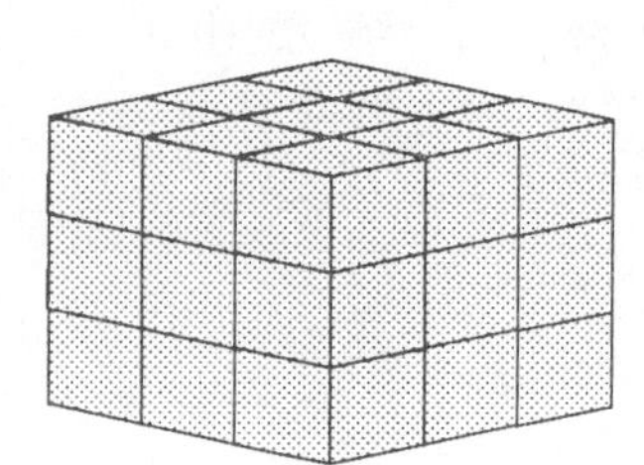

27 small cubes have been glued together to make one larger cube as shown on the right. This large cube is then painted blue all over. How many of the small cubes will have:

(a) 3 sides painted? (b) 2 sides painted?
(c) 1 side painted? (d) no sides painted?

Q5. The house to the right is drawn using a scale where 1 cm represents 3 m.

(a) What is the actual length of the bedroom?

(b) What is the actual length and the width of the kitchen?

(c) What is the actual length and the width of the living room?

(d) What is the actual area of the living room?

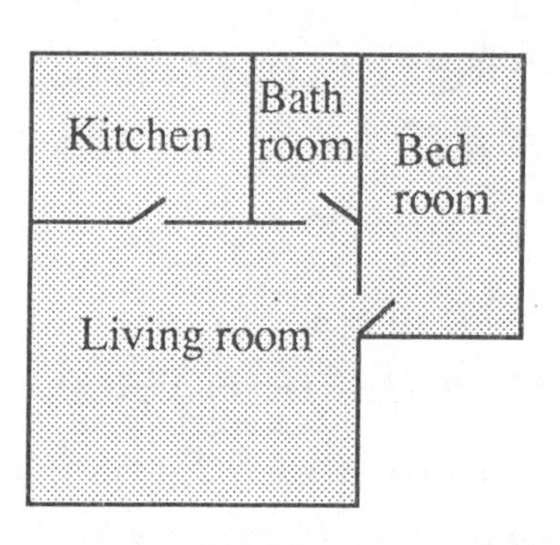

SPACE 2D

It is important that a student should have already acquired the skills outlined in the previous books in this series. By the end of Year 6 a student should be able to classify and construct shapes according to their properties (the number of angles, sides etc.), classify and measure angles using degrees and construct angles with a protractor. A student should have acquired the ability to identify vertical and horizontal lines and surfaces, to construct patterns and tesselations, to use simple perspective in drawings and have investigated shapes with turning symmetry.

VOCABULARY

Acute angle, angle tester, arc, bisect, centre, circular, circumference, compasses, corner, curve, degrees, diagonals, diameter, equilateral, flat, grid, grid paper, heptagon, hexagon, hexagonal, horizontal, identical, intersect, intersection, isosceles, line segment, obtuse angle, octagon overlap, parallel, pentagon, perpendicular, plumb, plumbline, polygon, polyominoes, projection, projector, protractor, quadrilateral, quarter turn, radius, rectangle, reflex, revolution, rhombus, right angle, rigid, scalene, semicircular, similar, slope, sloping, spirit level, square, symmetry, tesselate, tesselation, three quarter turn, tilting, trapezium, triangle, triangular, vertex, vertical.

CONTENTS

THE PROPERTIES OF POLYGONS

A polygon is a closed plane figure
with 3 or more straight sides.

Polygons can be REGULAR, with all sides equal and all angles equal, or IRREGULAR where the length of the sides and the size of angles vary. e.g.

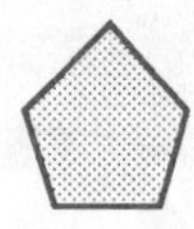

a regular pentagon

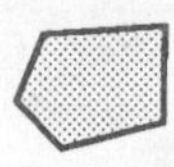

an irregular pentagon

DIAGONALS are straight lines which can be drawn from one angle (corner) of a polygon to another angle which is not adjacent to it.

the diagonals of a rectangle

ACTIVITIES:

1. Investigate the triangle (3 sides) the square (four equal sides and 4 right angles), the pentagon (5 sides), the hexagon (6 sides), the heptagon (7 sides) and the octagon (8 sides).

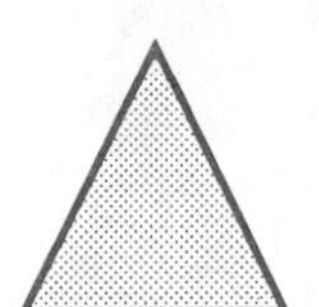

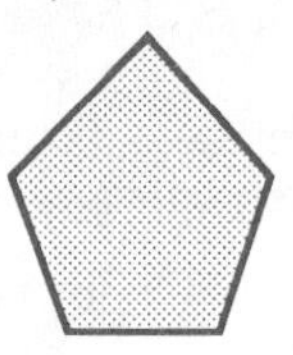
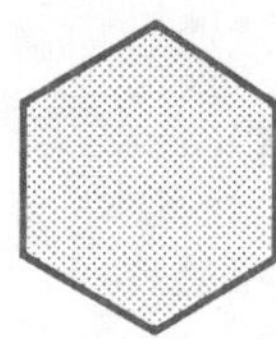
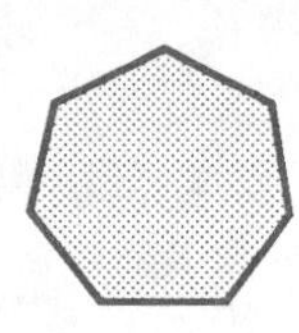
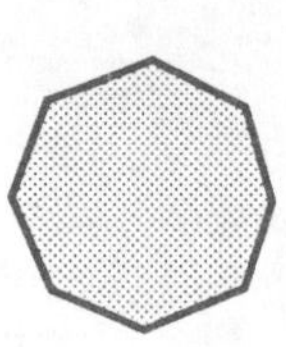

Construct the shapes, both regular and irregular, using geoboards or draw them on dot paper.

For each shape record the number of sides, the number of angles, the types of angles, the number of diagonals and the number of axes of symmetry.

An axis of symmetry divides an image in half so that the two halves are mirror images of each other or can be folded exactly on top of each other.

2. Some diagonals of polygons are also axes of symmetry. Investigate. What conclusions can be drawn?

3. Irregular shapes have the same number of diagonals as regular shapes. Is this true for axes of symmetry too?

NOTE: Ensure there is no confusion between diagonals and axes of symmetry.

CLASSIFYING ANGLES

The size of an angle refers to the amount of turn which has taken place between the arms of the angle. Different sized angles have different names.

A right angle is a square corner. Make a right angle tester with a piece of scrap paper.

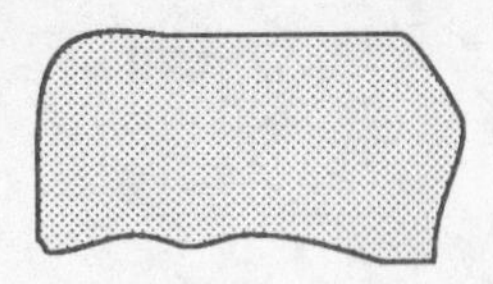
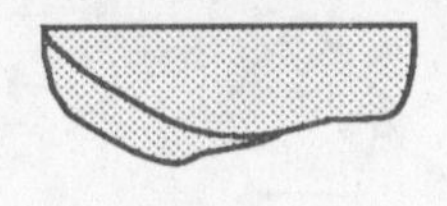

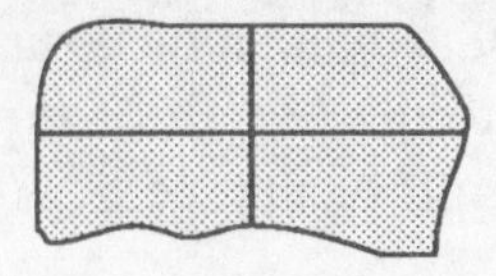

Use this tester to identify right angles, angles larger than a right angle and angles which are smaller than a right angle.

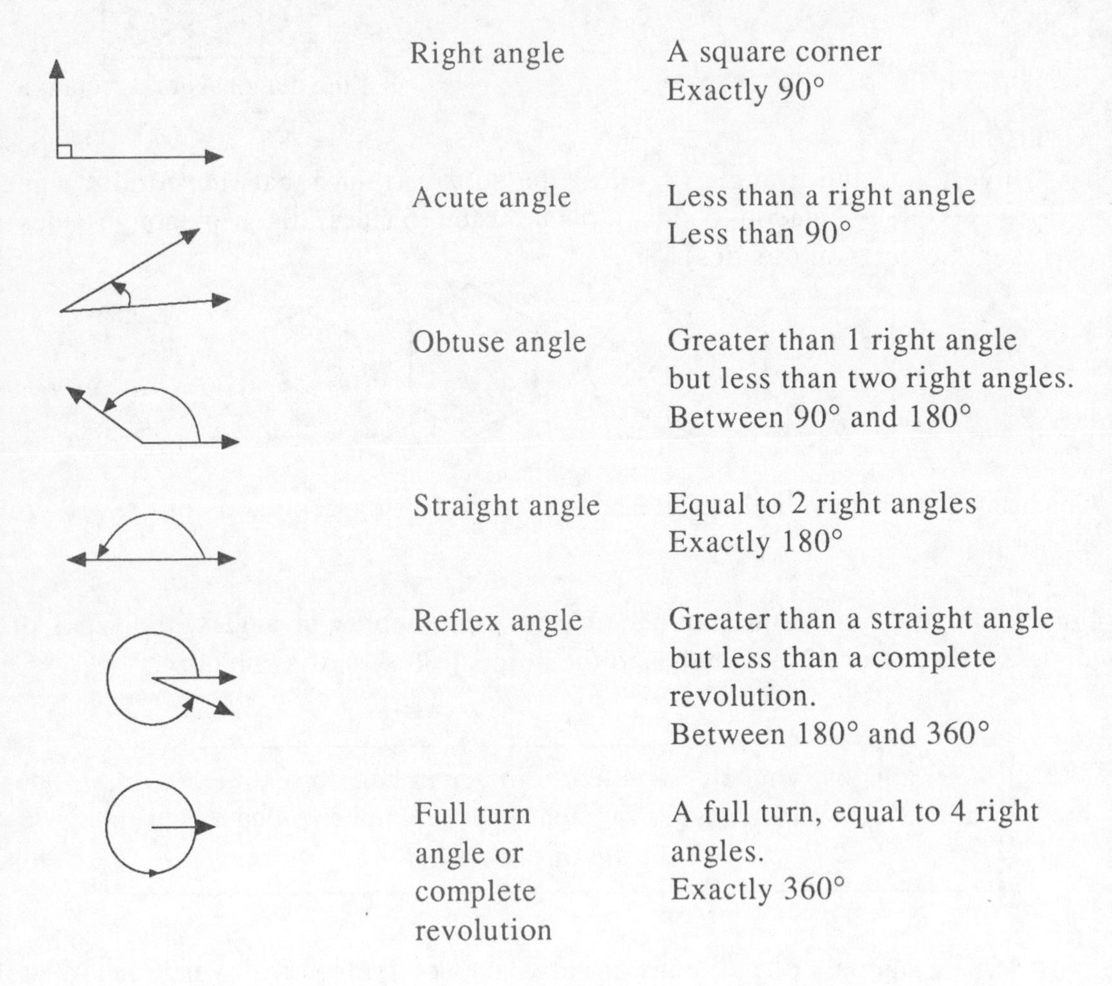

NOTE: The angle to be measured is always marked with a curved line. Right angles are a special angle and are marked with a square. A student should, in most cases, be able to identify the type of angle just by looking at it. It should not be necessary to use a protractor.

Examples: Classify the following angles:

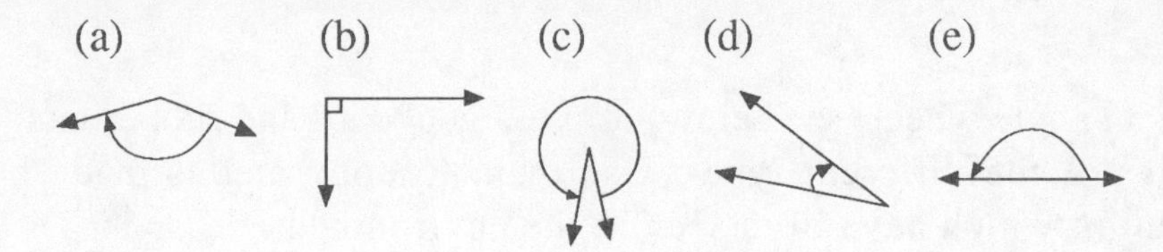

Solutions:

(a) obtuse angle, between a right angle and a straight angle.

(b) right angle, a quarter of a full turn.

(c) reflex angle, between a straight angle and a full turn.

(d) acute angle, less than a right angle.

(e) straight angle, equal to two right angles or half a full turn.

ACTIVITIES:

1. Look at the face of an analog clock and classify the angle between the hour and minute hands at different times.

2. Investigate the angles between the points of a compass, e.g. what type of angle is between NE and S? (Obtuse, greater than a right angle but less than a straight angle.)

3. Through how many degrees are various doors able to turn? More or less than 90°? More or less than 180°?

4. Set the arms of a compass to an acute , a reflex, an obtuse angle.

5. NOTE: At any point where 2 lines meet or cross there are always 2 angles not just one.

MEASURING ANGLES INFORMALLY

ACTIVITIES:

1. Make and use an angle wheel (see below) or use a geoboard and rubber bands to make angles of the different types. Use them to copy angles made by another student or which have been seen in the environment.

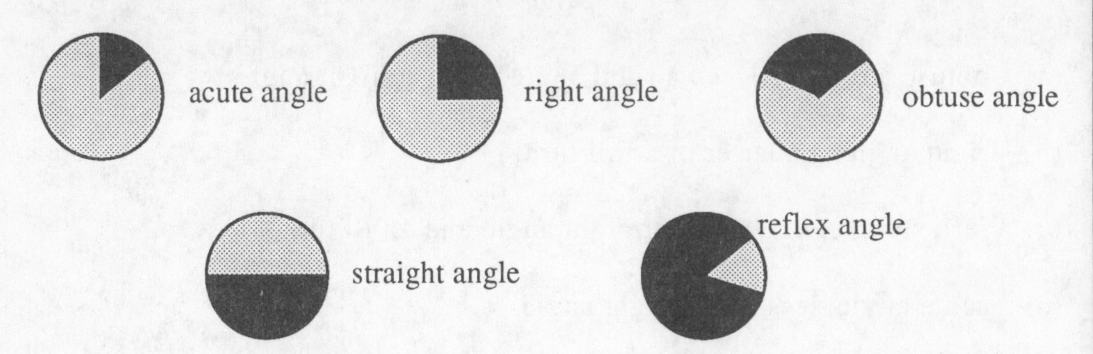

2. Make a number of identical angle testers from paper. Draw a number of different angles. Use the angle testers to measure the size of the drawn angles. Describe and record how many were used in each case ('exactly 3', 'a bit less than 5', 'about two and a half'). Make another set of identical angle testers but of a different size from the first set. Measure the size of the drawn angles. Record how many were used and compare with the previous results.

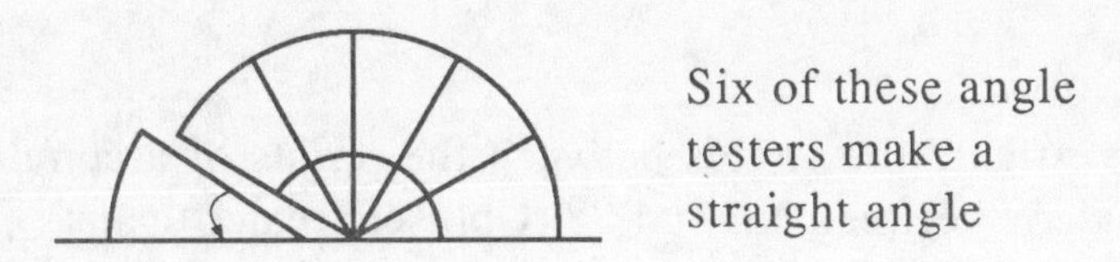

The results with different angle sizes will be different. It is necessary to have A standard unit to measure the size of angles.

AN ANGLE WHEEL

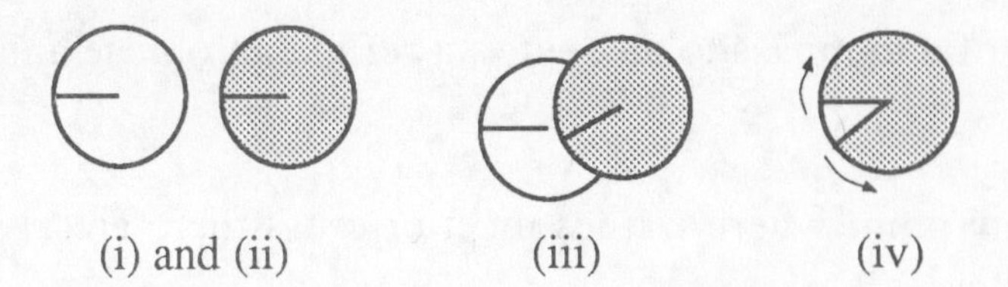

(i) Cut 2 identical circles from different coloured thin card.

(ii) Cut a straight slit in each from a point on the circumference (the boundary) across to the centre of the circle.

(iii) Fit them together as in the diagram.

(iv) By moving the circles on each other angles can be made.

MEASURING ANGLES FORMALLY

The ancient Babylonian year was 360 days long, the time it was thought it took for a whole year to go round. 360 was, therefore, the logical number of degrees to denote a full turn.

The device used for giving an accurate measure of the amount of turn in an angle is the PROTRACTOR. A protractor is most often semi-circular but can be circular.

A PROTRACTOR MEASURES THE AMOUNT OF TURN

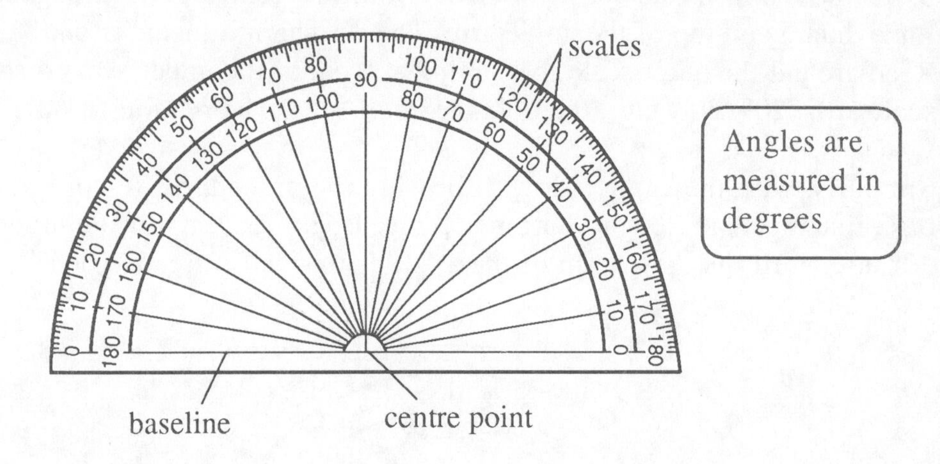

A protractor has a BASE LINE.

The base line has a CENTRE POINT where the 90 degree line meets the base line. The centre point is always placed exactly on the corner of the angle with the base line along one of the arms of the angle.

A protractor has two scales marked from 0° to 180° around the curve. One scale is read from right to left. The other scale is read from left to right. Look from the centre point along the arm on which the base line has been placed. Does this meet the 0° on the inner scale or the outer scale? Take care when reading the protractor scales when the protractor is upside down. Remember:

> Always start calculating the size of the angle from 0°

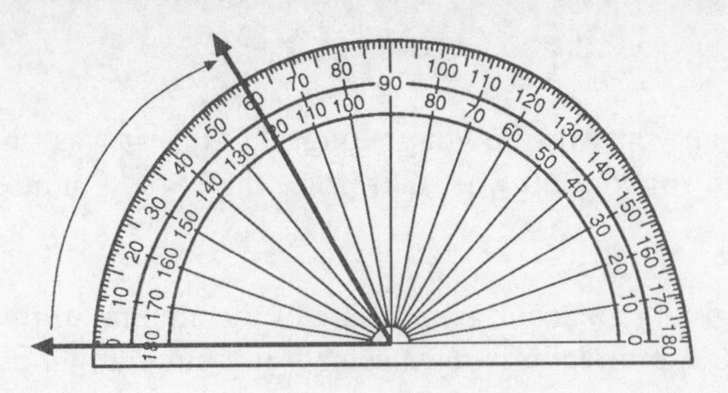

With the angle above, place the centre point on the corner of the angle, with the base line along the lower arm. Look from the centre point along the base line line which is on top of the angle arm. The 0° which it meets is on the outer scale. Read around the outer scale, beginning at 0° until the upper arm crosses the outer scale, 10°, 20°, 30°, etc. Read off the angle size. The reading is 60°.

Similarly, with the angle below, following the procedures it can be seen that the base line meets the 0° on the inner scale. Begin reading on the inner scale, 10°, 20°, etc. until the upper arm of the angle is reached. It reads 160.

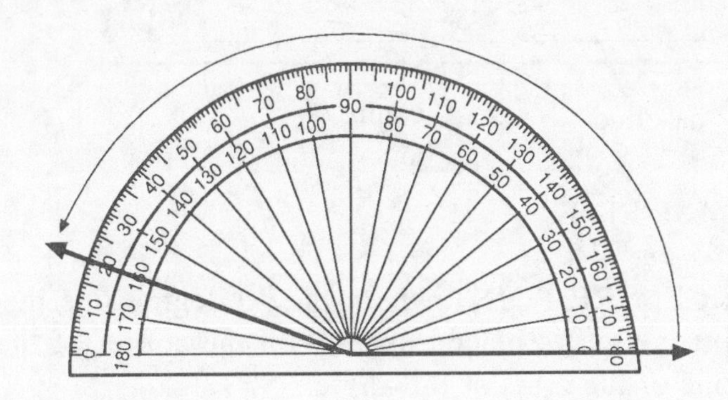

To measure reflex angles, measure the size of the smaller angle, whether acute or obtuse, and then subtract this from 360°. This will give the size of the reflex angle. In the example below, the smaller angle measures 80°. Subtract this from 360°. The reflex angle therefore, measures 260°.

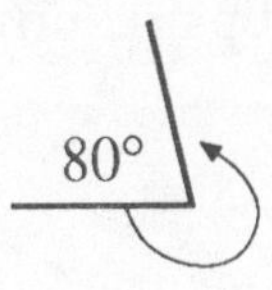

All students need lots of practice measuring a full range of angle sizes until the process of placing the the protractor correctly and reading the appropriate scale has become automatic.

NOTE: Remember to state the type of angle and then estimate the size of the angle before measuring.

CONSTRUCTING ANGLES WITH A PROTRACTOR

ACTIVITIES:

1. Construct a 50° angle.

   (a) Using a sharp pencil and a ruler, draw one arm of the angle on a sheet of paper.

   (b) Estimate and place a faint dot through which it is thought that the other arm of the angle will pass.

   (c) Place the base line of the protractor on this arm with the centre point at one end of the arm.

   (d) Look from the centre point along the arm to the 0°. Follow the scale reading round until 50° is reached. Place a small dot next to the protractor scale at that 50 mark.

   (e) Remove the protractor. Using a ruler, join the end of the arm that was under the centre point of the base line with the 50° mark .

Be accurate: 'Near enough' is not good enough!

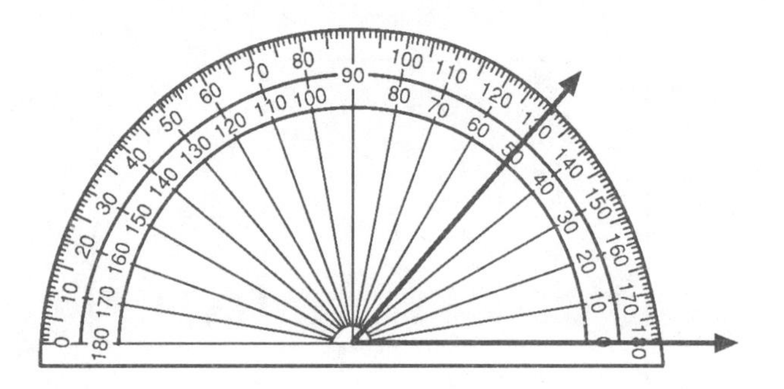

2. Draw a 110° angle.

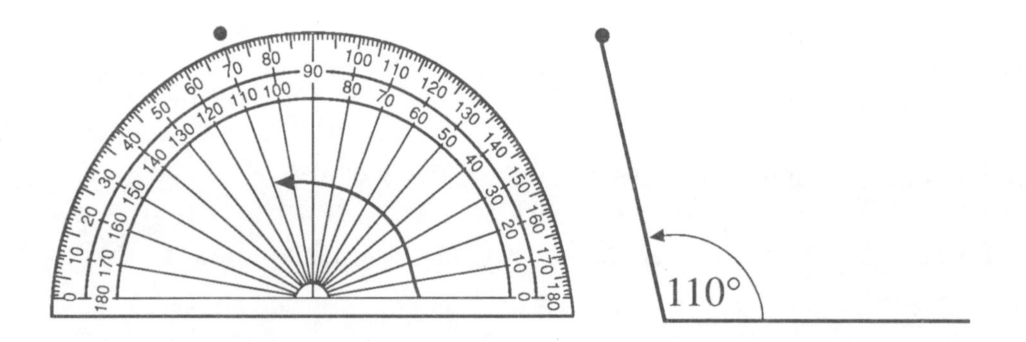

TRIANGLES NAMED ACCORDING TO ANGLES

NAME	DIAGRAM	TYPES OF SIDES
Right angled triangle	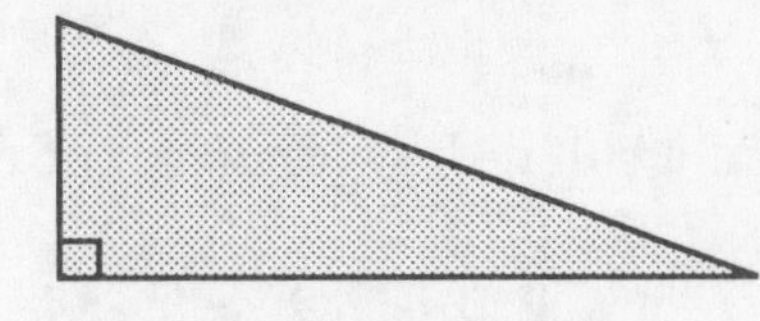	One of the angles is a right angle (i.e. 90°)
Acute angled triangle	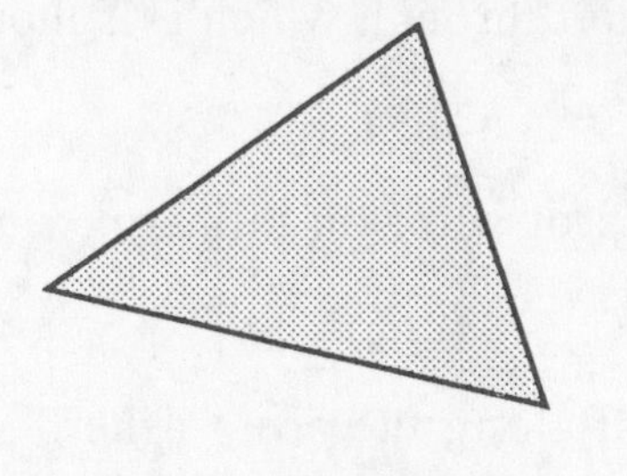	All 3 angles are acute (i.e. less than 90°)
Obtuse angled triangle	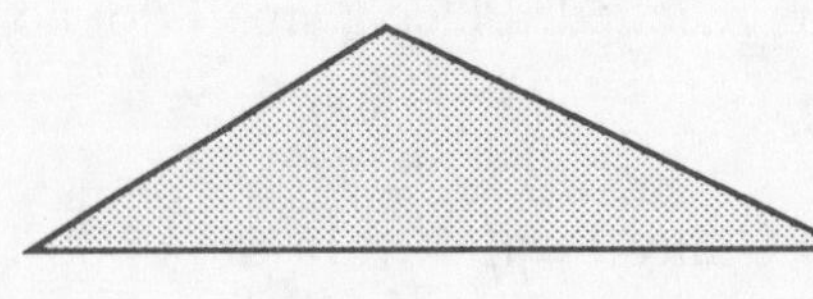	One angle is an obtuse angle (i.e. greater than 90°)

Examples:
State whether the triangles below are acute, obtuse or right angled.

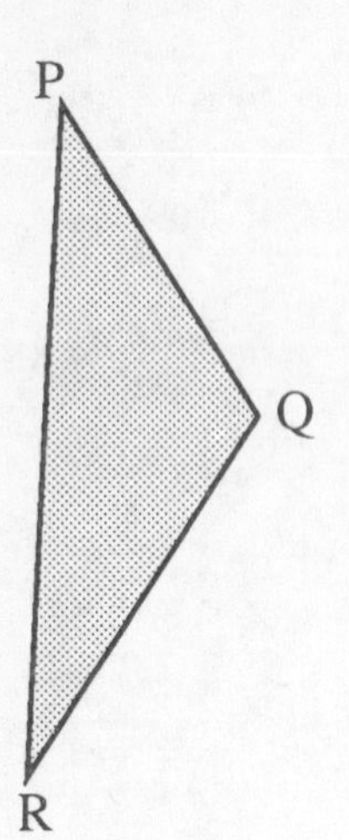

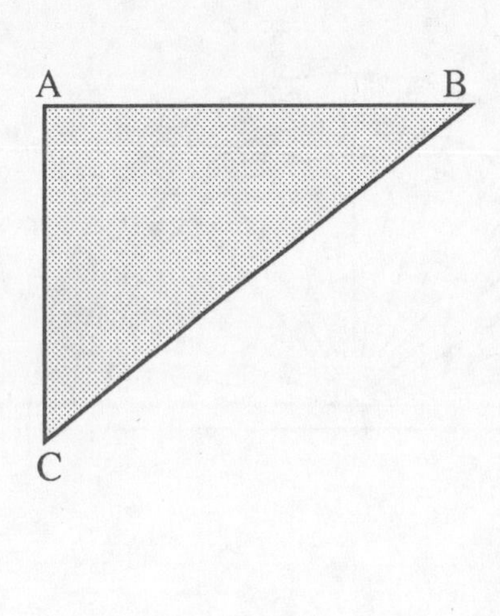

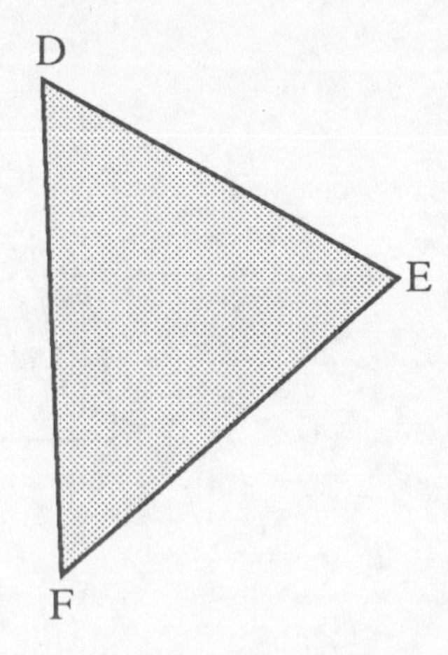

Solutions:

(a) This is an obtuse angled triangle, because $\angle$ PQR is greater than 90°.

(b) This is a right angled triangle, because $\angle$ CAB = 90°.

(c) This is an acute angled triangle, because all 3 angles are less than 90°.

TRIANGLES NAMED ACCORDING TO LENGTH OF SIDES

NAME	DIAGRAM	TYPES OF SIDES
Scalene triangle	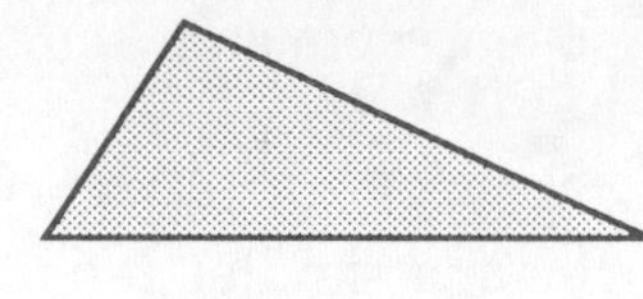	All three sides have different lengths. Also, all the angles will be different sizes.
Isosceles triangle	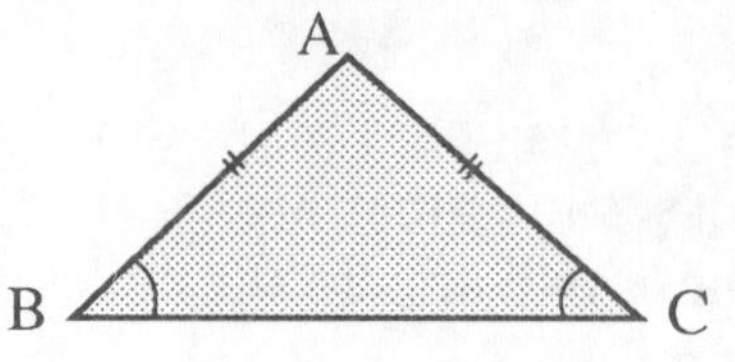	2 sides are equal in length AB = AC. Also, the angles at the base of the equal sides will be the same size.
Equilateral triangle	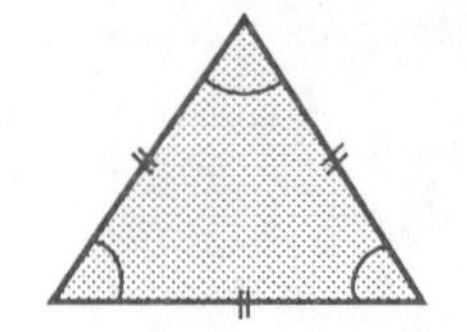	All 3 sides are equal in length. Also, the 3 angles will be equal in size.

THE ANGLE SUM OF A TRIANGLE

ACTIVITY:
Draw a triangle. Cut it out and tear off the corners. Put the corners together. What is the result? Repeat the experiment with a different kind of triangle. It will be seen that the sum of the angles of a triangle is always 180°, i.e. they make a straight angle.

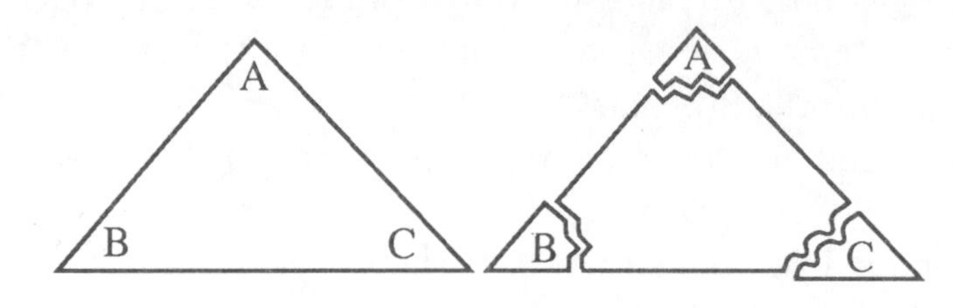

The sum of the angles of a triangle is 180°

CONSTRUCTING TRIANGLES

A compass can be used to draw triangles where the **lengths of the sides** are given.

Example:
Draw a triangle with sides measuring 6 cm, 5 cm and 3 cm.

(i) Draw a 6 cm line.
(ii) Set a compass at 5 cm. Place the compass point at one end of the 6 cm line. Draw an arc.
(iii) Set the compass at 3 cm. Place the compass point at the other end of the 6 cm line. Draw an arc which crosses the other arc.
(iv) Join the intersection point of these two arcs to the ends of the 6 cm line.
(v) Measure the sides to check accuracy.

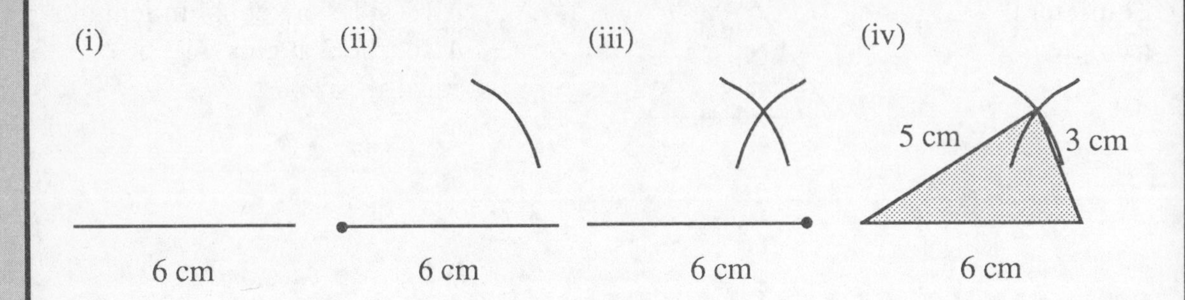

A **protractor** can be used to construct a triangle where **the angles** are given.

Example:
Construct a triangle with angles measuring 30°, 70° and 80°.

(i) Draw a line, AB, which is 6 cm long.
(ii) Place the centre point of the protractor on A. Reading from 0° on the appropriate scale, mark a 30° angle. Remove the protractor and draw the arm of the angle by joining point A with the 30° mark.
(iii) Place the protractor on B and construct an angle measuring 70°. Draw and extend the arm to cross the line previously constructed (point C)
(v) Measure angle C which has been constructed. It should measure 80°. (The sum of the angles of a triangle is 180°.)

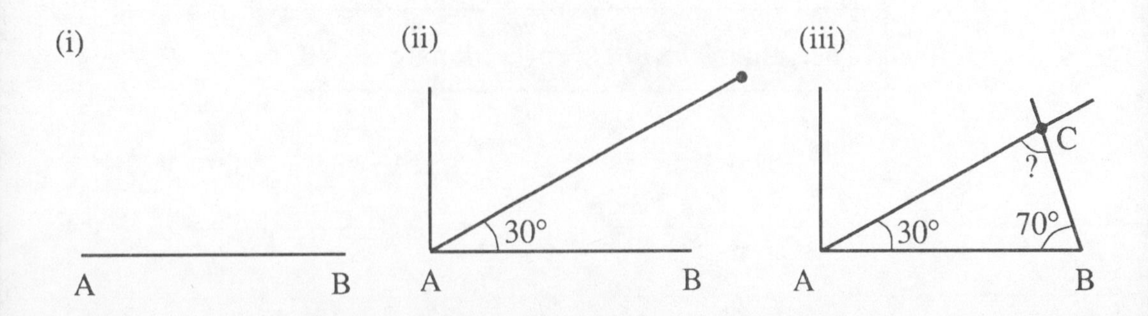

CONSTRUCTING SQUARES AND RECTANGLES

1. Draw round a square based object such as a cube.

2. Use grid paper to accurately draw squares and rectangles.

3. Fold and cut a rectangular piece of paper as shown below to make a square.

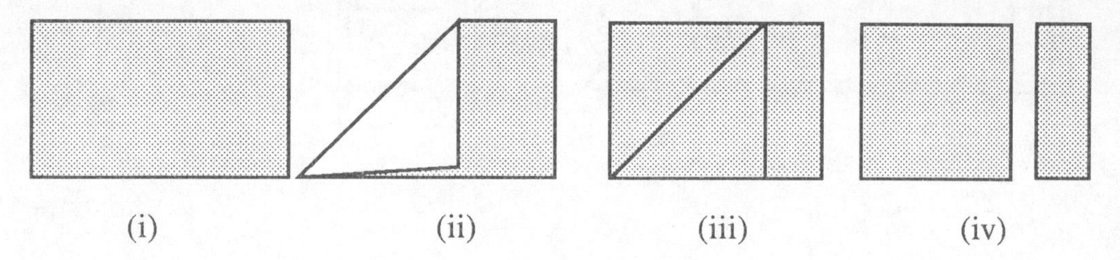

4. Fold a paper circle into quarters and then open out. Join the points where the folds meet the circumference to make a square.

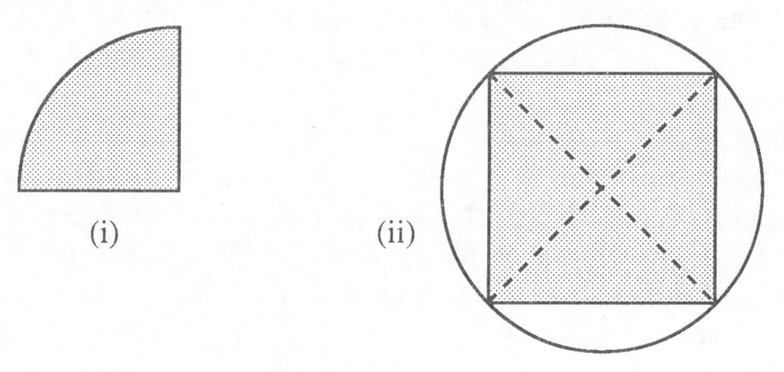

5. Use protractors and set squares to construct squares and rectangles.

6. Tear the corners of a square and put them together. Estimate the size of the angle they make. They make a complete turn of 360°. Repeat the procedure with a rectangle and then with a quadrilateral, estimating before measuring.

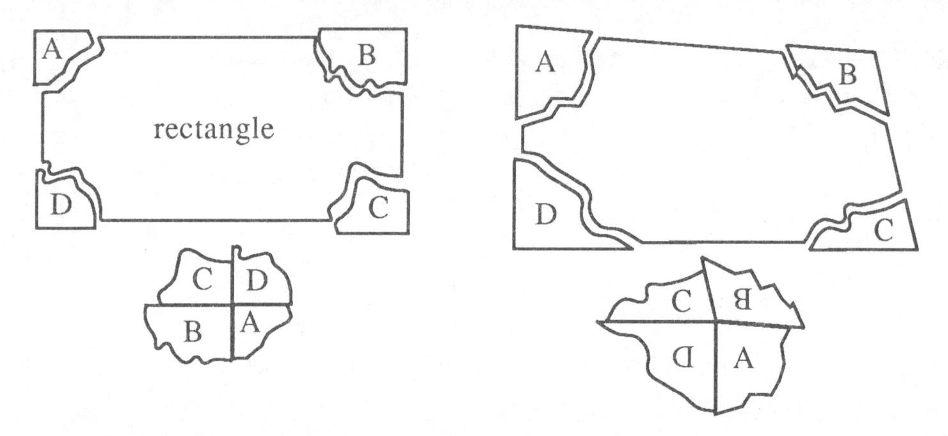

7. Investigate the angle sum of other polygons after estimating.

8. Check the properties of rectangles and squares—diagonals, angles, etc.

VERTICAL, HORIZONTAL AND SLOPING

Introduce the concept of vertical, horizontal and sloping by testing.

Surfaces can be tested with a spirit level or a plumb line.

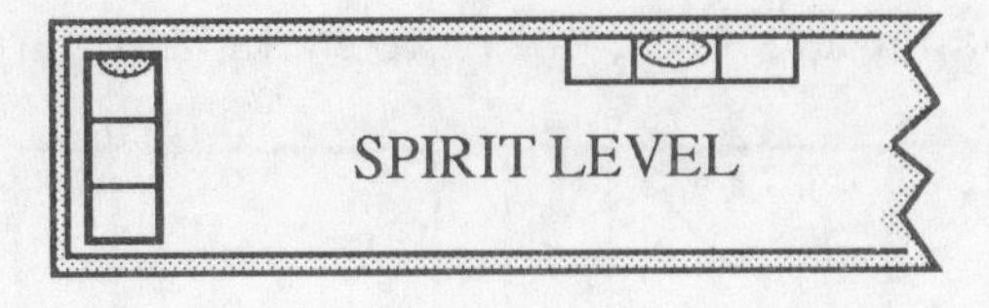

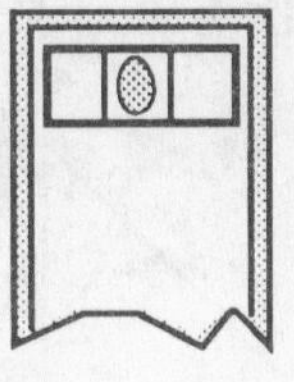

Spirit level

Plumb line

A spirit level is made from a length of metal into which have been set two small windows. One window lies down the length of the level, the other window lies across. Through the windows can be seen an air bubble in a liquid. The window is marked with two lines. When the bubble sits exactly between these two marks the surface being assessed is horizontal or vertical. If the bubble is off-centre the surface is sloping.

A plumb line can be made by attaching a heavy mass to a string or cord. The mass will pull the string straight down or vertical. (Originally the mass would have been lead, hence the name 'plumb' which is Latin for lead.)

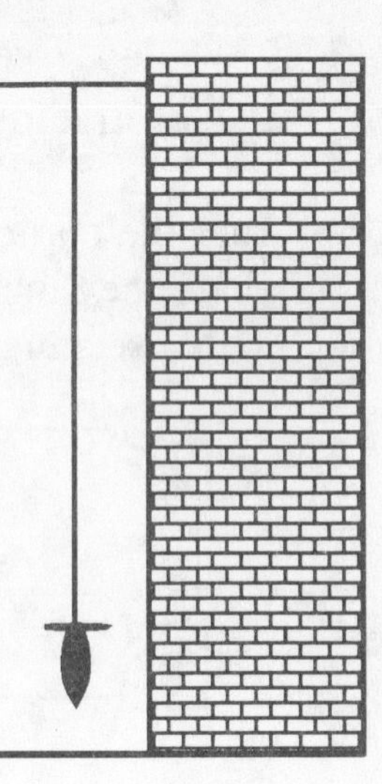

VERTICAL surfaces or lines go straight up and down. Compare the plumb line string with surfaces which look vertical, e.g. walls or door frames. If the surface and plumb line are parallel, the surface is vertical; if not, the surface is **sloping**. A spirit level can also be used.

HORIZONTAL surfaces or lines go straight across from side to side. Horizontal surfaces can be tested by placing a ball on the surface. If the ball does not roll the surface is horizontal. If the ball does roll then the surface is not horizontal but **sloping**. A spirit level can also be used.

ACTIVITY:
Investigate lines and surfaces to determine whether they are vertical, horizontal or sloping.

SHADOWS

In Years 3 and 4, experiments with the flipping, sliding and turning of shapes were undertaken. When each of these processes took place the shape did not change nor did its dimensions.

With shadows changes do occur, depending on conditions.

A shadow occurs when an object blocks a light source. In the following example the shape of the person's shadow gets longer or shorter depending on where he is in relation to the light source, in this case a streetlight.

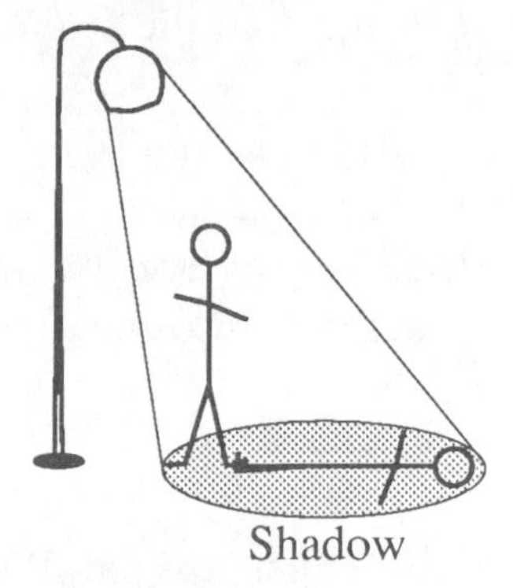

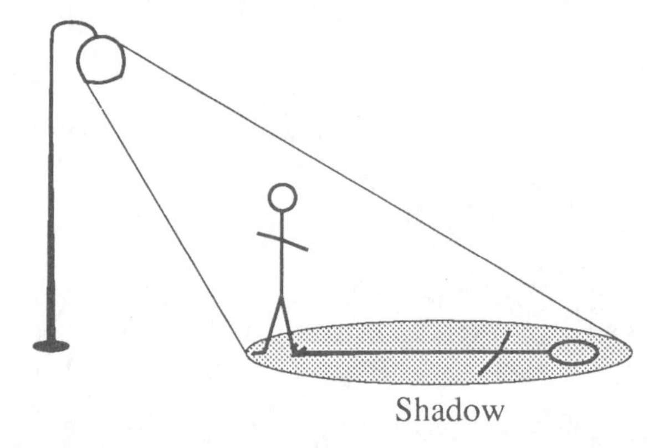

ACTIVITIES:

1. Conduct experiments with objects of different sizes and shapes, investigating the shadows they make in the sunshine at different times of the day.
2. Experiment with differently positioned light sources, high up or low down. What happens to the shadows in each case?
3. Make a sundial and investigate how it works.

PERSPECTIVE

Perspective is a means of realistically representing three-dimensional objects and scenes on a flat surface.

When viewing a landscape distant objects appear smaller than close up objects.

These trees are of similar height.
The distant tree appears smaller.

To give drawings a realistic look, distant objects need to be drawn relatively smaller.

Examine this drawing of a rectangular prism.

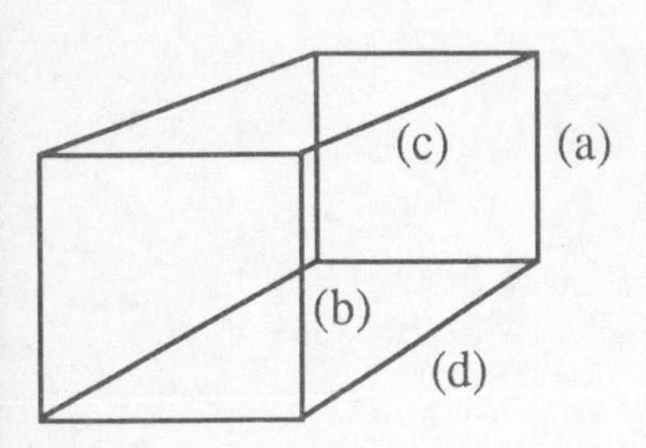

The back vertical edge of the prism (a) is drawn shorter than the front vertical edge (b).

The two edges (c) and (d) in reality are parallel. However they are drawn getting closer together to give the impression they are moving into the distance.

This effect is called perspective.

In the scene below all the lines which in reality are parallel appear to be moving towards a place on the horizon where they disappear. This point is called the vanishing point.

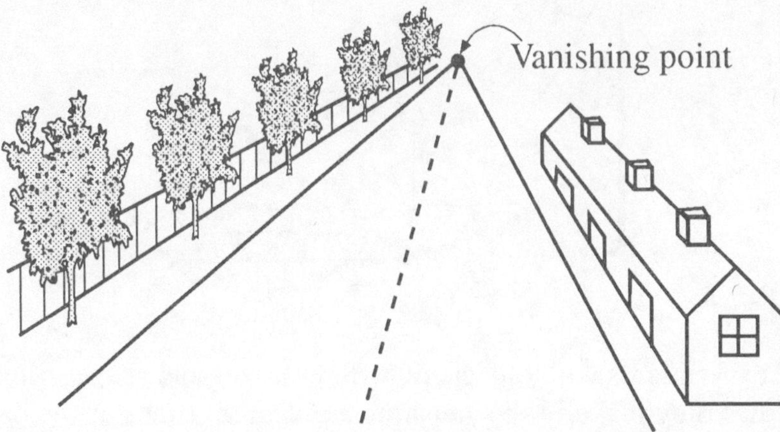

NOTE: All lines which appear vertical or horizontal to the viewer remain vertical or horizontal.

TURNING (ROTATIONAL) SYMMETRY

> A shape is said to have turning or rotational, symmetry if a tracing of the shape will fit on top of, and exactly match, the shape while the tracing is being rotated through a full turn.

To test whether a shape has turning symmetry, cut out the shape, trace around it onto paper and then push a pin through the centre of the shape and tracing. Slowly turn the shape around. If the shape fits exactly onto the tracing before a full turn has been completed then the shape has rotational or turning symmetry.

(a) (b) (c)

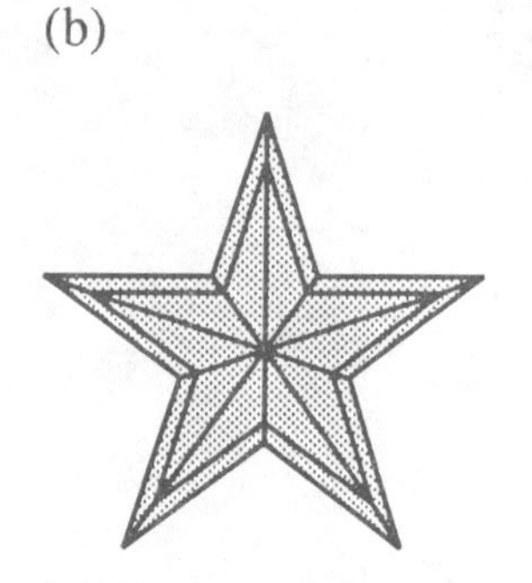

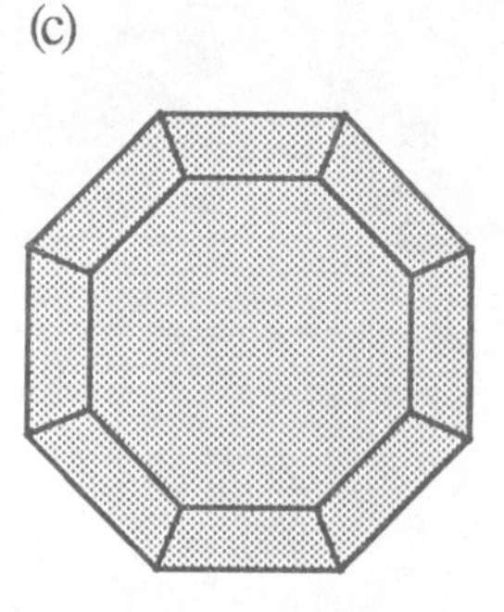

Shape (a) has 3 points of turning symmetry.
Shape (b) has 5 points of turning symmetry.
Shape (c) has 8 points of turning symmetry.

A shape which only matches after a full turn is not considered to having turning symmetry.

Example:
Which of the following letters has rotational symmetry?

A H N T Z

Solution:
The letters H, N and Z have rotational symmetry because if you rotate them through half a full turn (180°) they will look exactly the same.

ACTIVITY:
Investigate and make shapes which have turning symmetry. Record how many times the shape has turning symmetry during one full turn.

PATTERNS AND TESSELLATIONS

These activities build on those suggested in the previous book in this series. It is important these are experienced before progressing further.

ACTIVITIES:

1. Create patterns using the techniques of flip, slide and turn.

   Put a simple design into a grid square.

   Use flipping, sliding and turning of this design to create a pattern.

original design

flip, slide, turn

Original design

Slide the design along →

Flip the design down ↓

Turn each design ↷

2. Tessellating shapes are identical shapes which fit together exactly without overlapping or leaving gaps.

   Explore the environment for tessellating shapes. Are there any irregular tessellating shapes to be found?

3. Research the art of M. C. Escher who created remarkable visual effects. Investigate Escher's tessellating patterns.

4. Create a unique tile to make a tessellating pattern by 'cutting out and adding opposite'. Make a tessellating pattern with the tile.

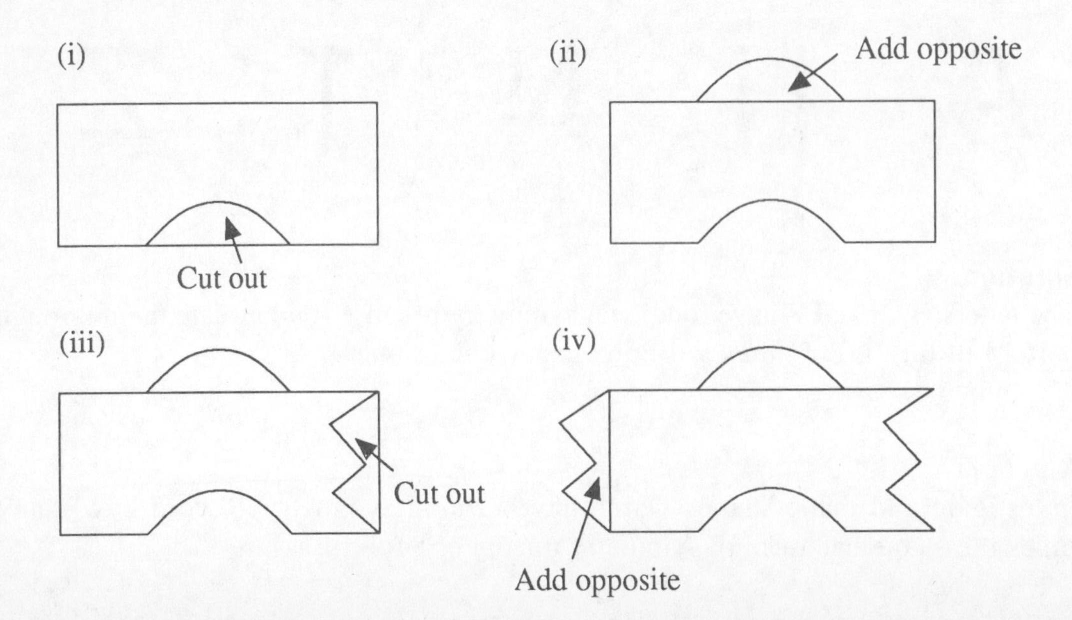

CONSTRUCTING CIRCLES INFORMALLY

Experiment with ways of constructing circles. In all the activities, estimate then measure the radius, the diameter and the circumference

The CIRCUMFERENCE is the distance around the circle.

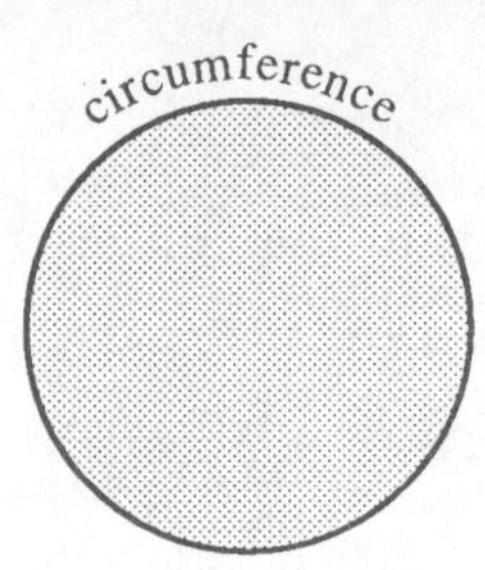

The RADIUS is the distance from the circumference to the centre of the circle (plural of radius is radii).

radius
centre

The DIAMETER is the distance across the circle through the centre and is twice the radius.

centre
diameter

The circumference is about 3 times the length of the diameter.

ACTIVITIES:

1. Draw circles by drawing round circular objects.

2. Make a loop of string or thread. Put the point of a thumb tack or pin through the loop and attach to a piece of card or paper. Put a pencil point in the other end of the loop. Draw a circle by making the loop taut with the pencil and taking the pencil round the tack which is the centre of the circle.

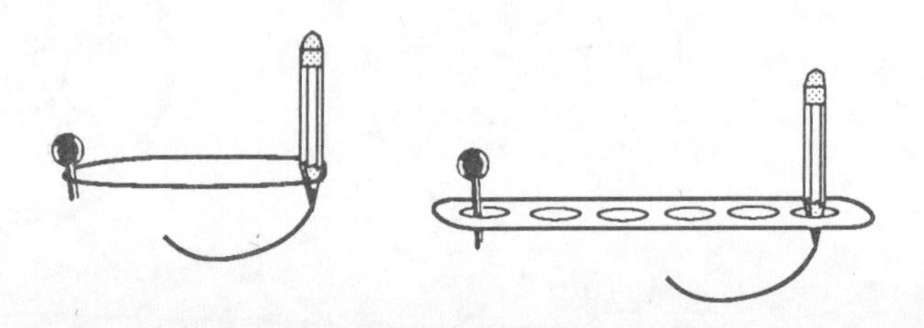

CONSTRUCTING CIRCLES

A **compass** is an instrument used to draw circles.

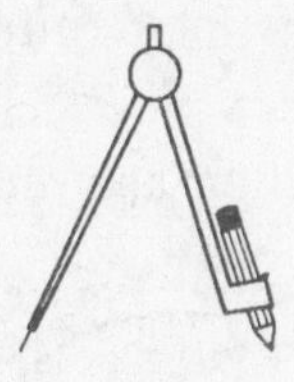

It is important to ensure the point of the compass and the point of the pencil are level when the compass arms are closed.

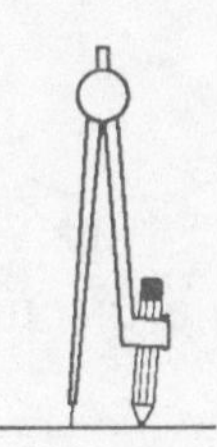

To draw a circle with a radius of 3 cm (a diameter of 6 cm), adjust the point so that the distance between the compass point and the pencil point measures exactly 3 cm.

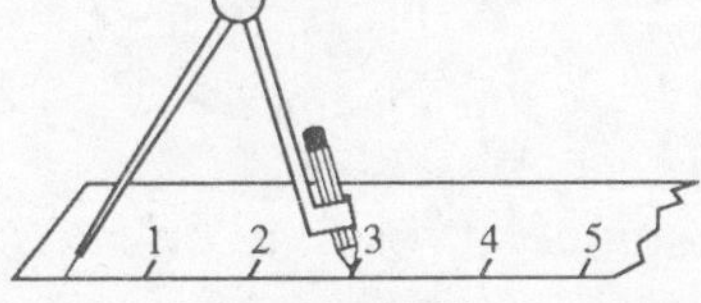

Holding the top of the compass, press the compass point into the paper and move the pencil arm around to draw a circle. Do not hold the pencil.

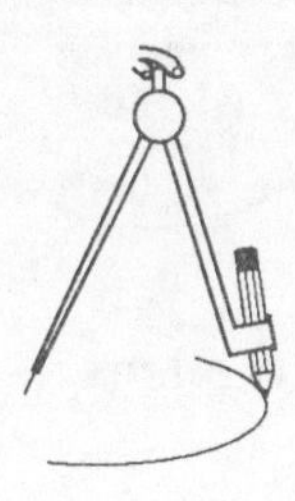

ACTIVITIES:

1. Practise drawing circles with different diameters and radii using a compass.

2. Create designs by drawing a series of circles or parts of circles with a compass.

  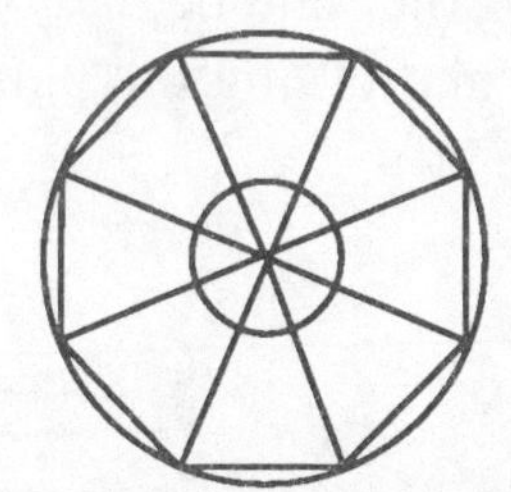

3. Copy designs created by a partner.

2D ASSESSMENTS

Students should understand the following ideas:

Properties of polygons

- demonstrate an understanding of the term 'polygon'
- demonstrate an understanding of the term 'diagonal'
- use a geoboard to show regular and irregular polygons
- use geo-strips to make different polygons with their diagonals
- for each polygon, describe the number of sides, angles, diagonals and axes of symmetry
- compare the number of diagonals and axes of symmetry of regular and irregular polygons
- create designs using polygons
- identify polygons in the environment

Classifying angles

- use a right angle tester to compare angles
- identify and name acute, right, obtuse, straight, reflex and full turn angles
- identify and name angles in the environment
- copy angles using an angle wheel or geoboard

Measuring angles

- demonstrate understanding of how to use a protractor
- classify angles according to their size
- measure a wide variety of angles using a protractor
- construct angles using a protractor
- classify triangles according to their angles

Vertical, horizontal, and sloping

- describe a spirit level and a plumb line, how they are used and for what purposes
- demonstrate the use of a spirit level and plumb line

Shadows and perspective

- demonstrate how to make long or short shadows
- describe how a sundial works
- predict the position, shape and length of shadows
- discuss perspective as demonstrated in a number of pictures and photographs
- draw pictures showing an understanding of the principles of perspective

2D ASSESSMENTS continued

Turning (rotational) symmetry

- identify shapes which have turning symmetry
- count the number of times the original and the tracing match during a complete turn
- identify shapes in the environment, e.g. logos, which have turning symmetry
- create shapes which have turning symmetry

Patterns and tessellations

- create patterns using flip, slide and turn techniques
- identify tessellating shapes in the environment
- create an original irregular tessellating tile and use it to make a design
- complete a variety of simple shape puzzles

Properties of circles/constructing circles

- understand the meaning of radius, diameter and circumference
- demonstrate different ways to construct circles
- demonstrate the correct manipulation of a compass to draw circles of various sizes
- create designs of circles and part circles constructed with a compass

Triangles/constructing triangles

- identify the properties of triangles
- classify triangles according to the angles
- classify triangles according to the lengths of the sides
- construct triangles with rulers and set squares
- demonstrate that the angle sum of a triangle is 180
- use a pair of compasses to construct a triangle with given sides
- use a protractor to construct a triangle with given angles

Constructing squares and rectangles

- use rulers and set squares or protractors to construct squares and rectangles
- identify the properties of rectangles and squares
- create designs using a variety of geometric shapes

LEVEL 1 — 2D

EASIER QUESTIONS

Q1. Name the following polygons, and then draw their axes of symmetry:

(a) 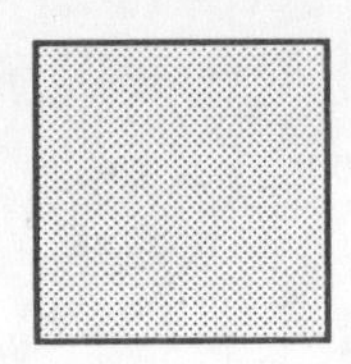

(b) 

(c) 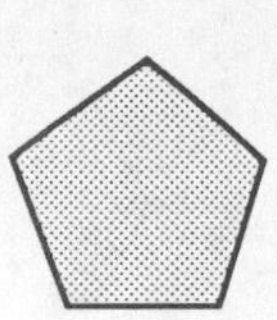

Q2. Classify the following angles without measuring:

(a) 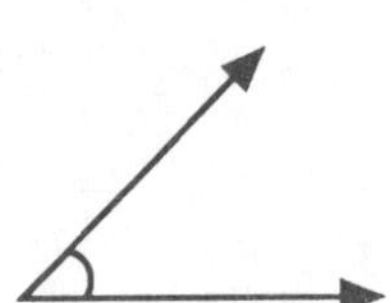

(b) 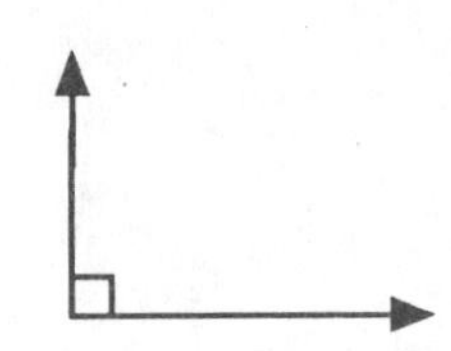

(c) 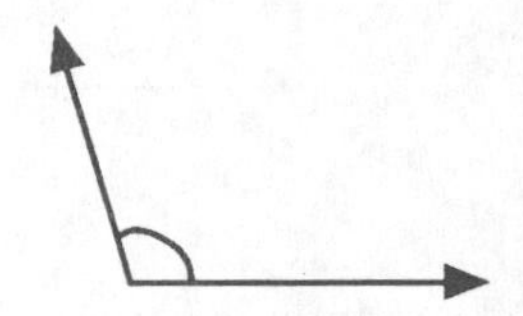

Q3. Measure the following angles using a protractor:

(a) 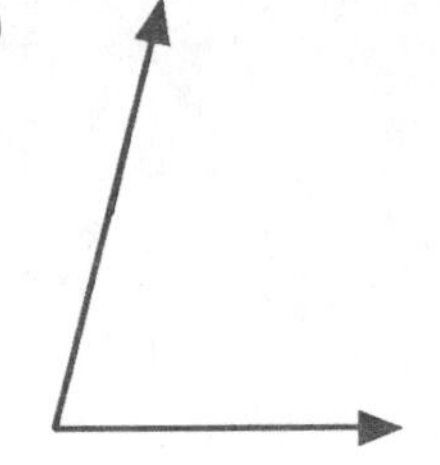

(b) 

(c) 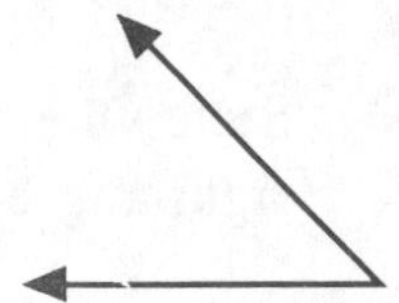

Q4. Which of the following shapes have rotational symmetry?

(a) 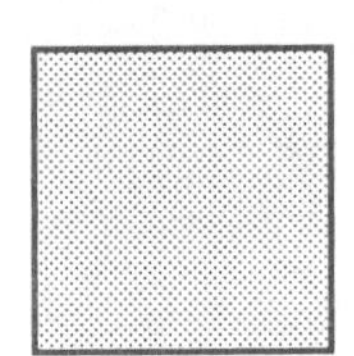

(b) 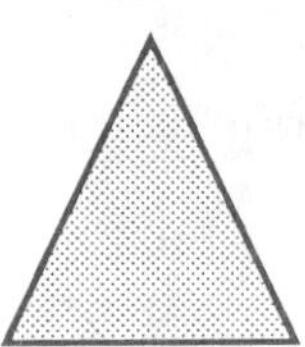

(c) 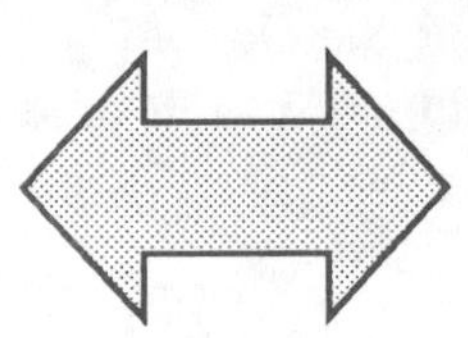

Q5. By measuring the sides of each triangle, classify it as either equilateral, isosceles or scalene:

(a) 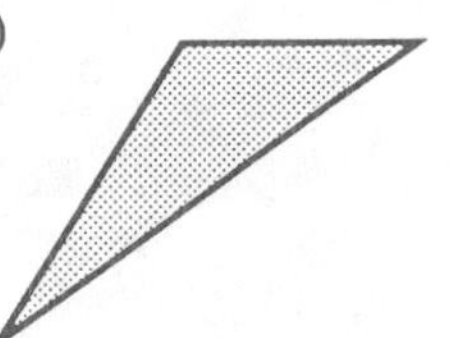

(b) 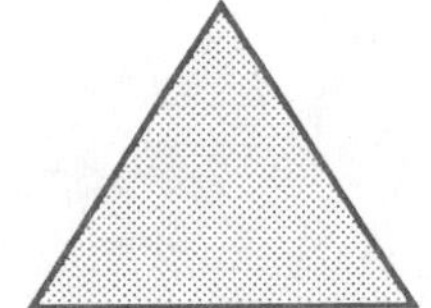

(c) 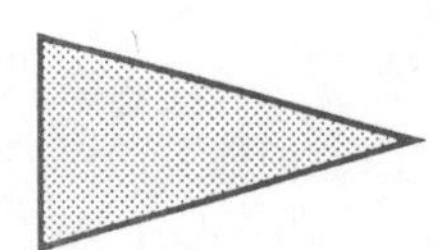

LEVEL 2 — 2D

AVERAGE QUESTIONS

Q1. Name each polygon, and then draw its axis of symmetry:

(a)

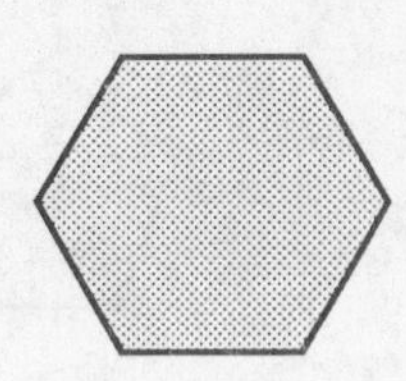

(b)

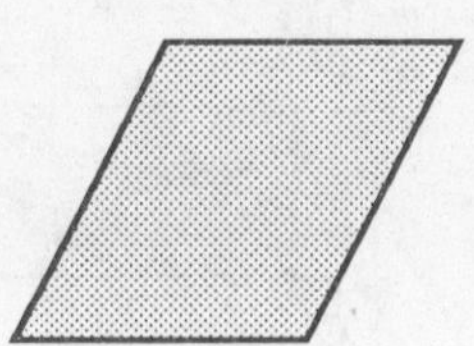

(c)

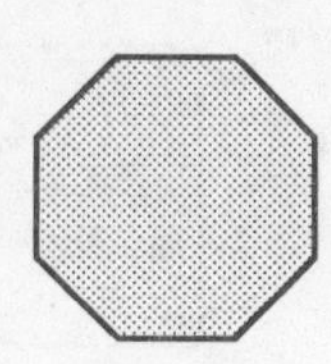

Q2. Without measuring, classify each angle and describe its size in words:

(a)

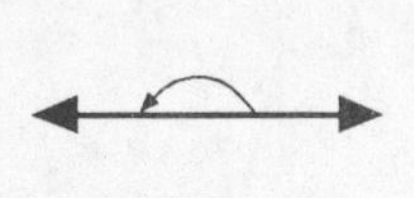

(b)

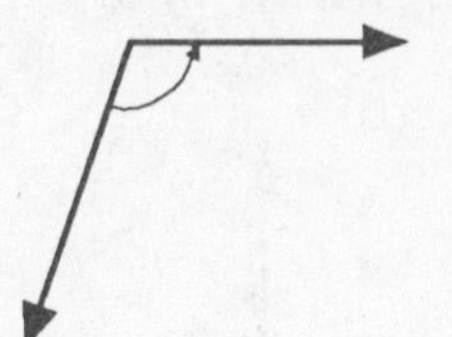

(c)

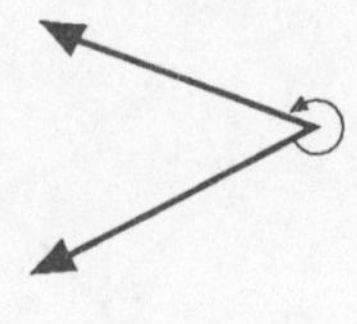

Q3. Measure the following angles with the use of a protractor:

(a)

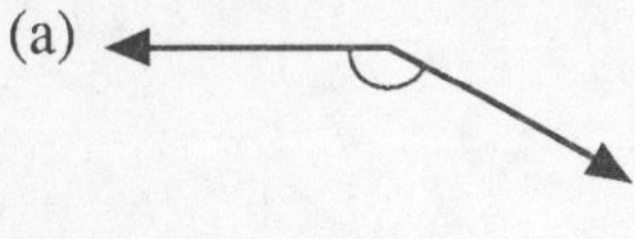

(b)

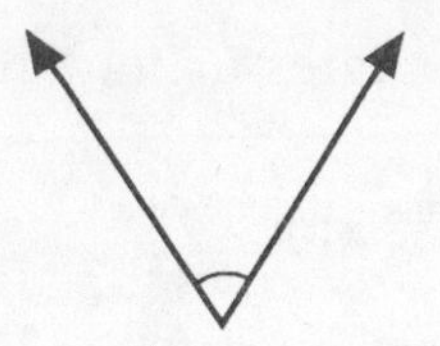

(c)

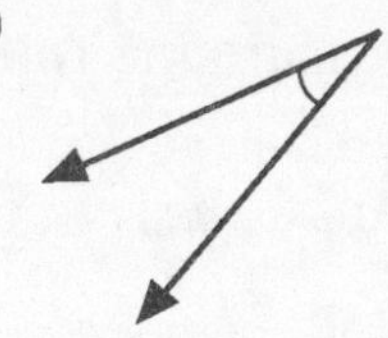

Q4. State whether the triangles shown below are acute angled, obtuse angled or right angled.

(a)

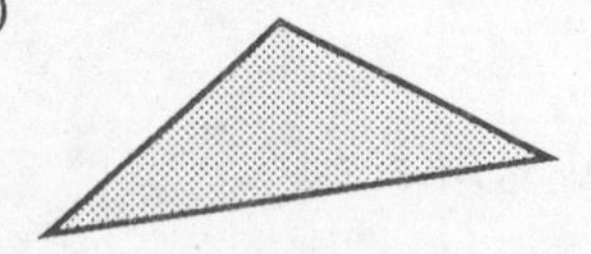

(b)

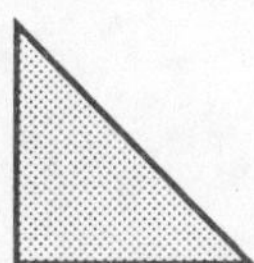

(c)

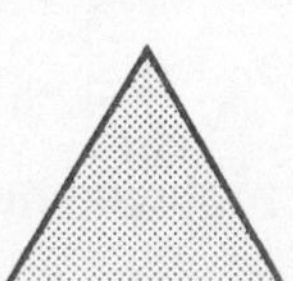

Q5. Which of the following figures have rotational symmetry?

(a)

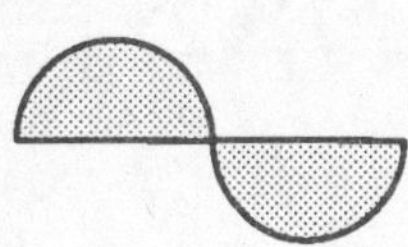

(b)

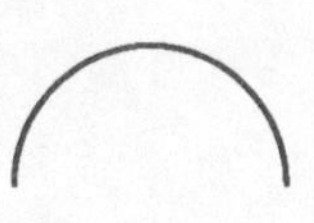

(c)

Q6. Without using a protractor, find the size of the unknown angle in each triangle:

(a)

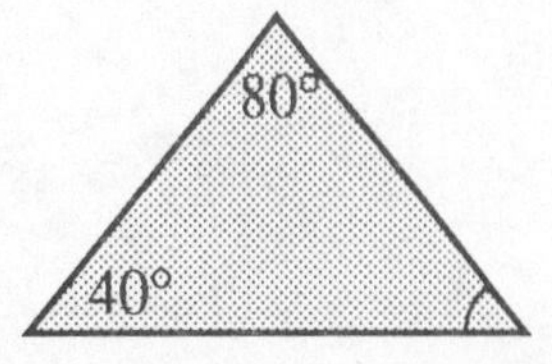

(b)

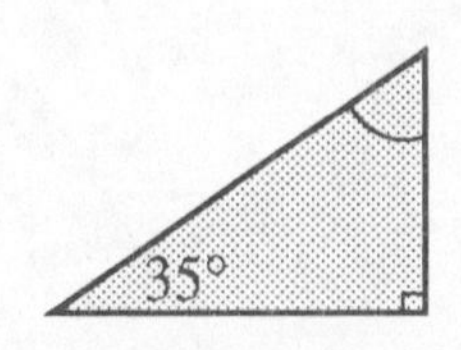

(c)

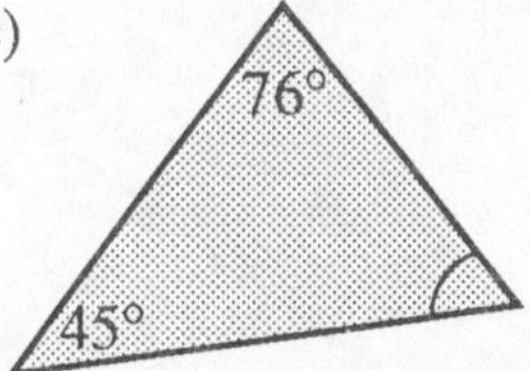

LEVEL 3 — 2D

DIFFICULT QUESTIONS

Q1. Name these polygons:

(a)

(b) 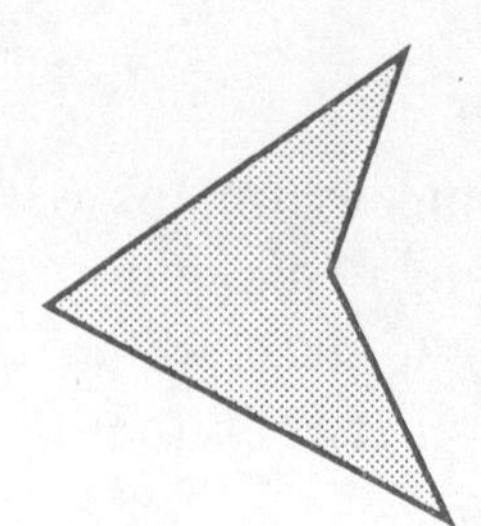

(c) 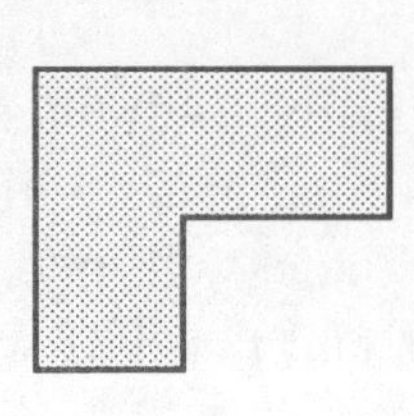

Q2. Using a protractor, measure each angle below:

(a)

(b) 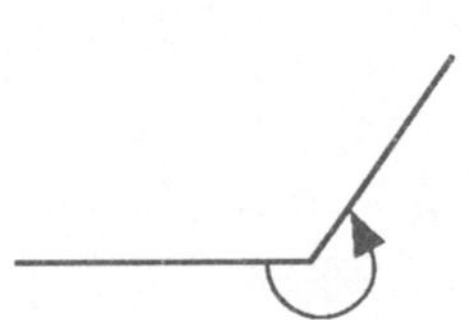

(c) 

Q3. Classify the following triangles according to both angle size and lengths of sides. e.g. acute angled, isosceles triangle.

(a) 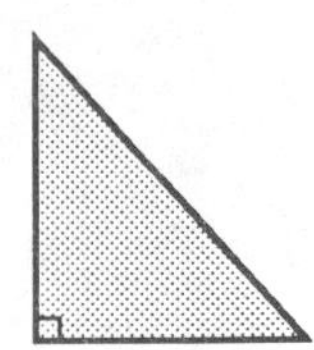

(b) 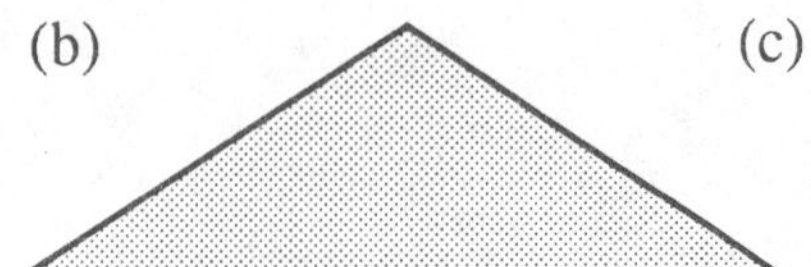

(c) 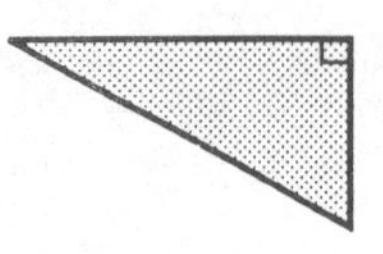

Q4. Without using a protractor, find the size of the unknown angles marked:

(a) 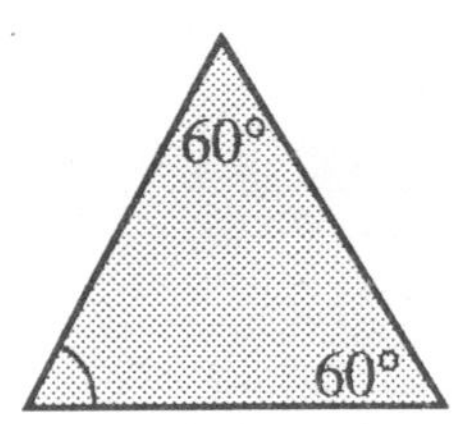

(b) 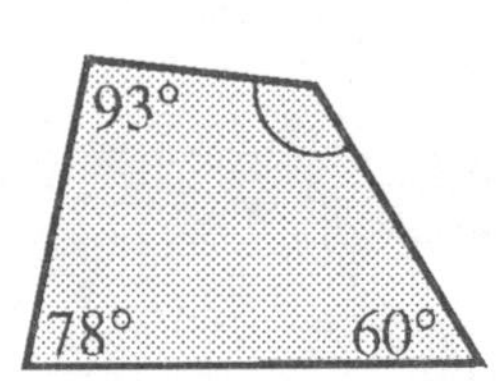

(c) 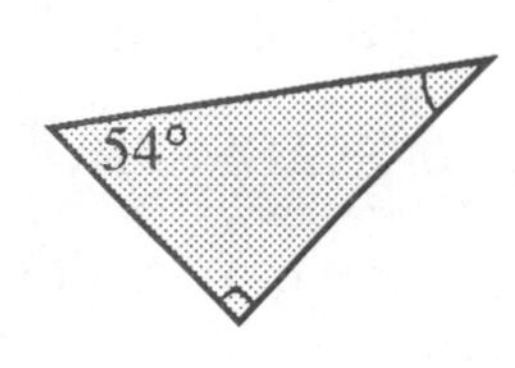

(d) 

(e) 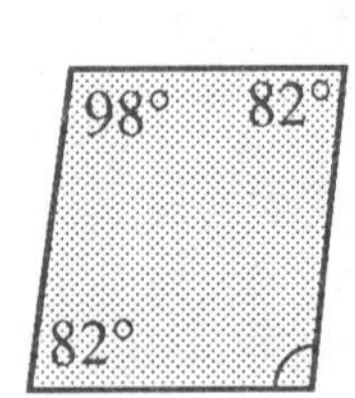

(f) 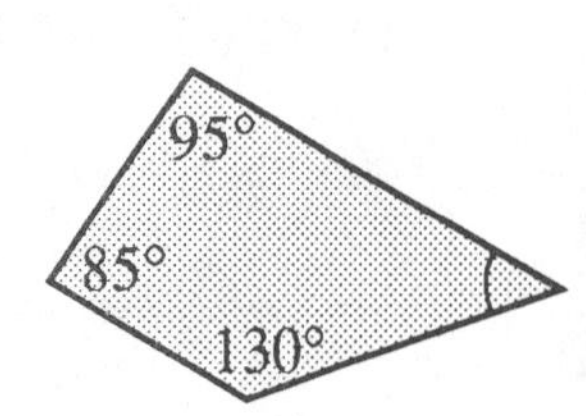

Q5. (a) What word is used for the perimeter of a circle?
(b) Name the line that joins the centre of a circle to the perimeter.
(c) Name the straight line that passes through the centre of a circle and touches the perimeter at each of its ends?

POSITION

Before progressing it is important that the skills outlined in the previous volumes in this series are acquired.

The ability to draw simple plans and maps will be developed during Years 5 and 6. Informal grids will be investigated and dot-to-dot puzzles and mazes completed. Coordinates will be introduced to describe position as will the four major compass points and the half way points between them.

VOCABULARY

Column, compass, compass points, co-ordinates, direction, east, easterly, first (second, etc.), grid, last, left, location, map, maze, middle, north, north-east, north-easterly, northerly, path, plan, plot, position, right, route, row, south, south-easterly, southerly, south-westerly, space, square, top, turn, west, westerly.

CONTENTS

Page

GRIDS

To develop an awareness of direction and to lay the basis for mapping skills, students should investigate grids, mazes and dot-to-dot puzzles.

Example:

Columns are vertical
Rows are horizontal

(a) What is pictured second from the left in the top row?
(b) What is pictured 3 below the fish?
(c) Describe the position of the fork in at least three different ways.
(d) The bell is to the right of what?
(e) What is at the top of the 2nd column from the left?

Solution:
(a) The fish is pictured second from the left in the top row.
(b) The apple is pictured 3 below the fish.
(c) The fork is (i) below the kite, and
(ii) above the watch, and
(iii) to the right of the plane, and
(iv) to the left of the shoe, etc.
(d) The bell is to the right of the boat.
(f) The chair is at the top of the 4th column from the left.

Example:
(a) On the grid draw a car in the middle square of the 2nd row up.
(b) Draw a tree to the right of the car.
(c) Draw a stick-man in the 2nd square above the cross.

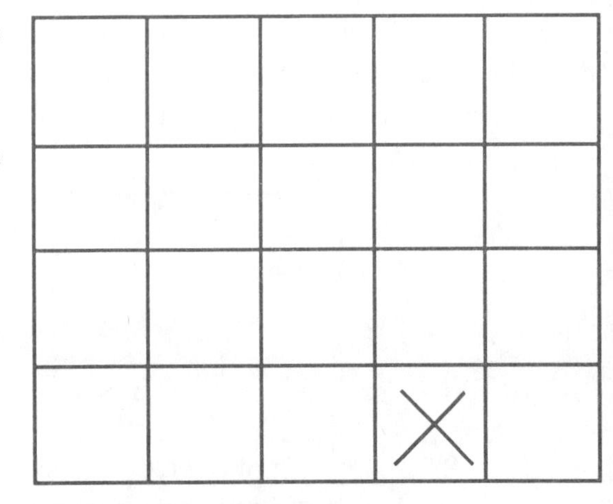

Solution:

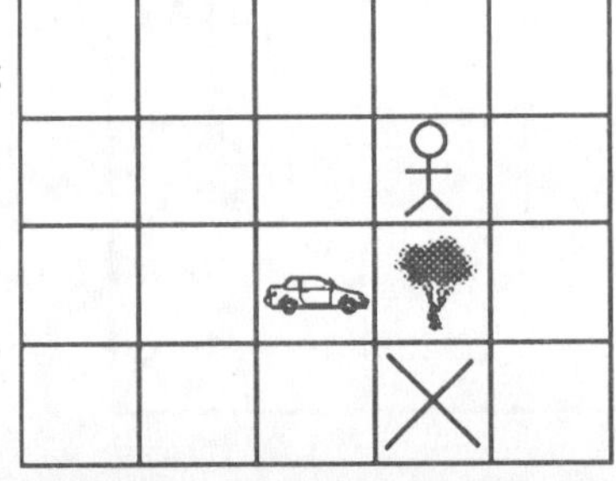

MAZES and MAPS

Example:

For each set of instructions say which hole in the lawn the beetle chooses.

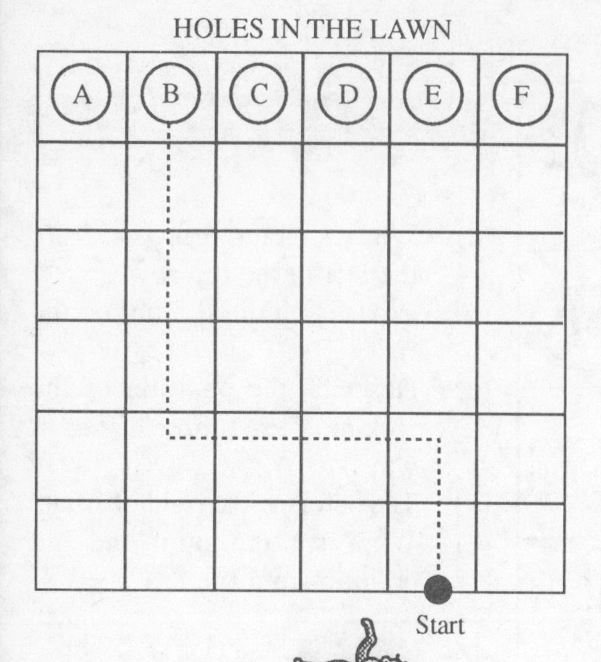

(a) The beetle crawls forward into the second space, turns left and crawls 3 spaces, then turns to its right and crawls 4 spaces (illustrated).

(b) Beetle crawls 4 spaces forward, turns right and crawls 1 space forward, turns left and crawls 2 spaces.

(c) Give a set of instructions so that the beetle chooses hole D.

Solution:

(a) The beetle chooses hole B.

(b) The beetle chooses hole F.

(c) One solution of many: 3 forward, 1 to its left, 3 to its right.

ACTIVITIES:

1. Plan a maze in the school hall, classroom or in the garden. Set up a number of obstacles. Plan a route through the maze which is relayed to a blindfolded friend. Do the instructions get the friend safely through the maze?
2. Draw a simple plan or map of the classroom, the student's bedroom, the school, the house, etc., to give a bird's eye view.

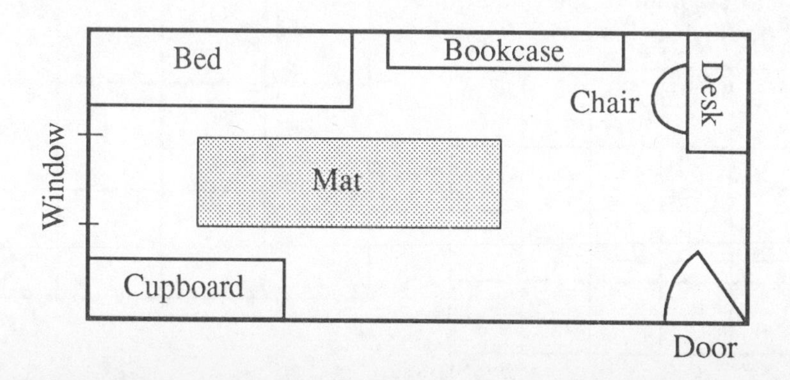

COORDINATES

Earlier activities will have given students opportunities to know how to describe their own position or that of an object. The use of coordinates is now introduced. Whilst it is most usual for the coordinates to refer to the intersection of the grid lines, students will meet instances when the coordinates refer to the spaces between.

> Coordinates are first read across from the left and then up or down.

Example (i):
On the grid, what are the coordinates for:

(a) the tree, (b) the car, (c) the fish?

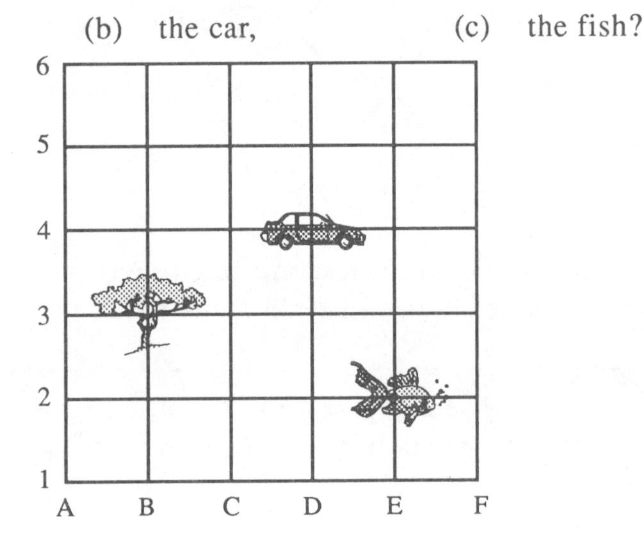

Solutions:
(a) The tree is at B3. (b) The car is at D4. (c) The fish is at E2.

Example (ii): Pirate Island

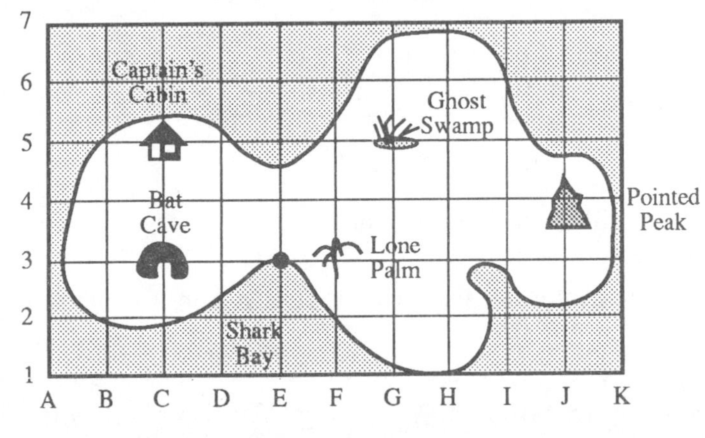

(a) Give the coordinates for the Ghost Swamp.
(b) What would be found at F3?
(c) The treasure is hidden at C3. Where would I find it?

Solutions: (a) Ghost Swamp is at G5. (b) The Lone Palm is at F3.
(c) The treasure would be found at Bat Cave.

ACTIVITY:
Investigate how coordinates are used in street directories and atlases.

THE COMPASS

When students have become familiar with the the compass points, North, South, East, West, NE, SE, NW and SW they are able to describe e.g. the direction of the wind and routes on a map and will also have acquired the directional skills needed for orienteering. A compass can help find directions. For example, if you were facing North and wished to walk in a north-easterly direction, then you would have to turn 45° to the right.

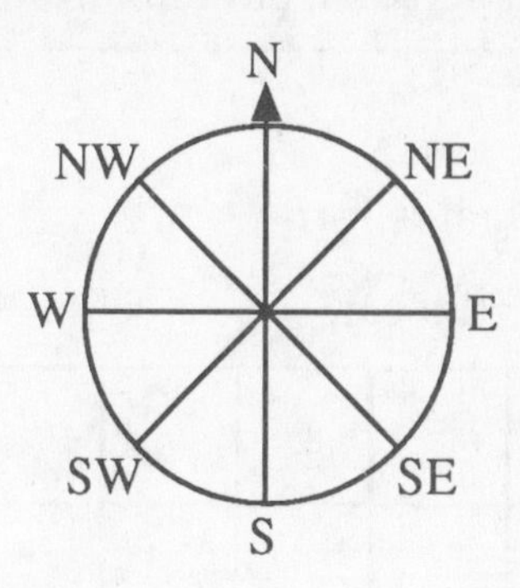

It is useful to link work with the compass to activities involving: grids and mazes; angles, as detailed in the Space 2D sub-strand; scale, in the 3D sub-strand.

The clockwise angle you must turn through from North to face an object is called the bearing of that object.

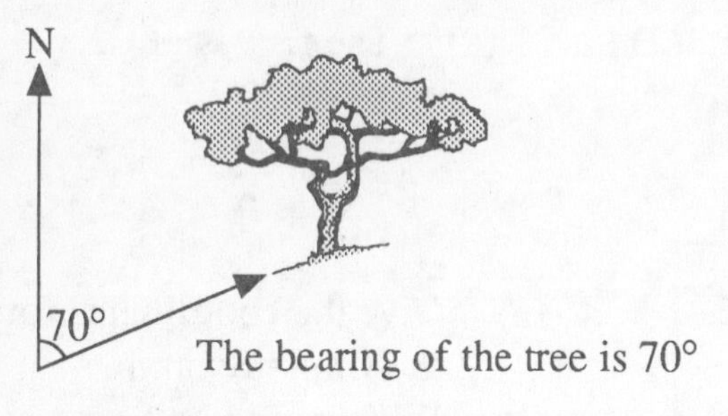

The bearing of the tree is 70°

The bearing of the house is 270°

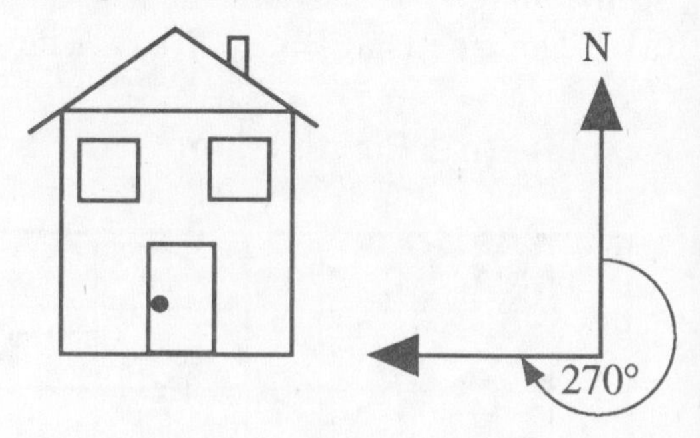

ACTIVITIES:

1. Look at a map of the Sydney suburbs. Name a suburb: (a) to the north of Epping, (b) to the south-east of Penrith, etc.
2. In which direction would you be travelling if you were flying from (a) Darwin to Sydney, (b) Brisbane to Adelaide, etc.
3, Using a compass, investigate the directions and number of paces required to walk over specified routes at school or at home, e.g. 'To travel from the classroom to the library I walked ten paces to the south-east and then turned to the east and walked twelve paces'.
4. Look at aerial photographs and draw maps or plans to represent what is shown.
5. Take part in orienteering activities.

POSITION ASSESSMENT

Students should understand the following ideas:

Grids. mazes. maps and puzzles

- describe the position of objects on a grid
- mark given positions on a grid
- give and follow directions through a maze
- draw a simple plan of a room, a building, etc.
- complete dot-to-dot and similar puzzles

Coordinates

- find a point on a grid from given coordinates
- describe the position of an object on a grid by giving the appropriate coordinates
- demonstrate an understanding of the use of coordinates in different directories and atlases

The compass

- find north on a map
- recall and identify the four major and four intermediate compass points
- find north using a compass; turn to face the major and intermediate compass points
- demonstrate an understanding of the use of coordinates in different directories and atlases
- demonstrate accurate reading of a compass during orienteering activities
- give and follow directions for a simple route in the school grounds or a reserve using compass points
- identify wind direction

LEVEL 1 — POSITION

EASIER QUESTIONS

Q1. On the grid, which picture is found:

(a) 1 to the right of the car?

(b) 3 to the left of the light globe?

(c) 2 up and 2 to the left of the pentagon?

(d) 1 to the right and 3 down of the house?

(e) 3 down and 3 to the left of the tree?

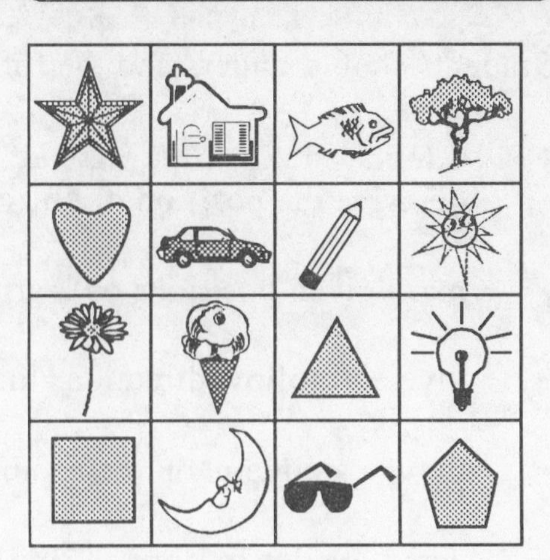

Q2. Banksiaville and its environs.

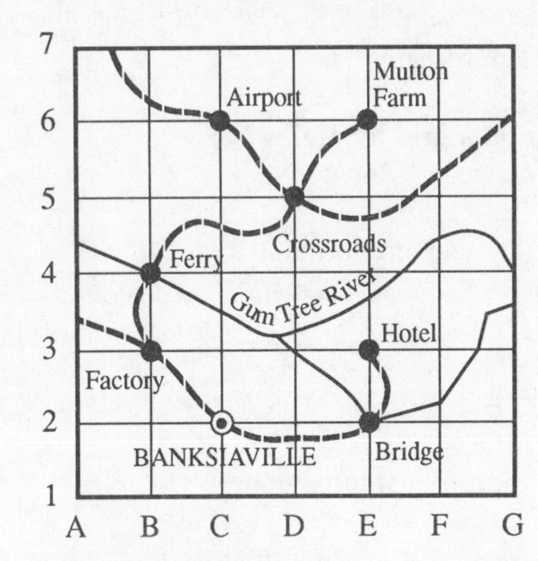

(a) What would be found at:

(i) C2 (ii) E6

(iii) B3 (iv) D5?

(b) At what coordinates would you find:

(i) the airport?

(ii) the bridge?

(iii) the ferry?

(iv) the hotel?

Q3. Mark the following positions on the grid and join them up as you go.

What have you drawn?

C5, B5, D7, E7, E8, F8, F7, G7, I5, C5, C2, E2, E4, F4, F2, H2, H5

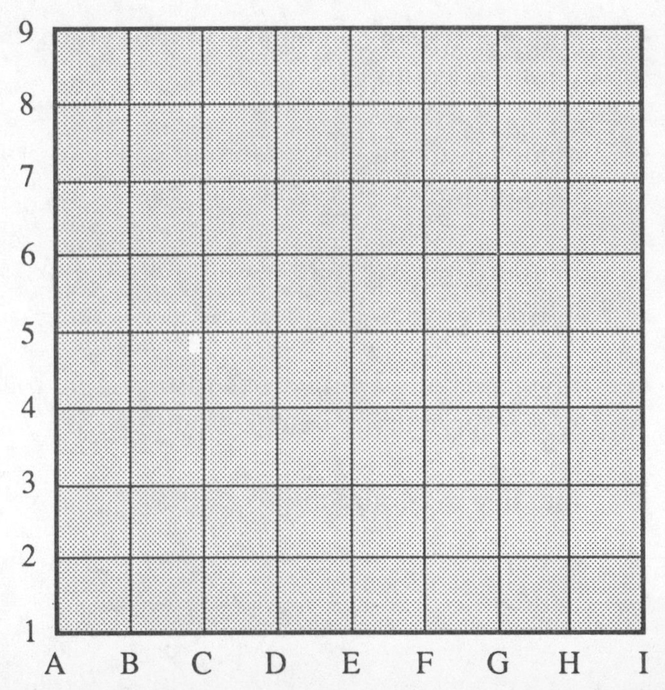

AVERAGE QUESTIONS

Q1.

Follow the directions below, marking the route as you go.

Start

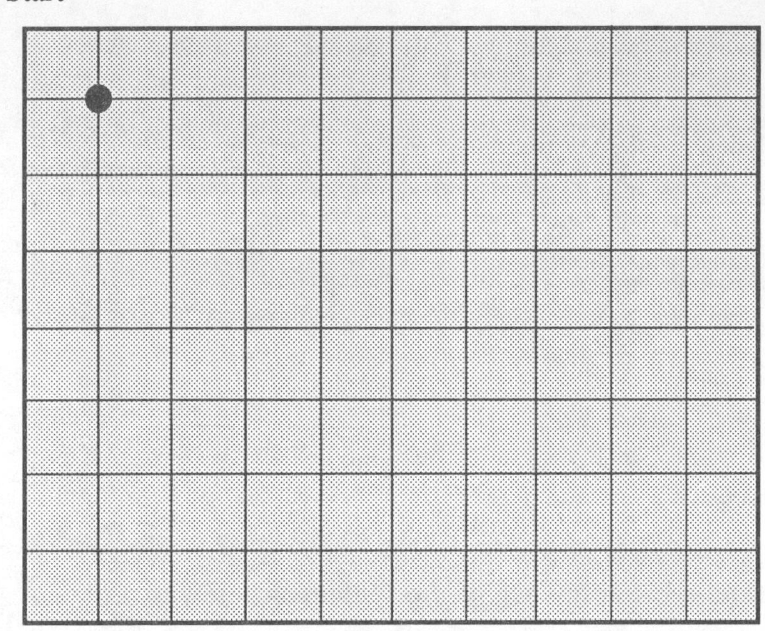

Scale: 1 cm represents 2 m.

10 m south, 4 m east,
2 m north, 4 m south,
2 m north, 4 m east,
2 m south, 8 m east,
6 m north, 8 m west
? m north, 8 m east.
Which number is revealed?

Q2. In each diagram below, find the bearing of the person **from** the house:

(a)

(b)

Q3. Solve this maze.

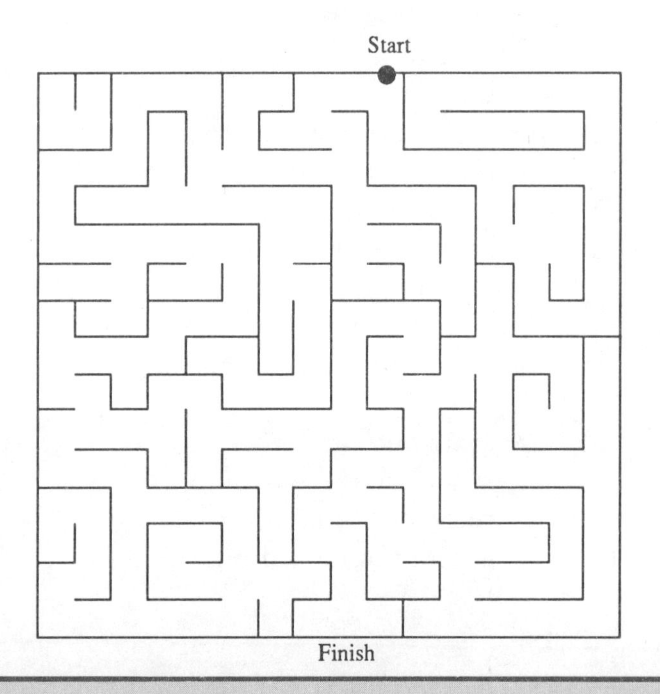

LEVEL 3 — POSITION

DIFFICULT QUESTIONS

Q1.

Map of Holiday Island

Sailing Centre
Airport
Light House
Lake
Forest
Crossroads
Resort
Swamp
Harbour
Lookout

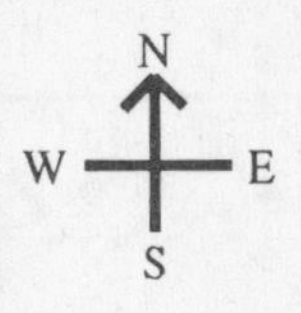

Scale: 1 cm represents 5 km

Q1. Insert the correct direction in each of the sentences below:

(a) The sailing centre is _____ of the Airport.
(b) The resort is _____ of the forest.
(c) The harbour is _____ of the lookout.
(d) The airport is _____ of the lighthouse.
(e) The crossroads are ____ of the lookout, and _____ of the resort.
(f) The harbour is ____ of the crossroads.
(g) The forest is _____ of the sailing centre.
(h) The lake is ____ of the lookout.
(i) The lookout is ____ of the resort.

Q2. How far by road (correct to the nearest km) is it from:

(a) the lookout to the crossroads?
(b) the resort to the sailing centre?
(c) the airport to the lookout?
(d) the sailing centre to the harbour?
(e) the lighthouse to the resort?

Q3. How far as the crow flies is it from:

(a) the swamp to the forest?
(b) the swamp to the lookout?
(c) the forest to the lake?
(d) the harbour to the sailing centre?

GRAPHS

A graph is a way of showing information in the form of a diagram. It is often much easier to understand a set of results by looking at a graph than it is by searching through lists of figures.

Graphs are used a great deal in many areas of Science, Human Society and its Environment, Economics and everyday living. There are several types of graphs, the use of which depends on the information being presented.

Having become familiar with tallying and column graphs in Years 3 and 4, students in Years 5 and 6 continue constructing and interpreting column graphs and progress to the interpretation and construction of picture graphs, line graphs, pie graphs and bar graphs.

VOCABULARY

Arrangement, axis, axes, bar graph, choice, category, column, compare, data, different from, equal to, favourite, horizontal, key, label, largest, least popular, line graph, information, interpret, investigation, more than, most popular, points, portion, next largest, picture graph, pie graph, predict, row, scale, sector, similar to, smallest, sort, stands for, survey, symbols, tally, the same as, title, vertical.

CONTENTS

Page

COLUMN GRAPHS

A column graph is often used for simple recording and interpreting. Column graphs can be drawn vertically or horizontally. The horizontal column graph should **not** be called a bar graph. A bar graph is a particular kind of graph with a special purpose.

Example:
The graph below records the favourite television programs of students in 5R.

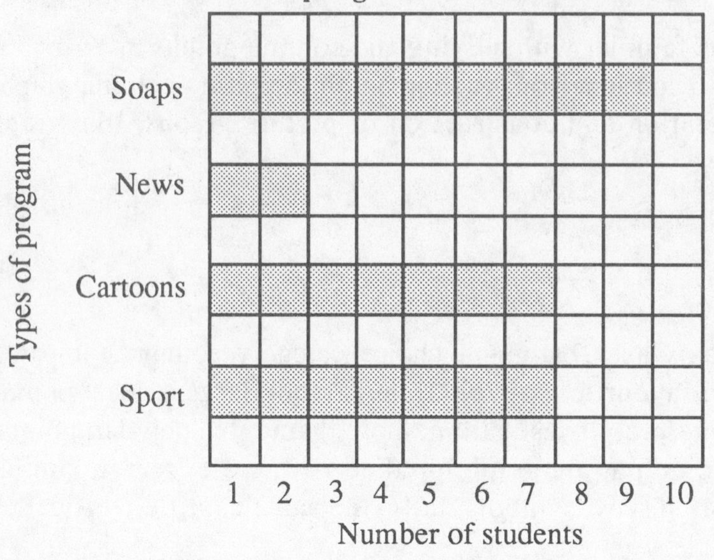

OBSERVATIONS

- The shortest column shows the students who prefer the News.
- More students in the class prefer to watch soaps.
- The cartoon and sport columns are the same length so the same number of students must prefer these programs.
- The least popular program is the News.
- More students prefer cartoons to the News.

QUESTIONS

(a) How many students prefer sports programs?
(b) Nine students prefer which kind of program?
(c) How many more students prefer cartoons to the News?
(d) How many students took part in this survey?
(e) Which is the least popular kind of program?
(f) Which two kinds of programs are equally popular?

Solutions:

(a) 7 students prefer sport.
(b) 9 students prefer soaps.
(c) 5 more students prefer cartoons.
(d) 25 students took part.
(e) News is the least popular.
(f) Sport and cartoons are equally popular.

ACTIVITY: Construct column graphs from tally marks of surveys. Formulate questions about the graph for a partner.

PICTURE GRAPHS

Picture graphs use symbols to represent several objects. They are often used where there are large numbers which could not possibly be represented on a one-for-one basis.

With picture graphs it is essential not only to look at the title of the graph but also at the key. The key states what each symbol represents.

Example: Sports played by girls in Green Street Primary School.

Little Athletics	
Swimming	
Netball	
Hockey	
Key: represents 20 girls	

In this example one stick person represents 20 girls.

QUESTIONS:
(a) Which is the most popular sport?
(b) Which is the least popular sport?
(c) How many girls take part in Little Athletics?
(d) How many girls take part in Swimming?
(e) How many more girls play Netball than Hockey?

Solution:
(a) Netball has more symbols than any other sport, so more girls must play this sport than any other.
(b) Hockey has the least number of symbols, so it must be the least played sport.
(c) Little Athletics has 3 complete symbols, so 60 girls must do Little Athletics.
(d) Swimming has 2 complete symbols and one half symbol, so 50 girls must do swimming (i.e. 20 + 20 + 10 = 50).
(e) 100 girls play Netball and 30 play Hockey, so 70 more girls must play Netball.

ACTIVITIES:
1. Interpret information given in picture graphs.
2. Construct picture graphs for a partner to interpret.

LINE GRAPHS

Line graphs are used to illustrate a continuous process and significant information can be gathered from between the plotted points. Otherwise a column graph should be used. There are two kinds of line graph, A straight line graph is often used for conversions. A line graph can also record irregular fluctuations of, for example, temperature, either as a series of straight lines joining the plotted points or as a curve.

Example:

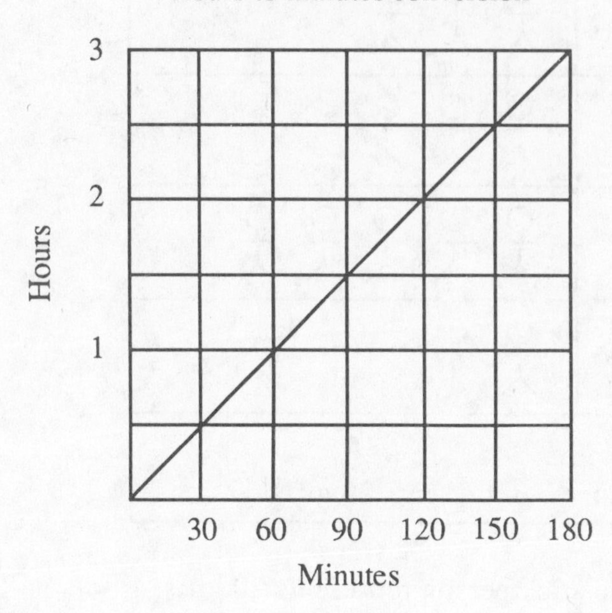

The title tells us that this graph allows us to convert hours to minutes and vice versa. The information on the vertical axis tells us each hour is represented by two rows.

QUESTION: What does one row represent?

The divisions on the horizontal axis tell us that each section represents 30 minutes.

QUESTION: How many minutes in 2 hours?

Look up the vertical axis until the three hour mark is reached. Next look horizontally along this two hour mark until the graph line is reached and then, from that point, look vertically down to the horizontal axis. The reading says 120 minutes. Therefore there are 120 minutes in two hours. The reverse procedure is followed when converting from minutes to hours

LINE GRAPHS—A FURTHER EXAMPLE

Four hourly temperature readings recorded at Broken Hill over a 24 hour period.

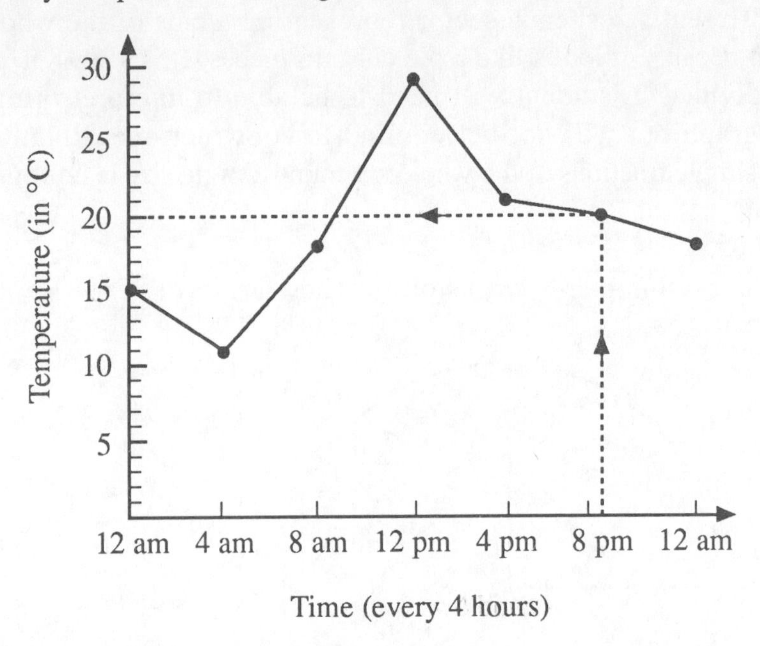

QUESTIONS:

(a) What was the temperature at 8 p.m.?
(b) What time did the temperature first reach 17°C?
(c) What was the lowest temperature and what time did it occur?
(d) By how much did the temperature fall between 12 p.m. and 4 p.m.?

Solutions:

(a) At 8 p.m. the temperature was 20°C. This can be seen by reading up from 8 p.m. to the graph line (as shown by dotted line).

Then read across to the temperature shown.

(b) It first reached 17°C at 8 am.
(c) Lowest temperature was 11°C and this occurred at 4 a.m.
(d) The temperature fell from 29°C to 21°C—a fall of 8°C.

ACTIVITIES:

1. Interpret data from a line graph.
2. Construct a line graph from given data.

PIE GRAPHS

A pie graph, sometimes referred to as a sector graph or pie chart, is a circle cut into sectors of different sizes, each sector representing a part of the whole. It is called a pie graph because it looks like a pie cut into pieces. It is a way of showing how a whole is divided. A student will need to be able to interpret information shown on a pie graph but will not be required to construct one. Relative sizes are discussed and simple fractions of the whole are found. **Angle size is not measured.**

Example:
A Pie Graph of Year 6 Summer Sport Choices. There are:

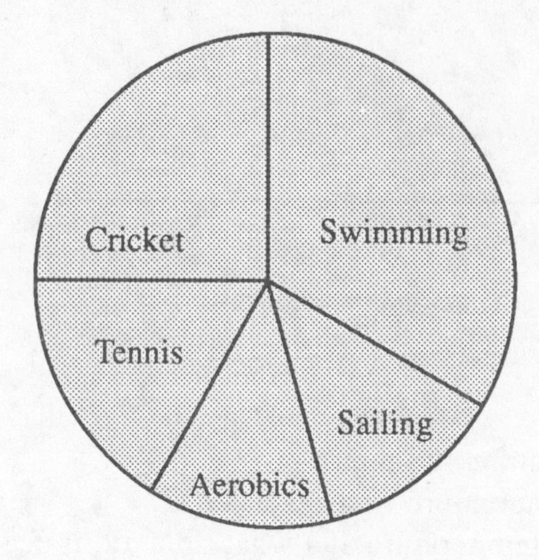

Observations:

- Because the swimming sector is larger more children chose swimming than any of the other sports. It is the favourite sport.
- Sailing was chosen by the least number of children as this sector is the smallest. It is the least favourite choice.
- A quarter of the children, 15, chose cricket because the cricket sector is approximately a quarter of the graph.
- Approximately 15 children chose aerobics or sailing because those two sectors together take up approximately a quarter of the graph.
- This means that approximately 30 children chose the other two sports. Since the swimming sector looks to be about twice as big as the tennis sector approximately 20 children chose swimming. 10 children would, therefore, have chosen tennis.

ACTIVITIES:

1. Collect pie graphs from magazines, newspapers, etc.
2. Interpret information given on pie graphs.

BAR GRAPHS

Like pie graphs, bar graphs are used to demonstrate how a whole is divided. A student should be able to interpret information given in a bar graph but is not required to construct one. Bar graphs should not be confused with horizontal column graphs. A bar graph shows the breakdown of the components in the relative sizes of the sections of the bar. For example, if half the boys in Year 6 chose soccer as a winter sport then half the bar depicting winter sport choices would be shaded to illustrate this. The use of colour is encouraged.

Example:
A bar graph to show how Lee spent his $20 pocket money.

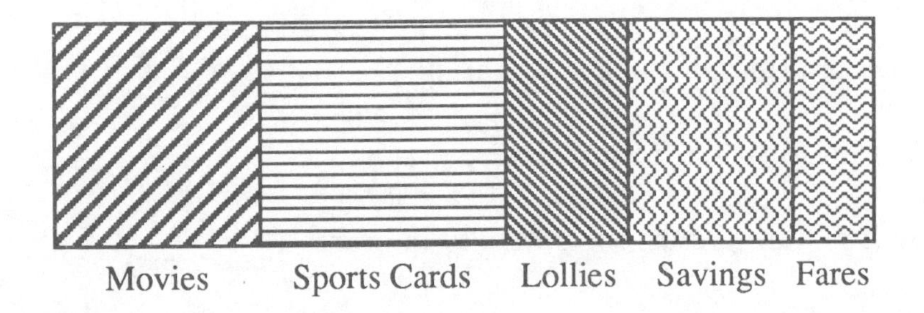

QUESTIONS:

(a) How much did Lee spend each week at the movies?

(b) Which item took the least of Lee's pocket money?

(c) Which 2 items used half of Lee's pocket money?

Solutions:

(a) Since the bar measures 10 cm and the movie section is $2\frac{1}{2}$ cm long then Lee would have spent a quarter of his pocket money at the movies—$5.
(b) The smallest section is Fares, so Lee would have spent least on fares.
(c) Sports cards (3cm) and Savings (2cm) total half the length of the bar. Therefore Lee would have spent half his money on these two items.

ACTIVITIES:

1. Collect bar graphs from magazines and newspapers, etc.
2. Interpret information given on bar graphs.

GRAPHS ASSESSMENT

Students should understand the following ideas:

Column graphs

- describe the principles of column graphs
- construct column graphs from tally marks of information gathered in surveys and then ask questions which encourage a partner to interpret the column graph
- interpret column graphs

Picture graphs

- describe the principles of picture graphs
- interpret information from a picture graph
- construct picture graphs for others to interpret

Line graphs

- describe the principles of line graphs
- represent data on a line graph
- give the value of a given point on a line graph

Pie graphs

- describe the principles of pie graphs
- compare and interpret information from pie graphs

Bar graphs

- describe the principles of bar graphs
- compare and interpret information from pie graphs

Q1. Wagga primary school students did a survey of the different colours of cars that passed close to their school. They recorded the information on the column graph below.

The colours of cars passing Wagga Primary School

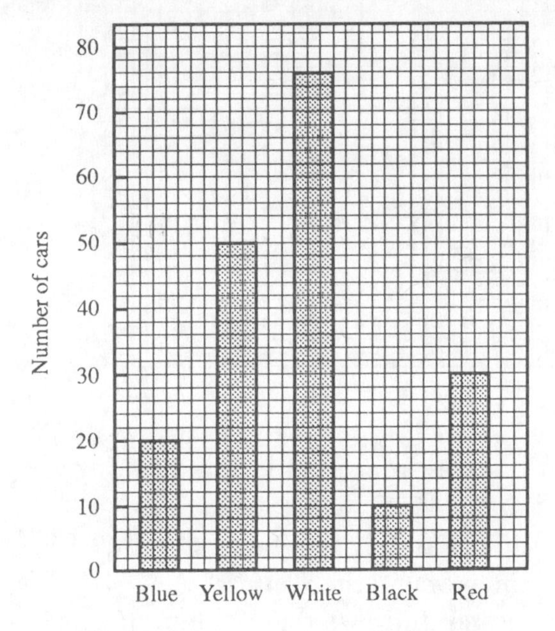

(a) How many cars were yellow?
(b) How many cars were red?
(c) What was the least popular colour?
(d) What was the most popular colour?
(e) How many cars were involved in the survey?
(f) Give a possible reason why lighter coloured cars are more popular?

Q2. Mr Smith owns an orchard and harvested his first crop of apples in 1990. The picture graph below shows how many apples he harvested over the first 5 years.

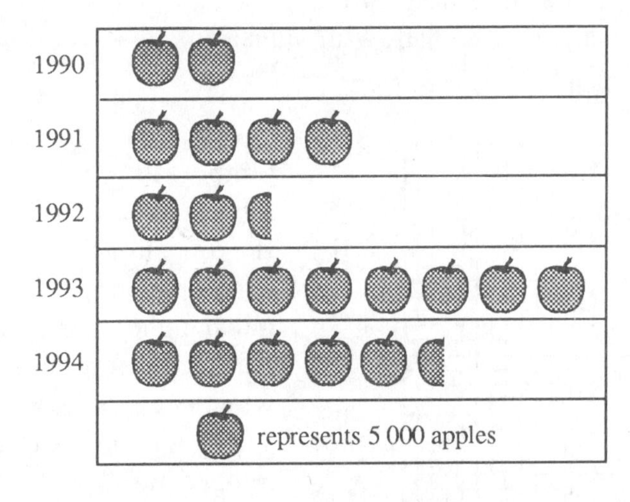

(a) How many apples did he harvest in 1991?
(b) Which year did he harvest the most apples?
(c) How many apples did he harvest over the 5 years?
(d) How many more apples did he harvest in 1993 than in 1992?
(e) Give a possible reason for fewer apples in 1992 than in 1991.

AVERAGE QUESTIONS

Q1. The column graph below shows the average monthly rainfall in Sydney over a 5 year period. Look at the scales closely and then answer the following questions.

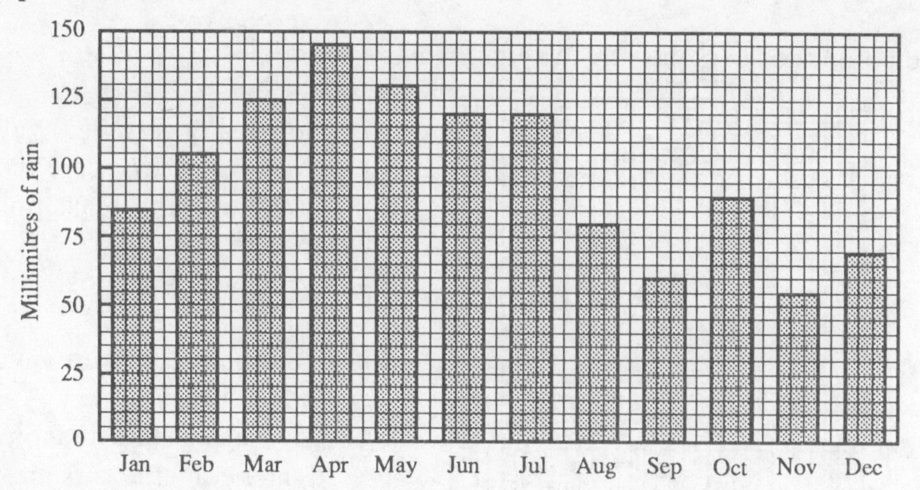

(a) What does each vertical graduation mark represent in mm of rain?
(b) What is the average rainfall for August?
(c) Which month has an average monthly rainfall of 90 mm of rain?
(d) Which 3 months of the year are, on average, the wettest?
(e) In how many months is the average rainfall less than 85 mm of rain?
(f) In how many months is the average rainfall greater than or equal to 115 mm of rain?
(g) Which months have an average rainfall of less than 100 mm and greater than 75 mm?

Q2. The line graph below is taken from the hospital chart of a sick girl. Read the scale carefully and then answer the following questions:

Alexandra's temperature graph

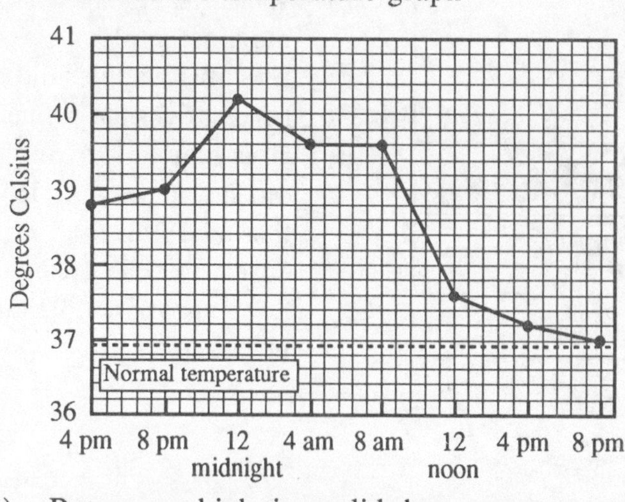

(a) What was the girl's temperature when she first went into hospital?
(b) If our normal body temperature is 37°C, how much higher than normal was her temperature when she first went in?
(c) What was her highest temperature?
(d) Between which times did the temperature remain the same?
(e) At what time did she start to dramatically improve?
(f) How much did the temperature drop between 8 am and 12 noon?

LEVEL 3 — GRAPHS

DIFFICULT QUESTIONS

Q1. Eye colours in class 6J. [Note: 6J has 32 students].

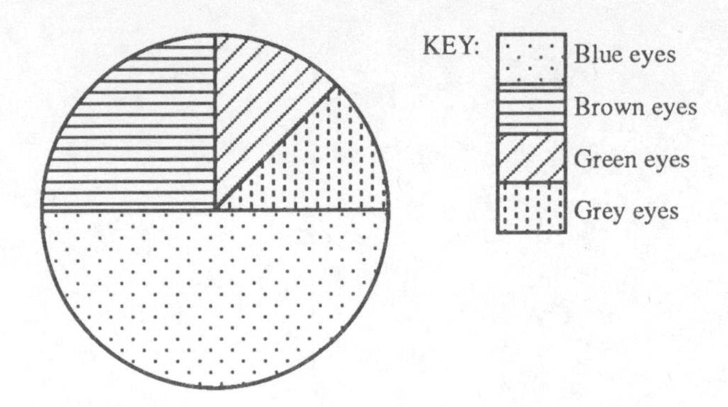

(a) How many students have green eyes?

(b) What fraction of the class has grey eyes?

(c) How many more students have brown eyes than grey eyes?

(d) Half as many students have brown eyes as blue eyes. True or false?

(e) How many times more students have blue eyes than grey eyes?

Q2. Plants sold by Growmore's Nursery. [Note: 84 plants were sold altogether]

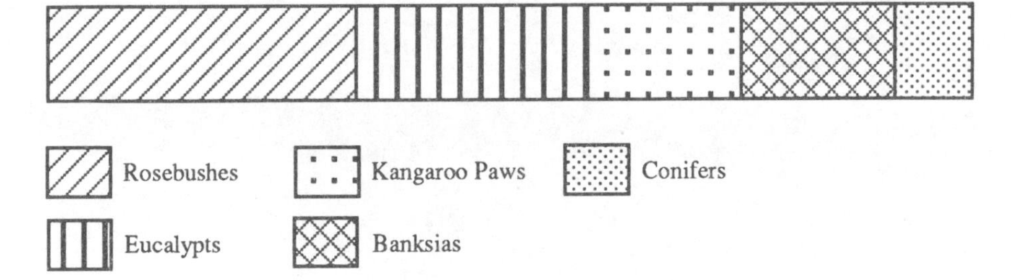

(a) The same amount was sold of two types of plants. Which plants were they and what was the amount of each sold?

(b) How many rosebushes were sold?

(c) How many more Eucalypts were sold than conifers?

(d) How many fewer Banksias were sold than rosebushes?

(e) What percentage of all the plants sold were Eucalypts?

An extra page for additional notes

MEASUREMENT

'he that nothing questions, nothing learns'

INTRODUCTION

Adults are constantly confronted by problematic situations involving measurement concepts: distances, capacity of containers, the mass of ingredients in a cake recipe or in mixing cement, the length of guttering for the roof, the amount of crazy paving for the path, petrol for the car, etc. The list is endless.

It is not sufficient to have learned a series of facts about how many metres make a kilometre or grams make a kilogram without a true understanding of what each of these units means. Can you visualise a metre? Would you recognise a kilogram if you lifted it? What is a square metre and how many square metres of lawn do you have so that you can calculate how much grass seed or turf fertilizer you need? Can you choose a thermometer that measures within the temperature range that you need? How much time will you need to travel from home to your holiday destination? Which container is the appropriate size to store the casserole in the freezer?

It is only through hands-on experiences that such knowledge is acquired .

Play is the starting point for the many activities concerning the different aspects of measurement. Then, by using informal measuring units~ the need for standard measuring units appropriate to vanous situations is recognised. All of these activities involve a great deal of shared experiences and discussion.

ESTIMATION AND APPROXIMATION PLAY A VITAL ROLE IN THE DEVELOPMENT OF UNDERSTANDING, EVERY OPPORTUNITY TO PRACTISE THESE SKILLS SHOULD BE GIVEN, ACCURACY AND UNDERSTANDING IMPROVE WITH PRACTICE.

CONCRETE MATERIALS

Storage

Bowls, boxes, cartons, containers, envelopes, jars, shoeboxes.

Materials

Alarm clocks, analog clocks, atlases, automatic timer, balance scales, balls—golf, tennis, cricket, etc., base 10 materials, bathroom scales, beads, beakers, beans, blocks of wood, books, bottles, bottle tops, bowls, buckets, bricks, building blocks, buttons, calculators, calendars, calibrated containers, calipers (inside, outside), cardboard (thin & heavy), cardboard boxes, cardboard shapes, Centicubes, clock face stamp, clock with second hand, coat hangers, coins, corks, counters, cricket stumps, cups, depth gauges, detergent bottles, diameter gauges, diary, digital clocks, dowel sticks, drinking glasses, droppers, Duplo bricks, egg cups, electric—blanket, frypan, heater, etc, equal arm balance, feathers, fish tanks, flour, foam rubber, frozen food packages, furniture, globes of the world, graph paper, grid paper, gumnuts, ice-cream, ice cubes, isometric dot paper, jars, juice containers, kettle, keys, kitchen scales, leaves, Lego bricks, LOGO, macaroni, magazines, marbles, masking tape, matchboxes, measuring cylinders, medicine glasses, metre rules, metre sticks, micrometer, milk cartons, mugs, Multilink, nails, newspaper, odometer, packets, paddle-pop sticks, paper, paper clips, peanuts, pebbles, pencils, pens, photographs, pine cones, ping-pong balls, pipecleaners, plastic bags, plasticine, polystyrene, polystyrene beads, recipe books, ribbon, rice, rope, rubbers, rubbish bins, 30 cm rules, salt, sand, sand timer, saucepans, sawdust, scissors, sewing thread reels, shells, spark plugs, speedometers, spoons of various sizes, spring balance, standard 1 kg, 500g, 100g & 10g masses, standard measuring jugs, sticks, stones, stopwatches, straws, string, tape, tape measures, teapots, telephone books, thermometers—unscaled & scaled, thimbles, thumb tacks, timetables, tins, tissue boxes, toothpicks, transparent grid overlays, trays, trundle wheel, tubs, Unifix, washers, water—tap, iced, warm, hot, boiling, etc, weather reports, wire, witches' hats, wood off-cuts, wool.

LENGTH

It is important that skills outlined in the previous volumes in this series are acquired before progress is made to those following.

Estimation is an essential component in this sub-strand and it should be used constantly in conjunction with actual measurement. During these two years a student will learn to recognise, estimate and measure a metre and half a metre. Having understood the need for a smaller unit the student will then learn to recognise, estimate and measure using centimetres and metres and to recognise the relationship between 100 centimetres and 1 metre. Links should be made with the Fractions and Decimals substrand as it is important to be able to record measurements using decimal notation. Experience should be given in the use of tapes, rulers, trundle wheels, calipers, etc. The need for a unit larger than a metre—the kilometre, and a unit smaller than a centimetre—the millimetre, should now be recognised. A student should be able to recognise, estimate, measure and record using these units.

VOCABULARY

Centimetre, circumference, decimal point, kilometre, estimate, measure, metre, millimetre, nearest, radius, scale of a map.

CONTENTS

THE CENTIMETRE—cm

Students should now be familiar with reading lengths and measuring using metres and half metres. Investigations should now take place with the centimetre.

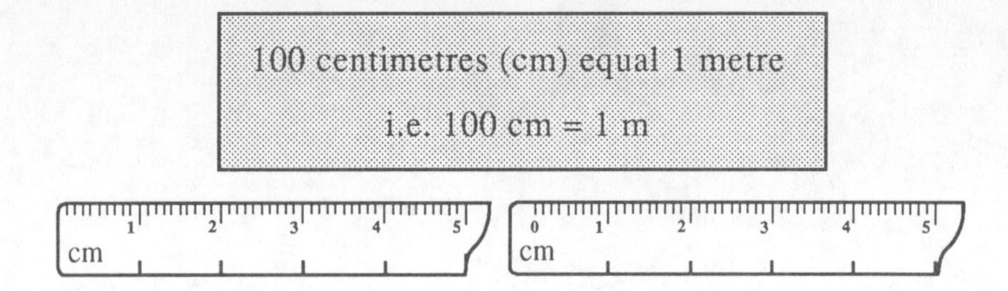

It is important to look at a variety of 30 cm rulers and to discuss the differences. Does the ruler have a spare piece on the ends to allow for damage so that accuracy is not lost if the corners are knocked. Will this influence how the ruler is placed for accurate measuring?

ACTIVITIES:

1. How many things can you find which you estimate to measure about a centimetre? When you measure them notice whether they are smaller or larger than a centimetre.

2. Estimate to the nearest centimetre then measure the length of various objects in centimetres.

3. How could you measure the length of a wavy line? (Carefully place thin string alongside the line following the curves. When the end of the line is reached mark the string, straighten it and place it against a ruler or shorts and longs to measure the length.)

4. Estimate and then measure the distance around balls of different sizes

5. Find by estimating then measuring, by comparison with a metre rule, a number of items that are less than a metre in length. Estimate and measure how much less than a metre each item is.

NOTE: By this stage many students will be ready to record lengths in the decimal form. Refer to the Fractions and Decimals sub-strand.

TAPES, TRUNDLE WHEELS AND CALIPERS

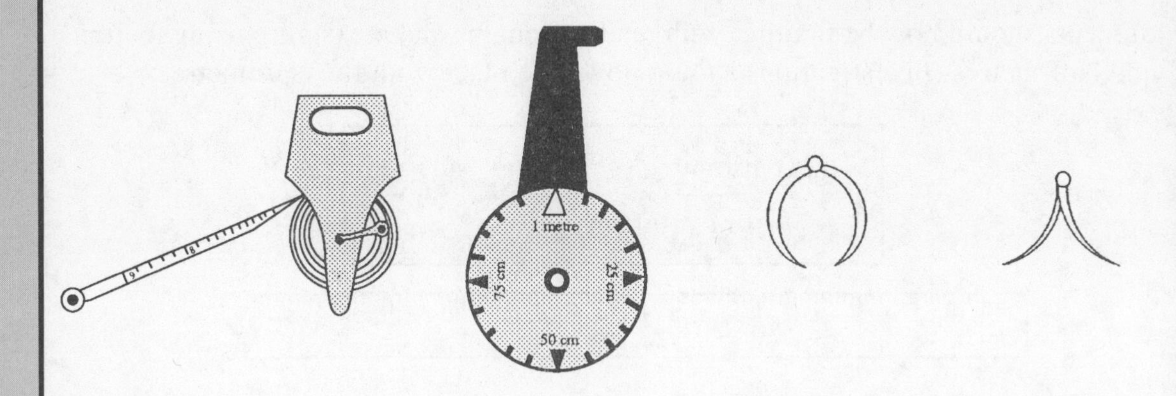

Tapes and trundle wheels are used to simplify the measuring of longer distances in metres.

Tapes come in a variety of lengths depending on the purpose for which they are intended. A 1 m dressmaker's tape is made of plasticised fabric. 5 m and 8 m tapes are used by carpenters and builders. They are made of steel so that they are as accurate as possible and are enclosed in a metal protective cover. They are spring loaded so that the tape rewinds itself into the case when not in use. Tapes which are used to measure distances on sports fields are also made of steel so that they don't stretch and come in a variety of sizes, 30 m, 100 m, etc. They too are enclosed in a protective case which has a retractable handle with which to rewind the tape into its case. Each tape should be examined to see what range it has, where zero is, how it is calibrated and how it unwinds and rewinds.

Trundle Wheels are wheels with a circumference of 1 m attached to a handle. By placing the wheel in the starting position and pushing it along with the handle the wheel will click to signify that one metre has been completed. Count the clicks to count the distance travelled in metres. Parts of a metre are marked on many wheels. Check how to read these.

The results produced by various measuring devices should be compared to determine the most accurate in a given situation.

Calipers are used to measure the inside and outside dimensions of objects. Diameter gauges and depth gauges can also be investigated.

It is important to learn to use the appropriate measuring device.

Activities should be undertaken to give students experience with all these devices so they will be able to determine their most appropriate use.

THE KILOMETRE—km

It would be impractical to measure longer distances using metres. There is a need for a larger unit to measure length—the kilometre. Kilometre is pronounced **kill-oh-metre**. The prefix 'kilo' means 1 000.

> 1 kilometre equals 1 000 metres
>
> i.e. 1 km = 1 000 m

It is difficult to visualise a kilometre. To aid comprehension it is necessary to walk a kilometre. Estimates of a kilometre distance along a nominated route should be made before actually walking it, using a trundle wheel to verify the distance.

ACTIVITIES:

1. Estimate a kilometre along another route and then measure it. How accurate were the estimates? When have a quarter, a half and three-quarters of a kilometre been completed?

2. Estimate which public buildings are less than, are more than or are just about 1 kilometre from school or home.

3. Estimate the distance that each student travels to school from their home.

4. Look at maps and discuss how distances are represented. Discuss scale. (Link to 3D substrand.) Measure in centimetres and then convert to find distances between towns. Graph the results. Also check the accuracy of the estimates in the previous activities (1–3) using local maps.

5. Write results in a variety of ways.

   Two and a half kilometres can be written 2 kilometres 500 metres, 2 km 500 m, 2 500 m or 2.5 km. (Link to fractions and decimals substrand.)

6. On car journeys, check distances travelled using the odometer.

PERIMETER

> Perimeter is the total distance around a closed shape.
> To find the perimeter add the lengths of all the sides.

Example (i): Calculate the perimeter of the triangle on the right.

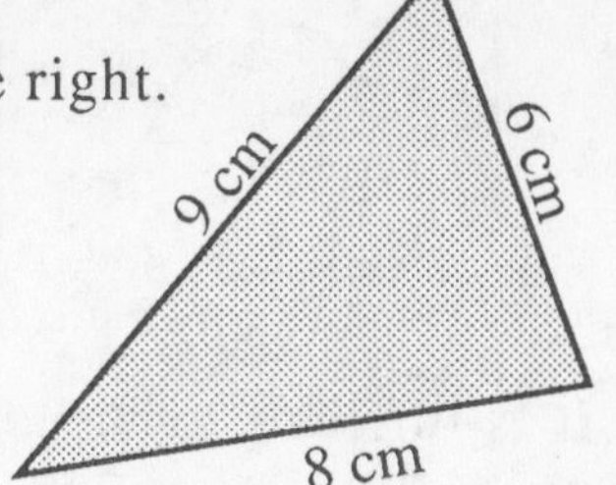

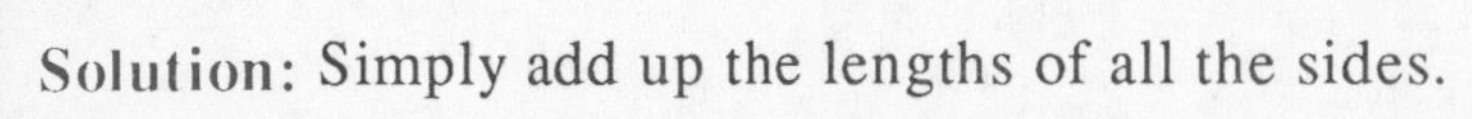

Solution: Simply add up the lengths of all the sides.

Perimeter $= 9 + 6 + 8$
$= 23$ cm

Example (ii): Find the perimeter of these shapes:

(a)

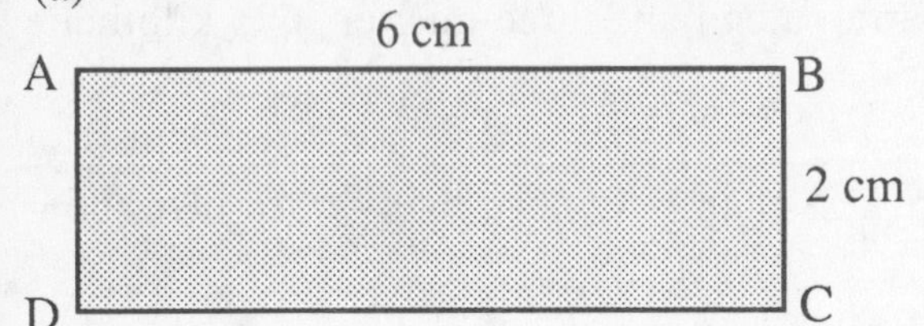

(b)

(c)

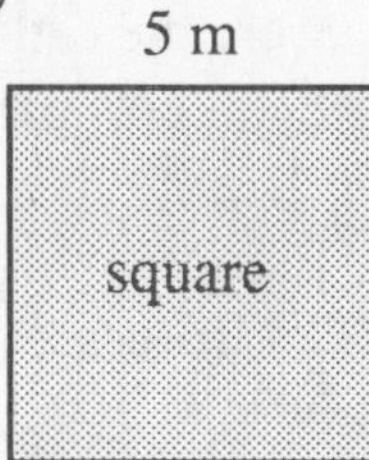

(d)

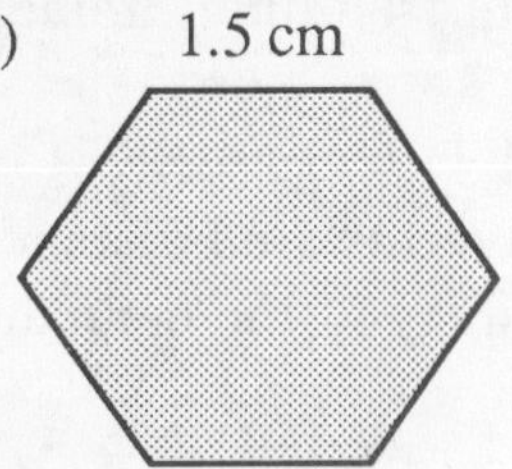

Solutions:

(a) AB = 6 cm
CD = 6 cm
BC = 2 cm
DA = 2 cm
The perimeter
= 16 cm

(b) 2.75
3.10
2.25+
8.10
The perimeter
is 8.1 km

(c) The perimeter of the square is
$4 \times 5 = 20$ m

(d) The perimeter of the hexagon
6×1.5 cm
$= 9$ cm

Investigations into measuring the radius, diameter and circumference (perimeter) of a circle should be undertaken.

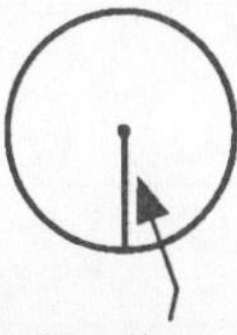

Radius

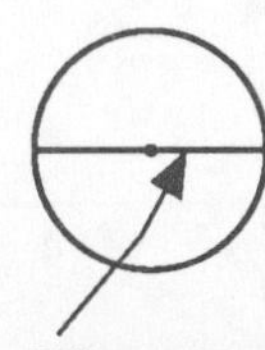

Diameter

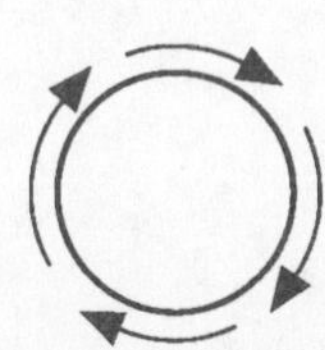

Circumference

THE MILLIMETRE—mm

Students will have recognised the need for a standard unit to measure lengths less than a centimetre.

Milli means a thousandth. A millimetre is $\frac{1}{1\ 000}$ of a metre. 1 000 mm = 1 metre.

10 millimetres equal 1 centimetre

i.e. 10 mm = 1 cm

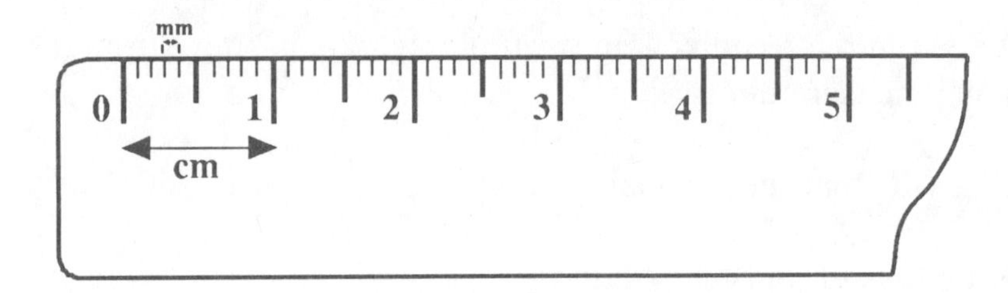

ACTIVITIES:

1. How many things can you find which you estimate to measure about:

   (a) 2 mm
   (b) 5 mm

   Measure these objects and assess how accurate the estimates were.

2. Draw lines which you estimate are:

   (a) 3 mm long
   (b) 8 mm long
   (c) 15 mm long

   Measure these lines and calculate the difference between the estimated and actual measurements.

3. (a) List a series of cm lengths.
   Convert these to mm.
   (b) List a series of mm lengths.
   Convert these to cm.

LENGTH ASSESSMENT

Students should understand the following ideas:

The centimetre

- explain the need for centimetres as a measure of length
- recall that m is the abbreviation for metre
- recall that cm is the abbreviation for centimetre
- recognise a metre, half metre and centimetre length
- estimate and measure objects in centimetres, comparing estimates with actual measurements
- recall that 100 centimetres make 1 metre
- identify objects of a given length
- draw lines of a given length
- understand that half a metre can be written as 0.5 m in the decimal form or $\frac{1}{2}$ m as a common fraction
- record lengths in decimal form

Tapes, trundle wheels and calipers

- estimate and accurately measure lengths and distances with a variety of measuring tapes recording results in decimal form
- estimate then accurately measure distances with a trundle wheel
- estimate then accurately measure dimensions of objects with calipers

The kilometre

- explain the need for kilometres as a measure of length
- recall that km is the abbreviation for kilometre
- recall that 1 000 metres make 1 kilometre
- estimate places 1 kilometre distant and check, where possible, with a trundle wheel or odometer
- explain how distances are represented on maps and convert these scaled distances to kilometres (link 2D)

- estimate and calculate the distances between the Australian state and territory capitals

Perimeter

- define perimeter and how it is measured
- estimate, measure and compare perimeters using Base 10 longs and shorts, string, rulers, measuring tapes, trundle wheels
- measure the radius, diameter and circumference of circles

Millimetre

- explain the need for millimetres as a measure of length
- recall that mm is the abbreviation for millimetre
- recall that 10 mm make 1 cm
- recall that 1 000 mm make 1 m
- estimate the length of objects in mm with reasonable accuracy

LEVEL 1 — LENGTH

EASIER QUESTIONS

Q1. Circle the most appropriate answer:

(a) the height of a 12 year old.

(i) 10 cm (ii) 180 cm (iii) 145 cm

(b) length of a new pencil.

(i) 10 cm (ii) 25 cm (iii) 15 cm

Q2. (a) 4 cm = ☐ mm (b) 8 km = ☐ m

(c) 70 mm = ☐ cm (d) 5 000 m = ☐ km

(e) 3 m = ☐ cm (f) 400 cm = ☐ m

Q3. Calculate the perimeter of each shape:

(a)

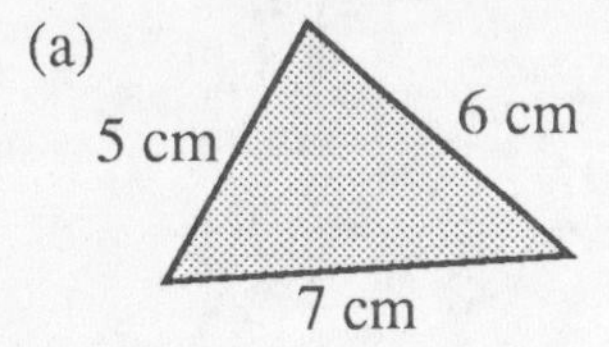

(b)

12 cm

4 cm ☐ 4 cm

12 cm

(c)

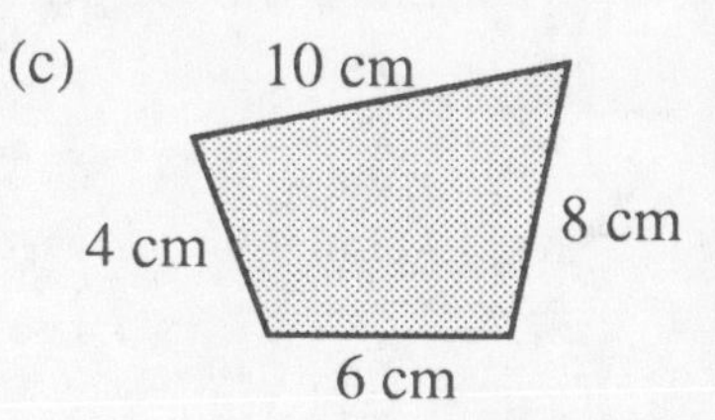

Q4. Peter measured his step to be 70 cm. If he takes 100 steps, how far has he walked?

Q5. (a) $\frac{1}{2}$ m = ☐ cm (b) 75% of 1 m (c) 0.25 of 1 km

Q6. The width of a classroom is 9.5 m. The length of the room is 2.2 m longer than the width. How long is the classroom?

Q7. How many 30 cm rulers must be laid end to end so that their total length is 2.1 m?

Q8. A piece of timber is cut into 4 equal pieces. If the timber is 2 m long, how long will each of the 4 pieces be?

Q9. A girl runs 3 times along the edge of the swimming pool which measures 18 m by 8 m. How far did she run?

LEVEL 2 — LENGTH

AVERAGE QUESTIONS

Q1. (a) $\frac{1}{5}$ m = ☐ cm (b) 6.5 cm = ☐ mm

(c) 500 m = ☐ km (d) 45 mm = ☐ cm

(e) 3.4 km = ☐ m (f) 9 250 m = ☐ km

Q2. Sydney Harbour Bridge is about 1 150 m long. How much longer or shorter is this than 1 km?

Q3. Joseph's step is 82 cm. How many steps does he have to take to travel 41 m?

Q4. A car travels at 80 km/h. How far will it travel in:

(a) $1\frac{1}{2}$ hours? (b) 2 h 15 min?

Q5. A string 25 m long had 4 pieces cut from it. The pieces were 1.45 m, 2.75 m, 4.1 m and 7.35 m long. How much of the string was left?

Q6. Calculate the perimeter of each figure:

(a)

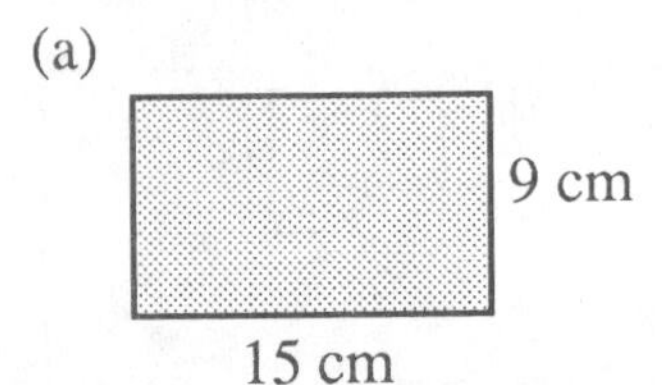

(b)

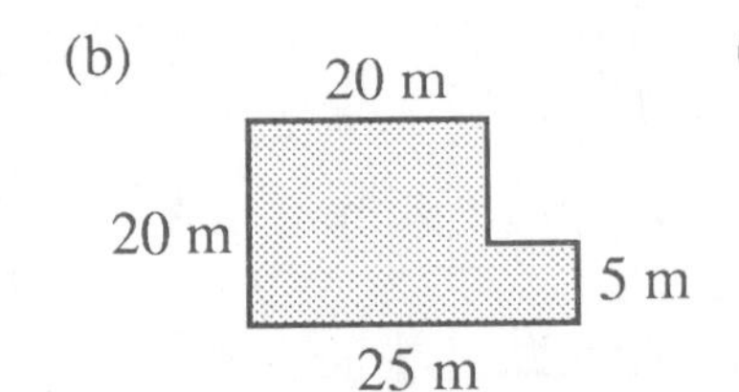

(c)

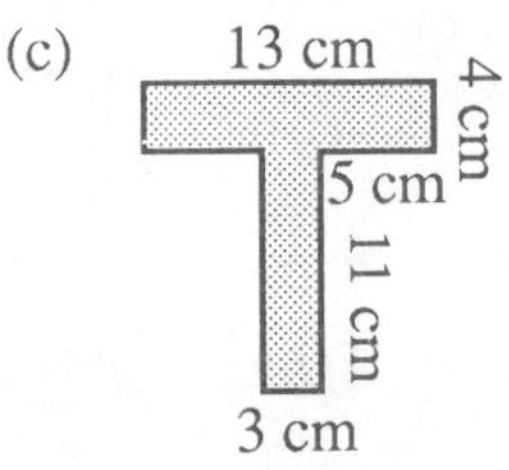

Q7. Find:

(a) $\frac{9}{10}$ of 3 m (b) 0.1 of 5 cm (c) 60% of 4 km

Q8. What is the perimeter of a square with length 14 cm?

Q9. This figure is made up of 2 cm squares. What is its perimeter?

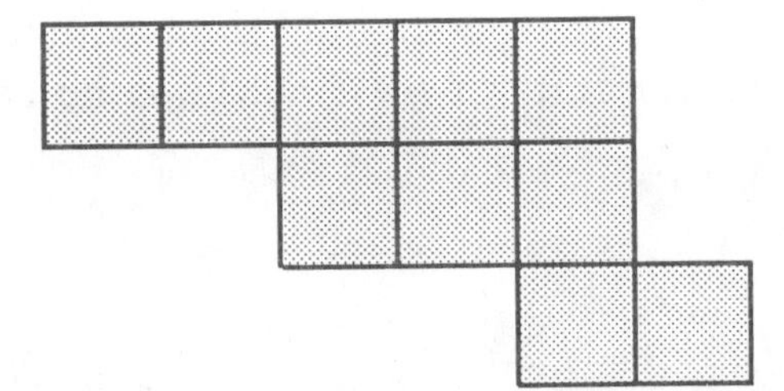

LEVEL 3 — LENGTH

DIFFICULT QUESTIONS

Q1. (a) 5.67 cm = ☐ mm (b) 432 mm = ☐ cm

(c) 4.2 m = ☐ cm

Q2. (a) 30% of 2m (b) 60% of 3 km (c) 0.7 of 5 cm

Q3. Jenny swims 12 lengths of a 50 m pool.

(a) How far has she swum?
(b) How many more lengths must she swim to complete 1 km?

Q4. Richard ran 3 km on Monday. Each succeeding day he increased his distance by 10% of the previous day. How far did he run on Thursday?

Q5. Geoffrey cycled $17\frac{1}{4}$ km. How much further did he have to cycle to complete 25.1 km?

Q6. Farmer Jones is fencing a rectangular paddock which is 1.8 km wide and twice as long as it is wide. How many metres of fencing does he need to buy?

Q7. Find the perimeter of each figure:

(a)

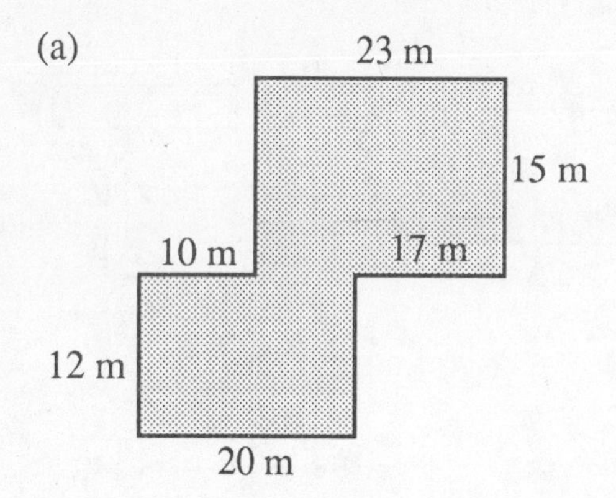

(b)

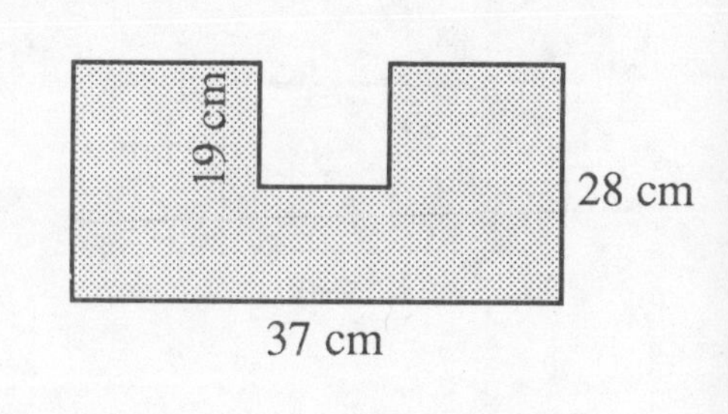

Q8. A rectangle has a length of 13 cm and a perimeter of 40 cm. What is the width of the rectangle?

Q9. Angus ran 4 times round the rectangular field which measured 65 m by 45 m. How many more circuits of the field must he complete to have run 2.2 km?

AREA

The concept of area, the measuring of the amount of surface, is perhaps one of the most difficult for young students to understand and a significant number carry this inability to conceptualise area into adulthood. It is therefore essential that each small stage is mastered before moving to the next. Readiness for this concept varies widely amongst children and it is important that it is not pushed too soon. If it is obviously beyond the understanding of the student then leave it and come back to it later. Otherwise the 'can't do' attitude can easily be adopted. Like fractions and decimals, area is a concept which must be constantly reinforced. Again, estimation is an important component.

By the beginning of Year 5 a student may be familiar with the square metre and also the square centimetre. To ensure these concepts have been understood please refer to the previous volume in this series. Further experience is needed with the square centimetre—measuring areas and comparing areas. To measure the area of larger tracts of land the concepts of hectares and square kilometres are introduced. The student also needs to explore and recognise the relationship between the length and breadth of a rectangle and its area.

VOCABULARY

Area, breadth, boundary, deep, depth, estimate, hectare, larger than, length, maps, measure, perimeter, plans, predicted area, smaller than, square centimetre, square metre, surface, surface area, the same as, width.

CONTENTS

THE SQUARE CENTIMETRE

It will have been realised that square metres cannot be used to measure smaller surfaces.

An appropriate unit for measuring smaller surfaces is the square centimetre.

> A square centimetre (cm^2) is an area equivalent to a square with sides 1 cm long.

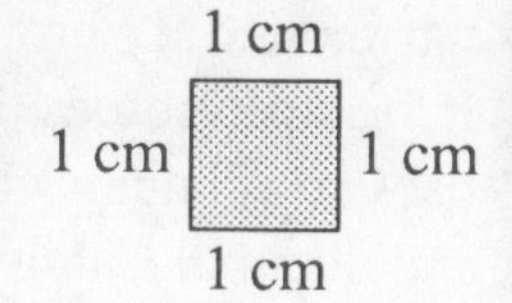

Some areas will have many square centimetres. Adopt strategies like tallying or writing in the grid to ensure accuracy.

Remember, take care to count the number of square centimetres accurately. For irregular shapes only count squares centimetres which have half or more than half covered. Do not count those with less than half.

ACTIVITIES:

1. List items found in the classroom or in the kitchen which have an estimated surface area of 1 cm^2, 5 cm^2, 10 cm^2, etc. Trace their outline and use a transparent overlay printed with a grid of square centimetres to check the estimates.

2. Draw shapes on square centimetre grid paper. Estimate then measure the area. These shapes could include half cm^2.

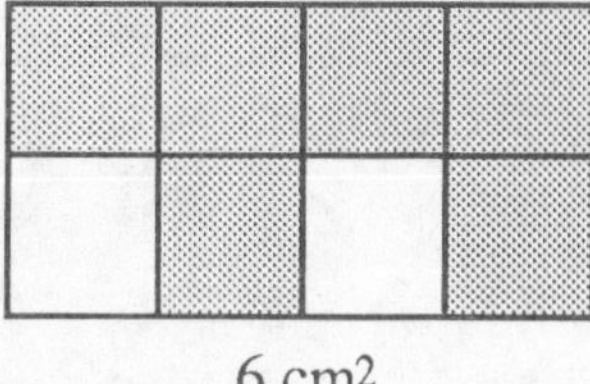

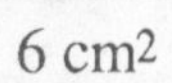

6 cm^2

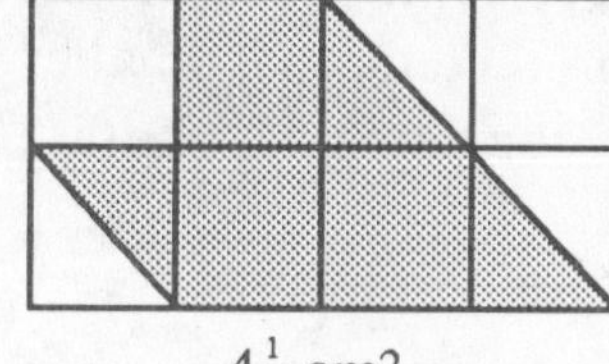

$4\frac{1}{2}$ cm^2

$6\frac{1}{2}$ cm^2

3. Collect a number of items which have a surface which can be appropriately measured in square centimetres. Use a square centimetre grid transparent overlay to check the estimates. Order them from smallest to largest according to area.

4. Draw round the foot and the hand. Estimate the areas, then measure with the overlay. Compare the two results.

5. Put the overlay on a circle and estimate then measure its approximate area.

   The area of a triangle

6. Cut a rectangle from square centimetre grid paper. Draw a diagonal and cut along it. The two pieces fit on top of each other exactly. What does this tell us about the area of a triangle in relation to the area of the rectangle from which it came? **It has an area half that of the rectangle**. Experiment with different sized rectangles to see if this is always true.

THE HECTARE AND THE SQUARE KILOMETRE

The **hectare (ha)** and the **square kilometre (km^2)** are the units used to measure land area.

> A hectare is an area of 10 000 m^2, in other words, an area equivalent to a square with sides 100 metres long.

i.e.

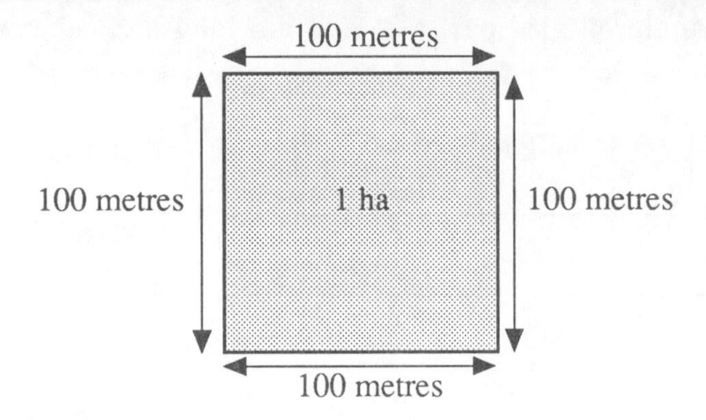

Ideally, students should take a trundle wheel to the local oval and measure out a hectare by measuring a square with sides of 100 metres. They would then be able to visualise the size. Alternatively they may be able to picture an area of land equal to two football pitches.

Paddocks and larger building blocks are measured in hectares. As with the square metre, it is important to realise that few hectares are regular, square blocks of land.

Square kilometres are used when giving the areas of national parks, shires, states or countries. Reference to square kilometres can be found in atlases.

ACTIVITIES:

1. Take several 10 cm × 10 cm squares of grid paper. Each of these squares represents a hectare. Cut the squares in different ways and rearrange them. How many different shapes can be made which represent an area of a hectare?

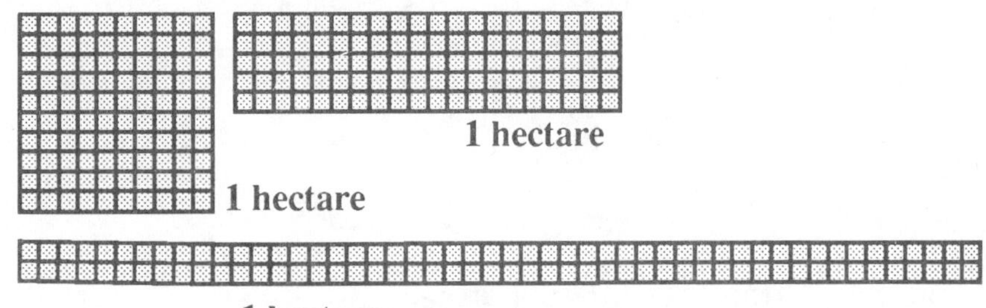

2. List tracts of land which are estimated to be about a hectare, and those less or more than a hectare.
3. Using a grid overlay and a map of Australia, estimate then calculate which state or territory has the largest area. Which has the smallest? Use reference books to research the area in square kilometres of the Australian states and territories. Order them from largest to smallest. Did the orderings match?
4. Investigate the land area of various countries of the world.

THE AREA OF A RECTANGLE

It is important that students come to an understanding of the relationship between the length, breadth (width) and area of rectangles as a result of their experiences. They should not be given a formula. If this relationship has not been recognised it is necessary that students are given more opportunities to develop this understanding.

Example:
'I drew this rectangle on grid paper. It is 7 cm long and 2 cm wide. It has an area of 14 cm^2.

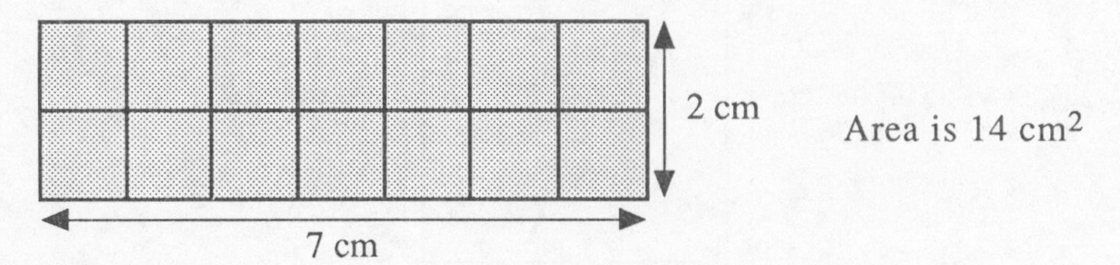

ACTIVITY:
Draw a series of different rectangles on quad paper. Make a table to record the length, breadth and area of each. Look at the results. Can a pattern be seen ?

Some irregular shapes can be divided into two or more rectangles so that it is easier to calculate the area.

The shape below is made of two rectangles.

The large rectangle has an area of 24 cm^2 and the small rectangle has an area of 4 cm^2. The total area is, therefore, 28 cm^2.

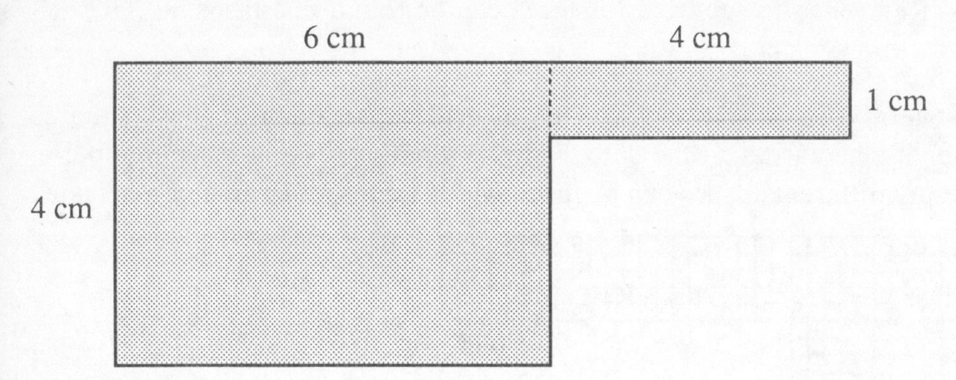

Example:
Calculate the area of the paved border around the swimming pool.

Solution:
The total area including the pool is:
$25m \times 15\ m = 375m^2$.
The pool measures $20m \times 10m = 200m^2$.
The paved area is $375\ m^2 - 200\ m^2 = 175\ m^2$.

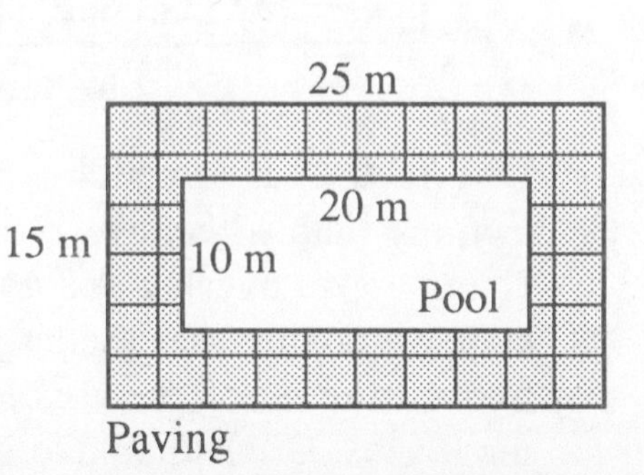

AREA ASSESSMENT

Students should understand the following ideas:

The square centimetre

- explain the need for square centimetres as a measure of surface area
- 1 square centimetre is abbreviated to 1 cm^2
- list items with an estimated area of e.g. 1 cm^2, 10 cm^2 and check with overlays
- draw shapes with a given area on grid paper
- estimate then calculate, using overlays, the area of regular, irregular and circular shapes
- explain and demonstrate how to calculate the area of a triangle using grid paper

The hectare and the square kilometre

- explain the need for the hectare as a measure of area
- the hectare is abbreviated to ha
- the square kilometre is abbreviated to 1 km^2
- on a playing field, describe the approximate boundaries of a hectare
- list tracts of land which are measured in hectares
- represent hectares with grid paper in a variety of ways other than as a square
- explain the need for the square kilometre as a measure of surface area
- compare and order the land area of various national parks
- use grid overlays to compare land area of different countries

The area of rectangles

- estimate then calculate the area of rectangles marked on grid paper
- draw rectangles on grid paper, estimate and calculate the areas
- draw rectangles on plain paper, estimate, measure and calculate the areas
- explain a quick way to calculate the areas

LEVEL 1 — AREA

EASIER QUESTIONS

Q1. Calculate the area of each shape □ represents 1 cm^2.

(a)

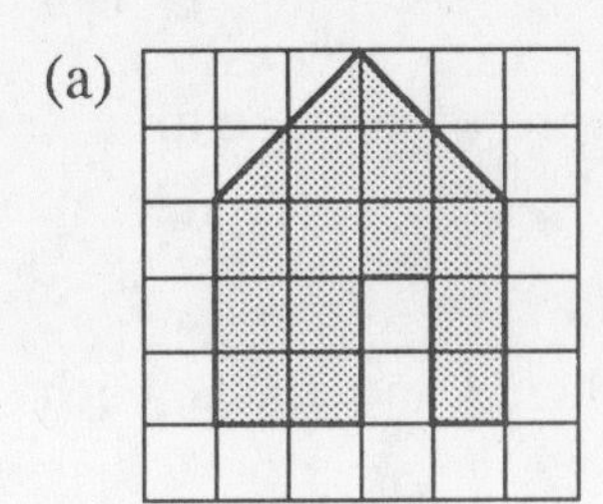

□ = 1 cm^2

(b)

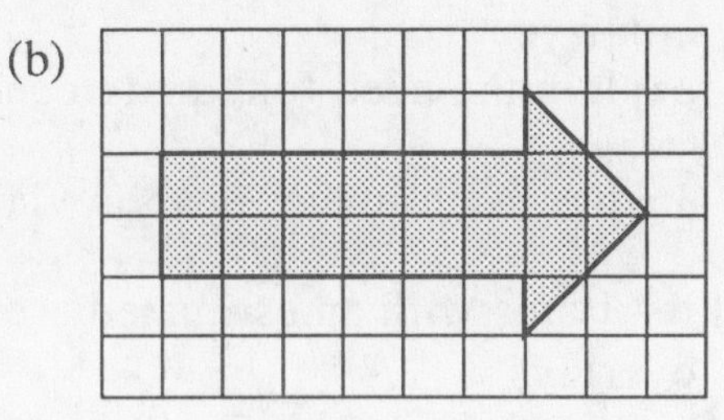

Q2. (a) 1 m^2 = □ cm^2 (b) 1 ha = □ m^2 (c) 20 000 m^2 = □ ha

Q3. Write down the most suitable unit for measuring the area of:

(a) Australia (b) school playground
(c) carpet (d) top of a matchbox
(e) kitchen tray (f) computer screen

Q4. Find the area of each figure:

(a)

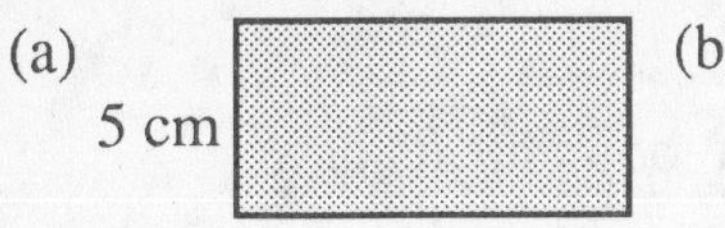

(b)

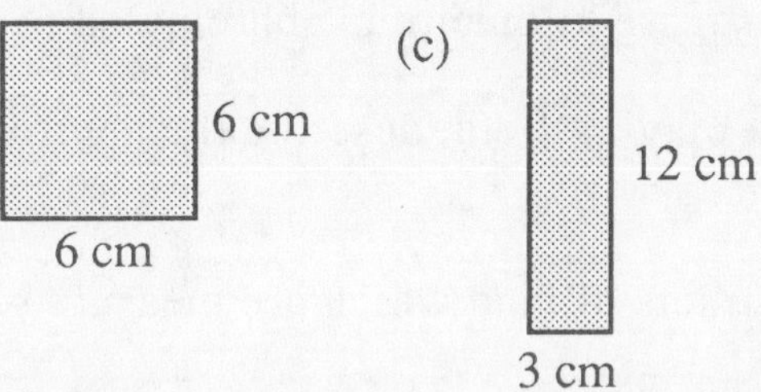

(c)

Q5. The page of a book is 10 cm long and 7 cm wide. What is the area of the page?

Q6. The wall of a house is 2 m high and 7 m long. What is the area of the wall?

Q7. 3 walls of a shower room are tiled to a height of 2 m. The shower room measures 3 m by 3 m. What wall area has been tiled?

Q8. The perimeters of 2 squares are 24 cm and 36 cm respectively. Find the difference in area between the two squares.

LEVEL 2 — AREA

AVERAGE QUESTIONS

Q1. Find the area of each shape. ☐ represents 1 cm^2.

(a)

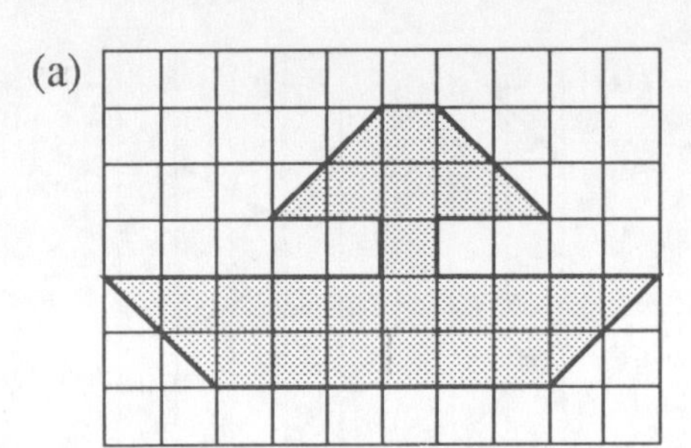

(b)

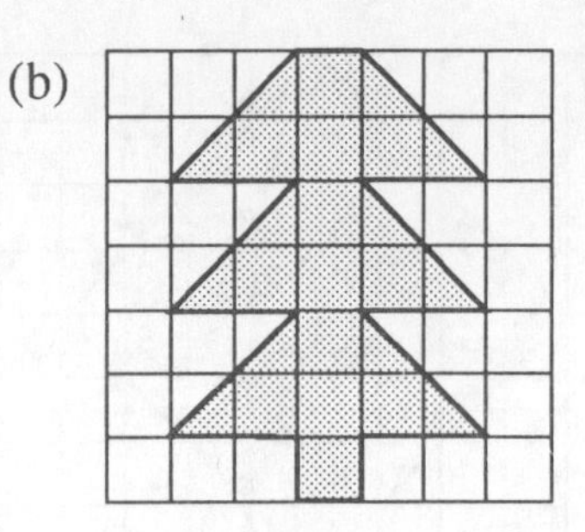

Q2. (a) 50 000 cm^2 = ☐ m^2 (b) 5 ha = ☐ m^2

(c) 1 km^2 = ☐ ha

Q3. Find the area of each shape:

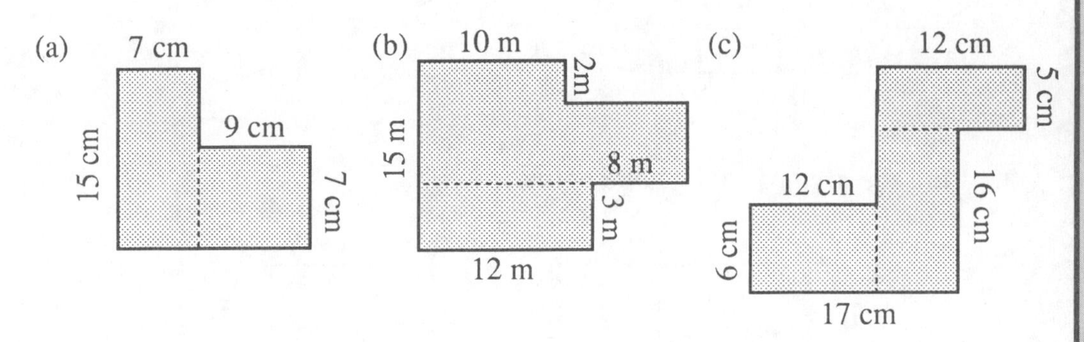

Q4. A playing field is 3.5 ha in area. How many square metres is this?

Q5. A room 4 m wide and 4.5 m long is to be carpeted. Carpet costs $65 per square metre. How much will it cost to carpet the room?

Q6. Drawn on the right is a swimming pool with a paved area surrounding it. Calculate the area of paving.

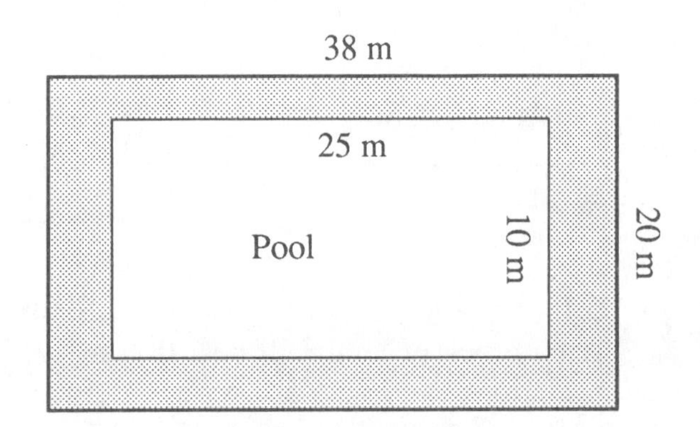

Q7. Which area is larger:

(a) 45 ha or 4 500 m^2? (b) 1.5 m^2 or 150 000 cm^2?

(c) 1 000 000 m^2 or 10 km^2?

LEVEL 3 — AREA

DIFFICULT QUESTIONS

Q1. Find the area of the following shapes □ represents 1 cm^2.

(a)

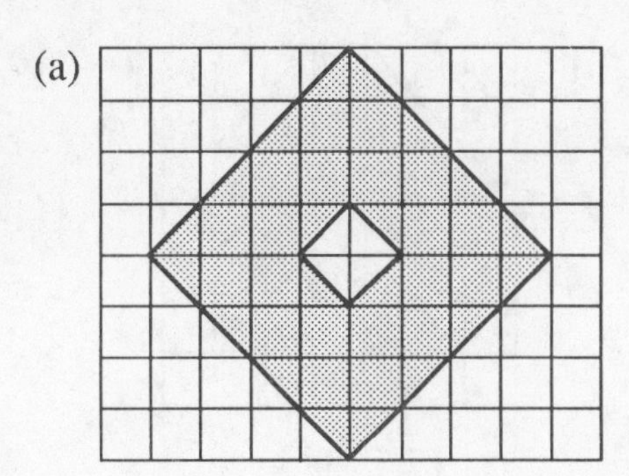

(b)

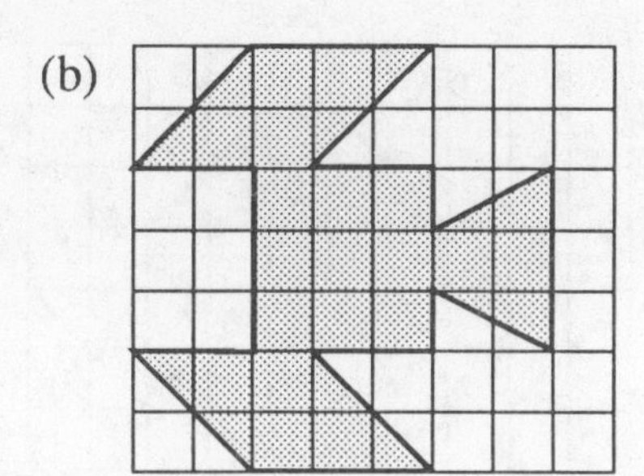

Q2. A table top is 2.3 m^2. How many cm^2 is this?

Q3. (a) 75 000 m^2 = ☐ ha (b) 0.83 ha = ☐ m^2

(c) 32 m^2 = ☐ cm^2

Q4. Find the area of each shape below:

(a)

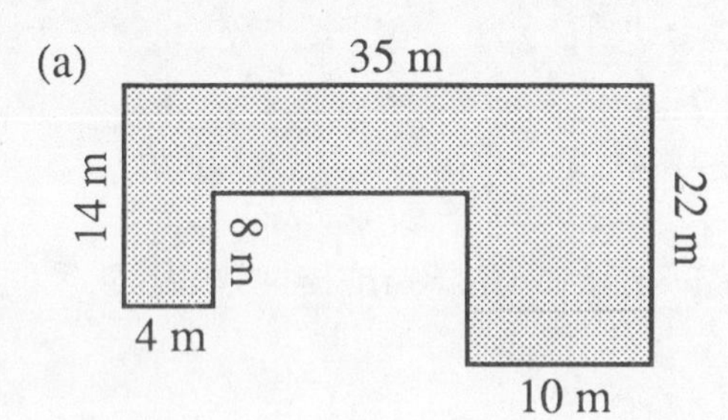

(b)

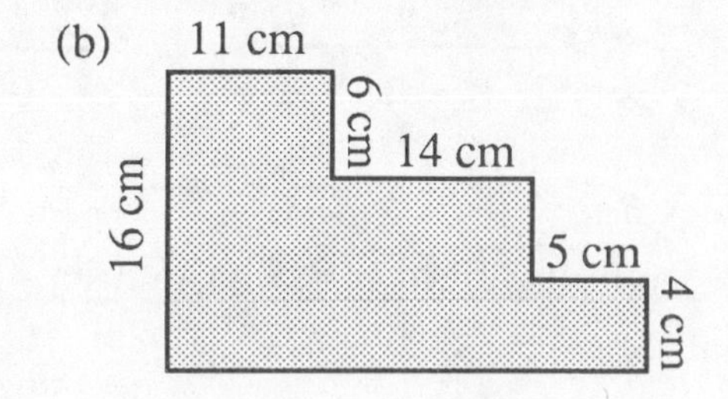

Q5. Find the length of each rectangle given their width and area:

(a)

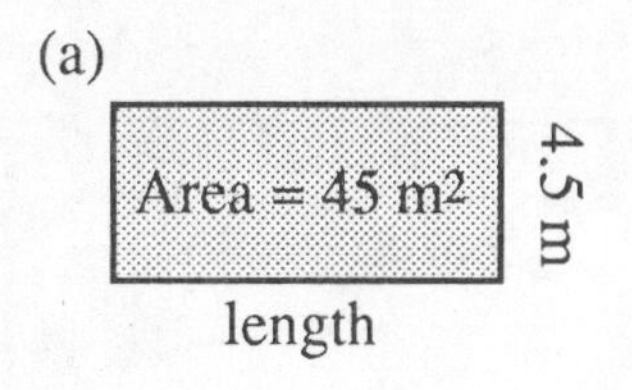

(b)

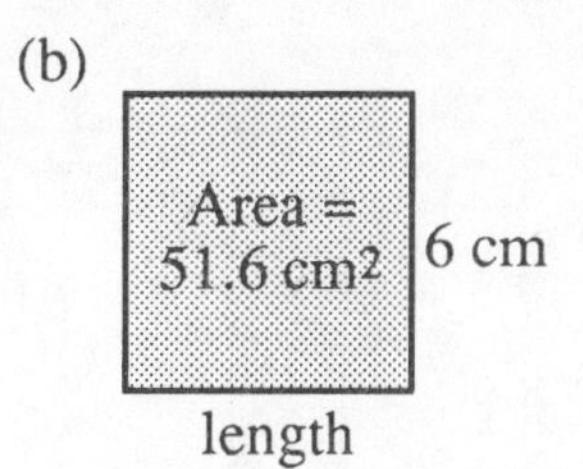

(c)

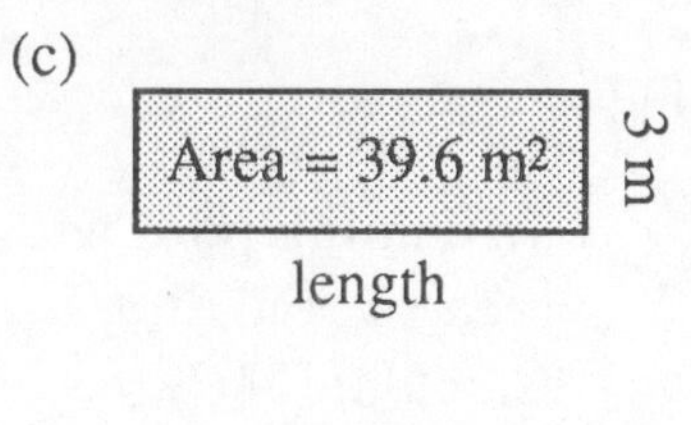

Q6. 6 ha of land have been released for building. $\frac{1}{4}$ of the area is for roads. Each block of land will be 1 000 m^2. How many blocks will be available?

Q7. I want to lay tiles on my kitchen floor. The floor is 5 m wide and 6.5 m long. The tiles I have bought are squares of side 25 cm. How many tiles do I need to cover the kitchen floor?

VOLUME

Volume is the amount of space taken up by an object, whereas capacity is the amount of space a container holds. Whilst these are individual definitions, in reality capacity and volume are terms which are often used in place of each other.

The concepts of volume and capacity can only be assimilated by regular experience with objects and containers of varying sizes. The relationship between the cubic centimetre, which is used to measure volume, the millilitre and litre, which are used to measure capacity, and the gram and kilogram, which are used to measure mass, forms the basis of investigations during these two years. It is important that these follow on from an understanding of the concepts outlined in the previous two volumes. Cubic metres are also introduced.

VOCABULARY

Adjacent, capacity, comparison, container, cubic centimetre, cubic metre, differences, dimensions, displaces, edges, equal, faces, floating, identical, intervals, mass by displacement, millilitre, perpendicular, rectangular prism, similarities, spaces, stack, standard unit, submerged, surfaces, too big (small), triangular prism, uniform, units, volume.

CONTENTS

THE LITRE AND THE MILLILITRE

1 litre equals 1 000 millilitres

1 L = 1 000 mL

It is important to strengthen the concept of capacity and to familiarise the student with the litre (L) and the millilitre (mL).

A collection of containers with contents measured and labelled in litres and millilitres should be made. A large array of shapes will be seen but some may be used more frequently. This should be discussed together with reasons why containers are not filled to the brim.

A calibrated measure marked in 100 mL divisions is now needed. This can be from the kitchen or, better still, made by pouring 100 mL of liquid into a transparent container and marking the level. Continue this process making further 100 mL marks up the side of the container. Check for accuracy.

It is very important that when reading a calibrated measure the eye must be level with the surface of the liquid being measured.

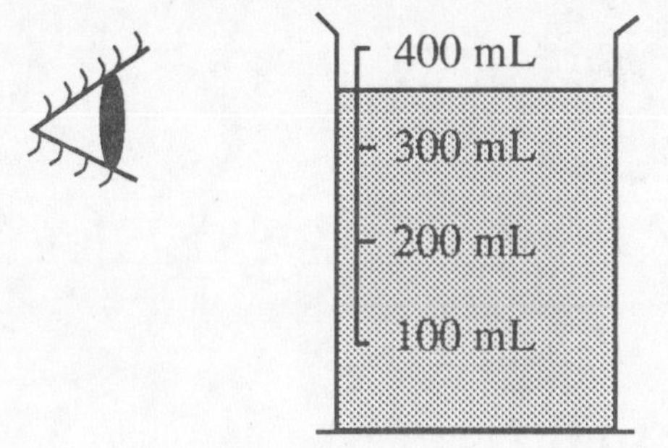

'This bottle contains between 300 and 400 mL'.

The calibrated measure can now be used to check the capacity of various containers.

e.g. 'This jar holds almost 200 mL'.

Calibrated measures are needed marked in 10 mL and 1 mL divisions. A medicine measure is useful for the latter.

Further investigations should be undertaken with these measures together with a variety of containers. Estimates should always be made before measuring.

ACTIVITIES:

1. Choose three transparent containers with bases of significantly different sizes.

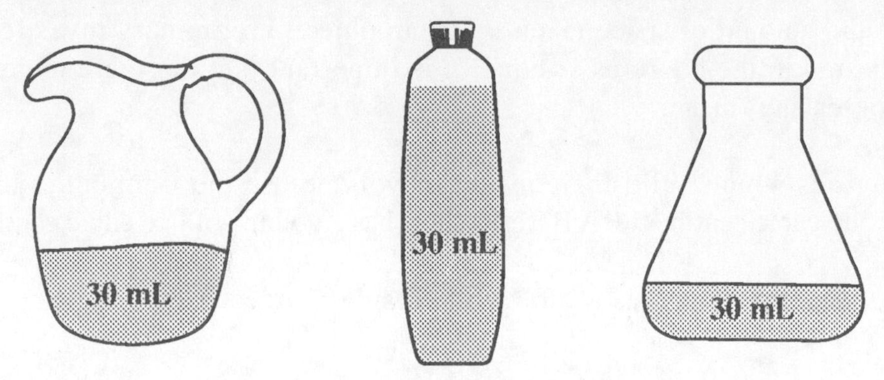

Pour 30 mL of water into each container.
Observe and discuss the observations.

Accuracy of reading should be emphasised as it is important, for example, in cooking and vital when measuring medicine.

2. Links should be made with the addition, subtraction and graph sub-strands.

   (a) The total capacity of two or three small containers can be calculated.

   (b) The amount of liquid left when an amount has been poured out of a container can be worked out.

   (c) Results of experiments can be graphed using simple picture or column graphs.

3. Why do manufacturers use bottles of particular shapes?

THE CUBIC CENTIMETRE

Volume is the amount of space taken up by an object. Preliminary investigations were suggested in the previous volume; it is important that these are undertaken before progressing further.

Many activities which build the concept of volume use the Centicube. It has a volume of one cubic centimetre. A Base 10 short has a volume of one cubic centimetre.

A cubic centimetre (1 cm^3) is a cube with all sides (edges) 1 cm long.

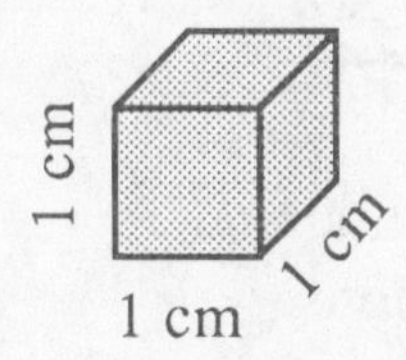

Use a quantity of Centicubes to make a variety of prisms. Calculate the volume of each prism in cubic centimetres by counting the number of Centicubes used.

Example:

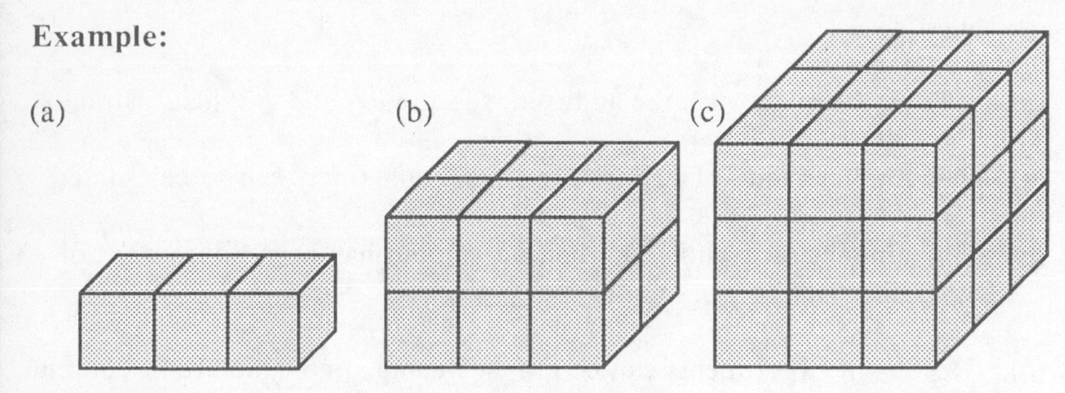

Solutions:

(a) This prism has a volume of 3 cubic centimetres.

(b) Prism has a volume of 12 cubic centimetres.

(c) The third prism has a volume of 27 cubic centimetres.

A student should come to realise that cubes are used to measure volume because the regular shape with flat, perpendicular surfaces can be stacked and packed with no gaps between.

The cubic centimetre is used to measure relatively small volumes.

ACTIVITIES:

1. Build a variety of prisms, estimate and then count the number of cubes used. Order from smallest to largest.

2. Make a variety of prisms each using 12 centicubes.

THE CUBIC CENTIMETRE AND THE MILLILITRE—THE LINK

The link between a cubic centimetre and a millilitre needs to be established.

ACTIVITIES:

1. (a) Take a container and fill it to the brim with coloured water. This container should be standing in a tray which will collect any displaced water.

   (b) Take five interlocking Centicubes, model them into a 3D shape and attach to a thread.

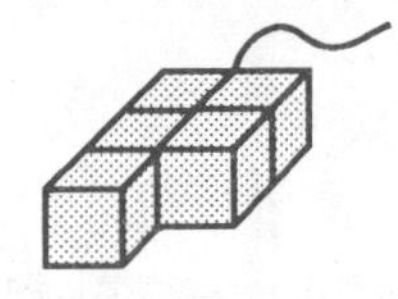

   (c) Lower the shape into the container of water ensuring the model is completely submerged using a sharp pencil point if necesssary. This will displace some water. Carefully raise the model from the water. Its container can now be removed so that the displaced water can be collected.

   (d) Pour the displaced water from the tray into a medicine measure.

   (e) Measure the amount of displaced water. What observation can be made? An object with a volume of 5 cm^3 displaces 5 mL of water.

2. (a) Pour 30 mL of water into a suitably calibrated container.

   (b) Carefully add ten Centicubes, one at a time.

   (c) With the eye at the level of the water observe what occurs to the water level as each Centicube is added and discuss your observations.

For example:
'The water rises to the next millilitre mark each time a cubic centimetre is added'.
'I estimate that, when ten Centicubes have been added, the water level will have risen to the 40 mL mark'.

1 millilitre of water is equivalent to 1 cm^3
$1 \text{ mL} = 1 \text{ cm}^3$

THE KILOGRAM AND THE LITRE—THE LINK

The link between the kilogram and a litre of water should be established.

Example:

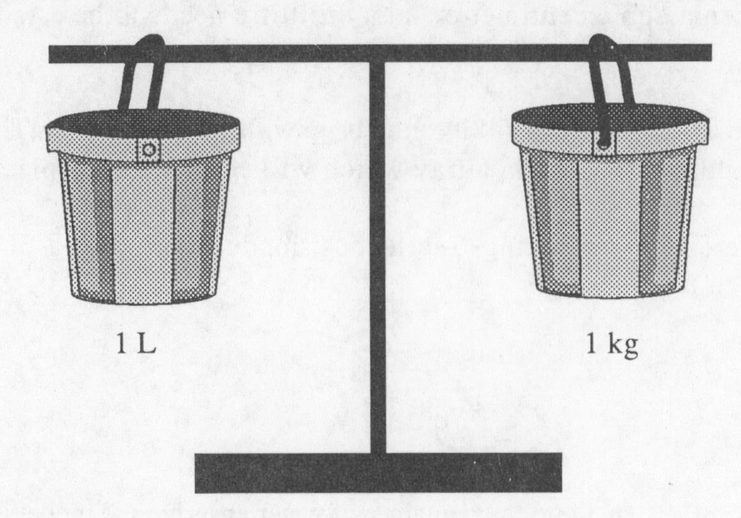

- Take an equal arm balance and pour 1 L of water into one of the pans. (If the pan is not suitable, place an identical container on each side of the balance and pour the water into one of them.)
- Estimate the mass of the water.
- Place suitable standard masses in the other pan until a balance is achieved.
- What is the mass of one litre of water?

Observation:
One litre of water has a mass of 1 kilogram.

Now, estimate what would be the mass of 1 mL of water. (lg)

1 mL of water has a volume of 1 cm^3 and a mass of 1 g

RELATING VOLUME AND CAPACITY

Further investigations into the relationship between volume and capacity should be made.

ACTIVITY:

- Take a number of similar shaped objects which have different masses, for example, identical cubes made from different materials.

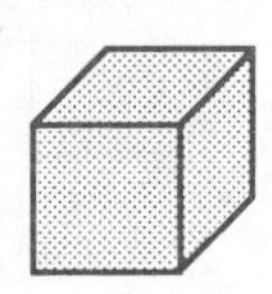

wood polystyrene plasticine

- Calculate their volume by displacement and record the results.

- Find the mass of each of the objects by measuring, using suitable scales or balances

- Is there a correlation between the volume and the mass?

Observation:
Each of the objects will have a similar volume but their masses will differ.

NOTE:

- Size determines volume. Size does not determine mass.

- Objects with similar dimensions will have the same volume.

- Objects with similar volumes will not necessarily have a similar mass.

THE CUBIC METRE—$1m^3$

The use of cubic centimetres to measure bigger volumes is obviously inappropriate. The need for a larger standard unit has been established—the cubic metre.

A model of a cubic metre should be made so that a student can visualise it.

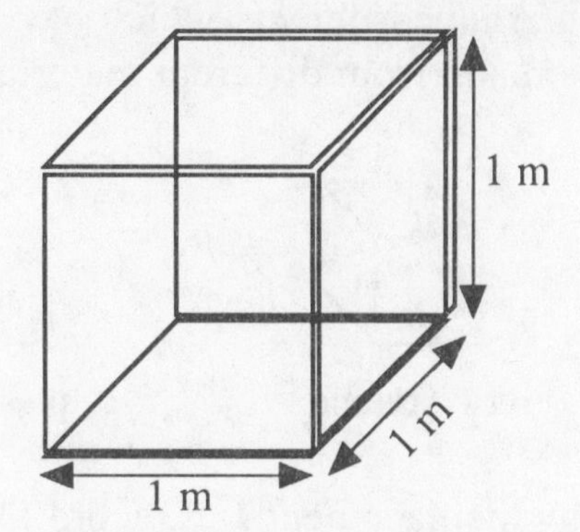

Cubic metre kits are available. Any rigid metre lengths of rod, wire or piping which can be joined can be used.

Alternatively, a cubic metre can be made from six 1 metre long pieces of cardboard taped together in the form of a cube.

ACTIVITIES:

1. Investigate for what purposes cubic metres are used.

2. Place the cubic metre in the corner of the room.
   Estimate how many cubic metres would fit in the room.

3. How many people would fit in a cubic metre?

4. Compare large objects with the cubic metre; are they larger or smaller than a cubic metre?

$1\ m^3$ has a capacity of 1 000 L

VOLUME ASSESSMENT

Students should understand the following ideas:

The litre and the millilitre

- recall the abbreviation for litre is L
- explain the need for the litre as a measure of capacity
- estimate and measure how many eggcups full of water are needed to fill a 1 litre container
- estimate then measure how many litres of water would be needed to fill a bucket
- recall the abbreviation for millilitre is mL
- 1 litre contains 1 000 millilitres
- explain the need for the millilitre as a measure of capacity
- use a calibrated container to measure given amounts of liquid
- use a medicine glass to measure small amounts of liquid
- measure the capacity of various containers to the nearest 100 mL
- choose appropriate standard measuring unit for any given container
- measure large and small amounts with accuracy
- record results of investigations in graph form

The cubic centimetre

- the abbreviation for cubic centimetre is cm^3
- explain the need for the cubic centimetre as a measure of volume
- explain why cubes are used to measure volume
- describe the dimensions of a 1 centimetre cube and the area of each face
- construct open-topped prisms, estimate then count how many cubic centimetres are needed to fill each container; order from largest to smallest
- build a number of different models, each with the same volume; check using the displacement method and by counting

VOLUME ASSESSMENT Continued

The cubic centimetre and the millilitre—the link
- describe the link between the cubic centimetre and the millilitre
- perform an experiment to show this relationship

The kilogram and a litre of water—the link
- describe the link between the kilogram and a litre of water
- perform an experiment to show this relationship
- calculate the mass of an amount of water given its volume; check
- calculate the volume of an amount of water given its mass; check

Relating volume and capacity
- perform an experiment which demonstrates that size determines volume
- perform an experiment which demonstrates that size does not determine mass
- explain the significance of the results of these experiments

The cubic metre
- explain the need for the cubic metre as a measure of volume
- model one cubic metre
- use the model to estimate the cubic capacity of large spaces or containers

LEVEL 1 — VOLUME

EASIER QUESTIONS

Q1. (a) 1 000 mL = ☐ L (b) 2 L = ☐ mL

(c) 500 mL = ☐ L (d) 3.5 L = ☐ mL

(e) 2 500 mL = ☐ L

Q2. How many 5 mL spoonfuls of medicine are contained in a:

(a) 50 mL bottle? (b) 350 mL bottle?

Q3. How many cubic centimetres are in each of the prisms below?

(a)

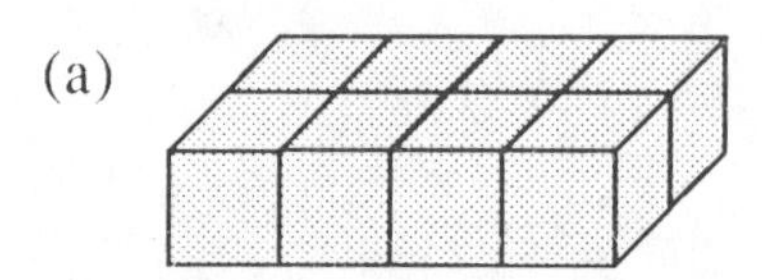

(b)

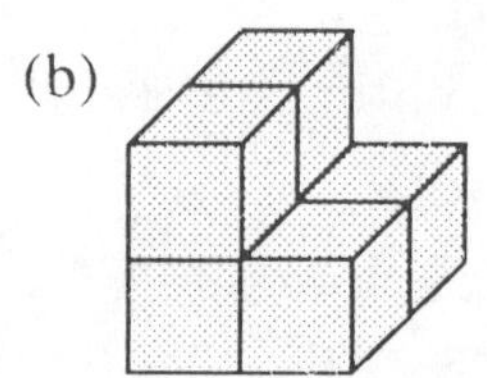

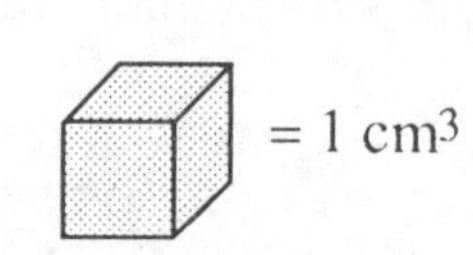

Q4. Change the following amounts of water to the units indicated.

(a) 650 mL of water = ☐ cm^3 (b) 55 mL of water = ☐ g

(c) 1 000 cm^3 of water = ☐ mL (d) 356 g of water = ☐ cm^3

Q5. What is the volume of each prism below:

(a)

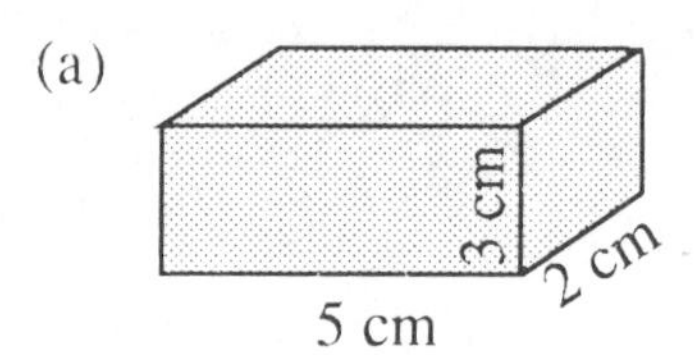

(b)

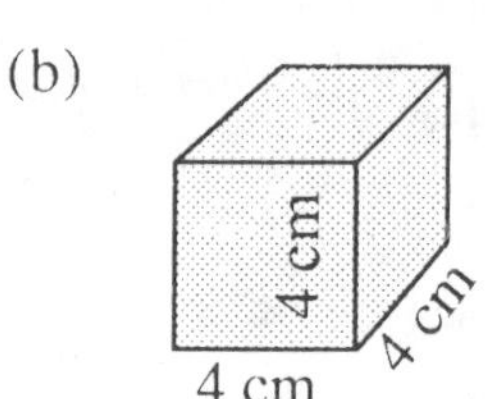

Q6. A box is 10 cm long, 7 cm wide and 4 cm deep.

(a) Draw a picture of the box.

(b) How many cubic centimetres will fit into it?

LEVEL 2 — VOLUME

AVERAGE QUESTIONS

Q1. (a) 250 mL = ☐ L (b) 3.25 L = ☐ mL

(c) 2 750 mL = ☐ L

Q2. A large bottle holds 1.5 L of cordial. A small bottle holds 60% as much cordial. How many millilitres does the small bottle hold?

Q3. Juice is sold in 2 different sized containers. 1 L for \$1.20 or 750 mL for \$0.90. Which is the cheaper way to buy juice?

Q4. How many cubic centimetres (cm^3) are in each prism below:

(a)

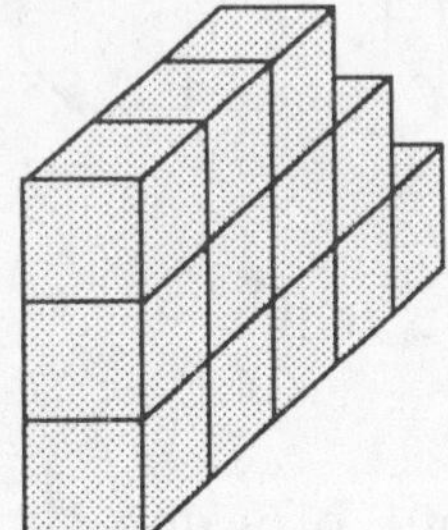

= 1 cm^3

(b)

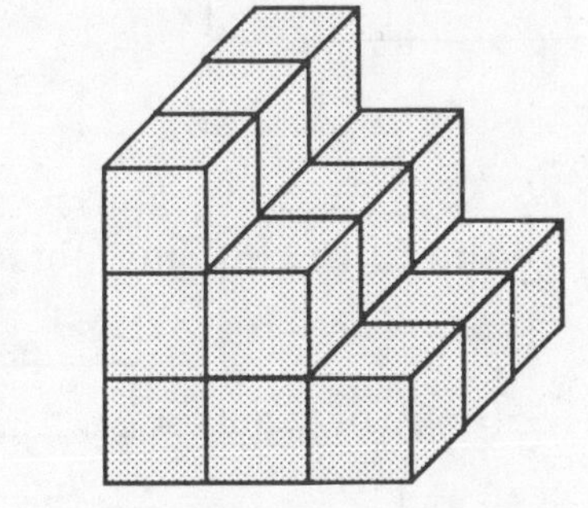

Q5. Calculate the volume of each prism.

(a)

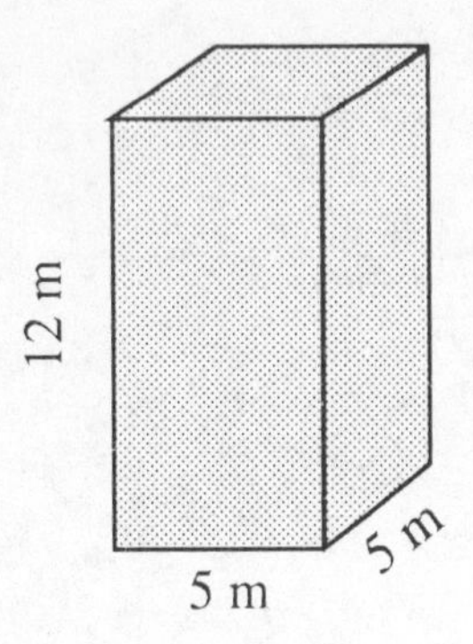

(b)

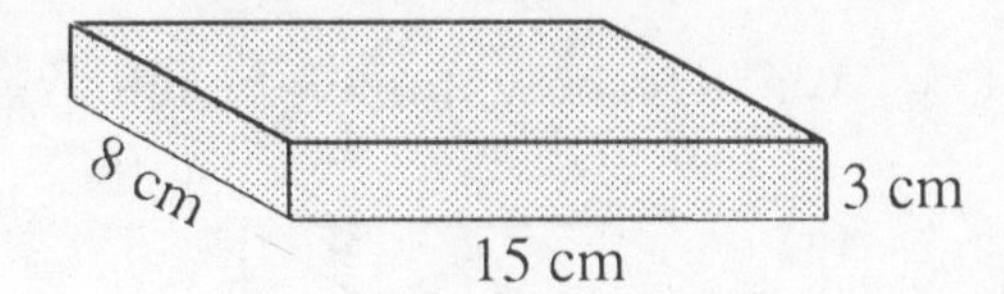

Q6. Change these amounts of water to the units indicated:

(a) 2 000 mL = ☐ kg (b) 3 000 cm^3 = ☐ L

(c) 5 kg = ☐ cm^3 (d) 1.25 L = ☐ g

Q7. A tank holds 90 m^3 of water. If the tank is 6 m long and 3 m deep, how wide is it?

LEVEL 3 — VOLUME

DIFFICULT QUESTIONS

Q1. 1 L of guava juice costs \$5.60. What would be the cost of:

(a) 125 mL of juice? (c) 1.75 L of juice?

Q2. A swimming pool is 25 m long, 7 m wide and 2 m deep. How many litres of water does the pool hold when full?

Q3. A tap is leaking at a rate of 50 mL per minute? How long will it take for the tap to fill a 5 L bucket?
(Answer in hours and minutes.)

Q4. How many cubic centimetres (cm^3) in these prisms?

(a)

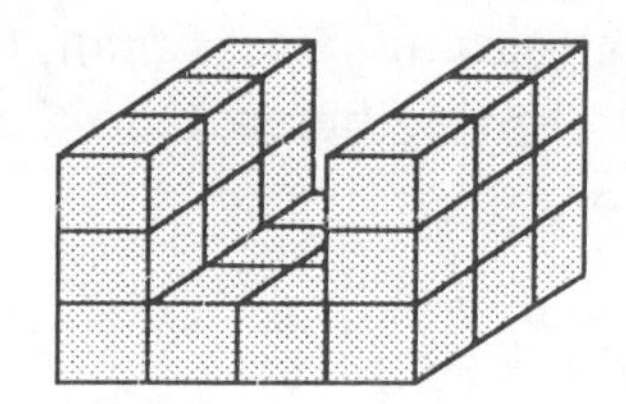

(b)

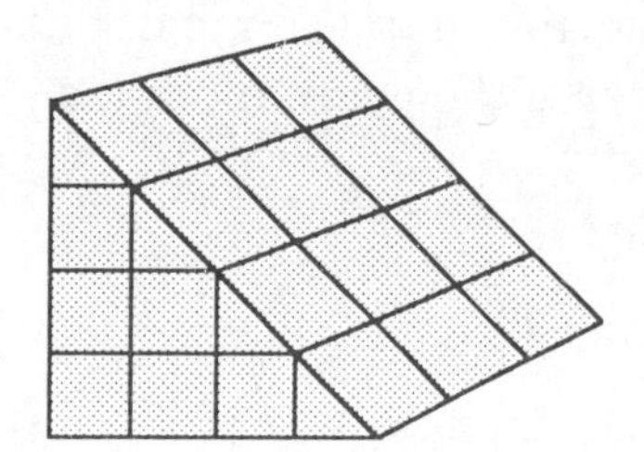

Q5. Given the volume, length and depth of each prism, find the width.

(a)

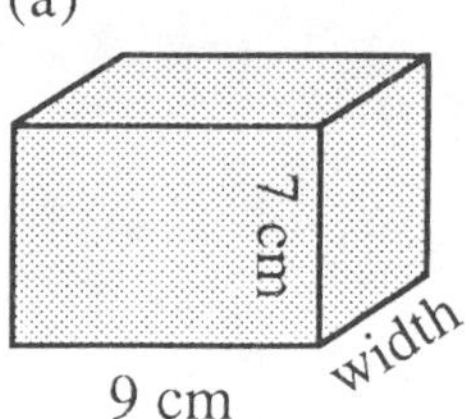

Volume = 189 cm^3

(b)

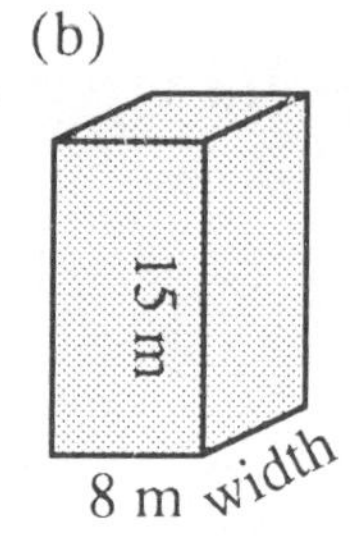

Volume = 600 m^2

(c)

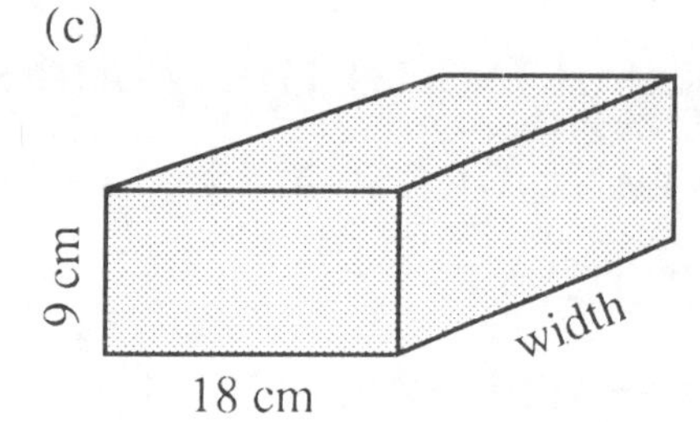

Volume = 2 430 cm^3

Q6. When a box is $\frac{1}{4}$ full, it holds 30 m^3 of sand. The box is 6 m long and 5 m wide. How deep is the box?

Q7. A rectangular jug holds 320 mL when it is $\frac{1}{5}$ full. The jug is 10 cm long and 20 cm deep. How wide is the jug?

MASS

Mass is the amount of material present in an object. Weight is the most usual form of measurement.

It is important that the activities outlined in the first two volumes in this series are undertaken before progressing further.

During Years 5 and 6 a student builds on the experiences of hefting to assess the mass of an object and the use of the kilogram as a standard unit of measure. Grams are introduced for measuring lighter masses and a variety of different scales and balances are investigated. The tonne is also introduced.

VOCABULARY

About, approximately, calculate the mass, calibration, decimal, dial, displaced tonnage, estimated mass, gram(s), greater than, gross mass, kilogram(s), less than, measured mass, measure the mass, more than, net mass, scales, spring balance, to the nearest, tonne(s).

CONTENTS

THE GRAM

During Years 3 and 4 students should have had opportunities to investigate mass with the many activities which were suggested to familiarise them with the kilogram mass. It is important to ensure that these activities have been experienced before progressing. The need for a standard unit to measure masses of less than a kilogram will have been recognised. The gram—**g**—should be introduced.

1 000 grams (g) = 1 kilogram (kg)

Begin with 500 g and 100 g standard masses.

ACTIVITIES:
Investigate how many 500 g masses balance 1 kg and how many 100 g masses balance 1 kg. What conclusions can be drawn?

'2 × 500 g standard masses balance 1 kg. Half a kilogram must have a mass of 500 g. 1 kg must be the same as 1 000 g.'

'10 × 100 g masses balance 1 kg. 5 × 100 g masses balance a 500 g mass.

2 Using balance scales investigate the mass of everyday items when compared with combinations of 500 g and 100 g masses. Heft before measuring.

'This apple has a mass between 200 g and 300 g.'
'The mass of this shoe is almost 400 g.'

3. Make masses of, e.g. 200 g or 300 g, by putting sand into bags until they balance with the standard masses. Use these home-made masses when estimating by hefting and checking the mass of objects.

4. Estimate by hefting the amount of metal nuts needed to balance 400 g. Check using the balance scales. Was the estimate less or greater than the actual mass? When using kitchen scales read the result to the nearest 100 g.

5. Create lots of similar activities to compare objects with standard masses of multiples of 100 g. Great accuracy can be achieved with plenty of practice. Use graphs to record the results of investigations.

MEASURING TO THE NEAREST GRAM

When students are familiar with and can reasonably estimate the mass of an object in 100 g divisions they can progress to measuring to the nearest gram. By now there should have been the realisation that more precise measures of mass are required.

10 g, 5 g, 2 g, and 1 g standard masses are available. A Centicube has a mass of approximately 1 g.

Equal arm balance scales, bathroom scales and kitchen scales should be used. The need for zeroing should be discussed.

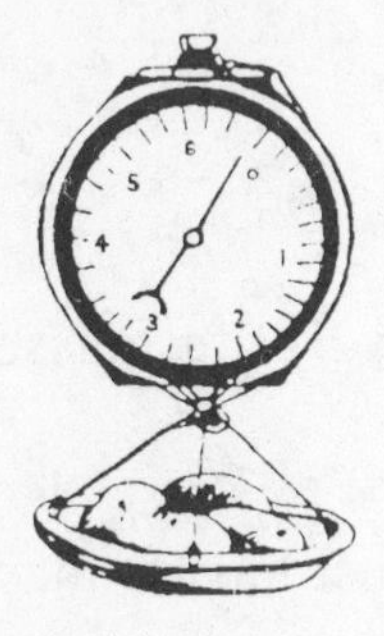

Greengrocers scales

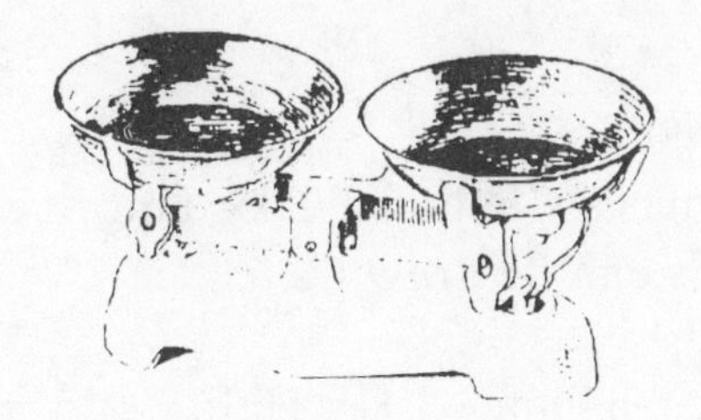

Balance scales

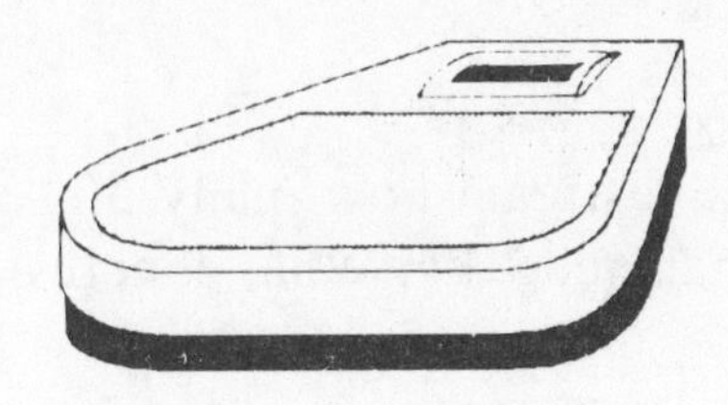

Bathroom scales

ACTIVITIES:

1. Estimate by hefting and then measure the mass of a number of relatively light objects: a pencil, a ruler, scissors, fruit, tennis ball, a cricket ball, etc.

2. Estimate by hefting and then measure the mass of objects which have a mass greater than 1 kg but less than 4 kg. An object needing a 1 kg standard mass, 2×100 g standard masses and a 10 g standard mass to balance it would have a mass of 1 kg 210 g.

3. Some students will be ready to record masses above 1 kg in decimal form. The mass in (2) would be recorded as 1.210 kg in decimal form. It could also be recorded as 1 210 g. For such students it is important to encourage them to be aware of and use the different forms of recording.

4. Investigate different devices for measuring mass—bathroom scales, kitchen scales, electronic scales, spring balances. Choose the appropriate scales in any given situation.

Opportunities will arise to link with the addition and subtraction sub-strands. Here is a simple example.

The mass of flour in this bag is 300 g and the mass of flour in the other bag is 400 g, what is the total mass of flour?

What was the difference between the estimate and the actual mass? How much more rice was needed to make the mass that was required? By how much was the mass over-estimated?

ACTIVITIES:

1. Create a series of different shapes using 20 Centicubes. Estimate the mass of each then check by measuring. Discuss the results.

2. Measure the ingredients for a recipe and bake it. The need for accuracy should be emphasised.

3. Measure the mass of objects on different types of measuring instruments and compare their accuracy. Using a standard mass, how is it possible to determine which is the most accurate? Inaccurate scales will give a reading less or greater than standard.

4. Research spring balances and find out how to make a simple one. Use it to measure a number of objects. What are the disadvantages of a spring balance?

NOTE: It is important to establish the link between the kilogram and the litre of water. This is dealt with in the volume sub-strand.

NET AND GROSS MASS

Gross mass measures the mass of the contents together with the container. **Net mass** refers to the mass of the contents alone.

ACTIVITIES:

1. Look at many items available in a supermarket. Some students may notice that net is sometimes written nett.

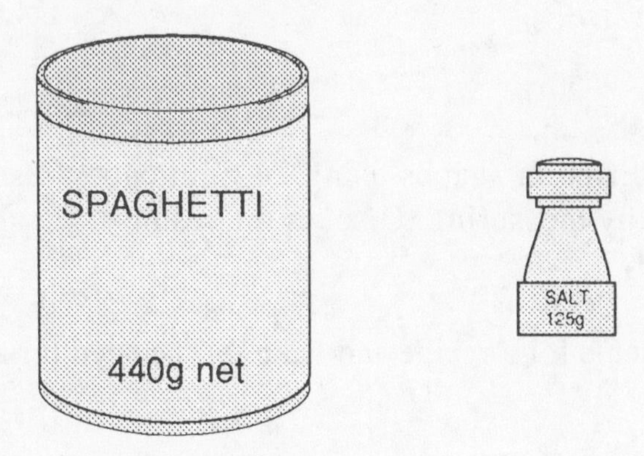

   By reading the net and gross mass information on the packaging it is possible to calculate the mass of the packaging. Investigate.

2. Many items only have the net mass recorded. How can the gross mass be calculated and also the mass of the packaging? Investigate.

3. Fill a variety of containers with different substances, e.g. sand, rice. Estimate the net and gross mass of each and then measure. How accurate were the estimates? Is there a tendency to over-estimate or underestimate? If so, by adjusting the estimates can they become more accurate?

THE TONNE

One tonne (t) = 1 000 kilograms (kg)

Following discussion about measuring the mass of large objects such as cars, trucks of grain or large animals, the need for a unit of measure greater than the kilogram should be recognised. The tonne is used to measure large masses.

ACTIVITIES:

1. Research items that have their mass measured in tonnes.

2. Research and compare the average masses of large animals.

3. Compare the masses of different vehicles.

4. Research 'tare' and 'aggregate'.

A mass recorded in tonnes and kilograms can be written in decimal form. 2 tonnes 725 kg would be written 2.725 t.

It can also be written 2 725 kg.

NOTE: 1 m^3 of water = 1 tonne.

MASS ASSESSMENT

Students should understand the following ideas:

The gram

- explain the need for the gram as a measure of mass
- recall that gram is abbreviated to g
- recall 1 000 grams balance 1 kilogram
- recall that kilogram is abbreviated to kg
- heft containers holding items with differing multiples of 100 g to compare which has the greater mass
- estimate how many items balance multiples of 100 g
- demonstrate and describe the relationship between 100 g and 100 mL of water
- estimate then use balance or kitchen scales to measure given masses lighter than 100 g
- estimate the mass of lighter objects by hefting
- measure the exact mass of items using standard masses and also kitchen scales
- find items with a mass of 1 g, 2 g, 5 g, 10 g
- measure the exact mass of items with a mass up to 4 kg recording in grams and kilograms in the decimal form
- estimate then measure the total mass of a small number of items
- estimate then, from the total mass of a number of items, calculate the mass of one of the items
- accurately measure the mass of ingredients for a recipe, mix, bake and eat!
- use a spring balance to compare the mass of light objects

Net and gross mass

- explain the difference between gross and net mass
- estimate then, using the net mass information on the container, and having found the gross mass, calculate the mass of the container

The tonne

- explain the need for the tonne as a measure of mass
- recall that tonne is abbreviated to t
- recall 1 000 kilograms balance 1 tonne
- make reasonable estimates of the masses of a variety of large vehicles
- express tonnes as kilograms
- express kilograms as tonnes

LEVEL 1 — MASS

EASIER QUESTIONS

Q1. (a) 1 kg = ☐ g (b) 1 000 kg = ☐ t

(c) 2 000 g = ☐ kg (d) 0.5 t = ☐ kg

(e) 5.5 kg = ☐ g (f) 500 g = ☐ kg

Q2. What is the total mass of 3 parcels, each having a mass of 1.75 kg?

Q3. Judy buys 3 kg of potatoes, 1 kg 200 g of onions and 750 g of fish. What mass does she have to carry home?

Q4. Brighto washing powder comes in 3 different sizes.

500 g at $1.49, 1kg at $2.88 and 2 kg at $5.80.

Which size is the best buy?

Q5. Violet needs 1 kg of apples to make her apple pies. If each apple has a mass of 200 g, how many apples will she have to buy?

Q6. The net mass of a tin of tuna is 468 g. The gross mass is 537 g. What is the mass of the tin?

Q7. A truck weighing 3 t is loaded with 100 boxes—each box weighing 15 kg. What is the mass of the truck when it is loaded?

Q8. Michael has a mass of 42 kg 750 g. Gregory is 750 g heavier than Michael. What is Gregory's mass?

Q9. An apple has a mass of 140 g; a rockmelon is 5 times heavier. What is the total mass of 4 similar rockmelons?

LEVEL 2 — MASS

AVERAGE QUESTIONS

Q1. Rick posted 3 parcels with masses of 2 kg 150 g, 1.5 kg and 760 g. What was their total mass?

Q2. A bulk container held 25 kg of oranges. $6\frac{1}{2}$ kg, 3 kg, $1\frac{1}{4}$ kg and 750 g of oranges were removed. What mass of oranges remained?

Q3. (a) 2 750 kg = ☐ t (b) 3.6 kg = ☐ g

(c) 5.25 t = ☐ kg (d) 5 100 g = ☐ kg

(e) 0.9 kg = ☐ g (f) 200 kg = ☐ t

Q4. A crate of pineapples has a gross mass of 25.3 kg. The crate has a mass of 3.7 kg. What is the net mass of pineapples?

Q5. A truck has a mass of 4 215 kg and it is carrying 30 crates of tomatoes, each with a mass of 7.5 kg, and 8 crates of potatoes, each with a mass of 14.7 kg. What is the total mass of the truck and vegetables?

Q6. Find:

(a) $\frac{3}{10}$ of 2 kg (b) 0.1 of 3 t (c) 80% of 60 g.

Q7. A can of tuna has a gross mass of 250 g. The can has a mass of 96 g. A recipe requires 770 g of tuna. How many cans will I have to buy for the recipe?

Q8. The team of 7 netballers had an average mass of 49 kg. What is the total mass of the team to the nearest ten kilograms.

LEVEL 3 — MASS

DIFFICULT QUESTIONS

Q1. 6 packets of biscuits have a total mass of 750 g. What would be the mass of 16 packets?

Q2. The cooking time for a 500 g leg of lamb is 15 minutes. How long would it take to cook a 5.2 kg leg of lamb?

Q3. The mass of a jar is $\frac{1}{5}$ that of its contents—raspberry jam. The gross mass of the jar of jam is 690 g. What is the net mass of jam?

Q4. 750 g of fertiliser covers 1 m^2. How many kilograms of fertiliser are needed to cover an area of 25 m^2?

Q5. Find:

(a) $\frac{2}{3}$ of 1.2 kg (b) 75% of 0.5 kg (c) 0.4 of 1.5 t

Q6. A box containing 5 apples has a gross mass of 695 g. The same box containing 7 apples has a gross mass of 945 g. What is the mass of the box?

Q7. On a peanut butter label it states that there is 5.6 g of protein and 1.4 g of sugar per 20 g serve. What mass of:

(a) protein would be present in a 50 g serve?

(b) sugar would be present in a 150 g serve?

(c) protein would be present in a 1.2 kg serve?

Q8. Honey was available in 2 sizes of jar. One had a gross mass of 400 g, the other was $1\frac{1}{2}$ times greater. A box containing 16 smaller and 12 larger jars was delivered to the Sunset Motel. The total mass of jars and box was 14.4 kg. What was the mass of the empty box?

TEMPERATURE

Temperature is a measure of the level of hotness and coldness.

During the early years a student should have passed beyond the informal assessment of temperature to a recognition of the need for measuring equipment and for a standard unit of measure, the degree Celsius. The previous volumes in this series give suggested activities to lay the foundation of the concept of temperature. These activities should have been completed before progressing further.

The final two primary years give continuing opportunity to estimate, measure and record temperatures in degrees Celsius. A wide variety of thermometers is examined, used and assessed.

VOCABULARY

Aquarium thermometer, body temperature, boiling point, climate, clinical thermometer, cooking thermometer, degree(s) Celsius, freezing point, insulation, less than, maximum, minimum, minus, more than, negative, predicted temperature, read a thermometer, thermostat, vacuum flask.

CONTENTS

THERMOMETERS

A thermometer is a device for measuring temperature. It is a fine glass tube which contains mercury, spirit or alcohol which is stored in a bulb at the bottom of the tube. As the temperature increases the substance takes up more space so it rises in the tube. This rise is measured against a scale on or by the tube.

Large thermometers are now easily available. They should be used where possible as they are much more easily handled and read than the small sized thermometers.

There are a number of safety factors which should be strictly adhered to when using thermometers.

- As mercury is a potentially hazardous substance, it is important to use a thermometer that contains alcohol.
- Thermometers should be handled carefully as they are made of glass and are easily broken.
- Care should be taken that a thermometer is only used in situations which are within its specific range, e.g. a clinical thermometer should only be used to measure body temperature; if it is used to measure boiling water it will break as the temperature is beyond its limits. It is important to estimate the probable temperature of the substance being measured.
- The thermometer should return to room temperature after each use and before storing.
- Thermometers should be stored away from direct sunlight in a vertical position with the bulb downwards.

THE STANDARD THERMOMETER

In 1742, a Swedish astronomer, Anders Celsius, devised a scale for measuring temperature. This scale was named after him. The point at which water turned to ice is called 0° Celsius and the point at which water boiled is called 100° Celsius. It is a centigrade scale, that is based on 100°. A 0° to a 100° thermometer will usually have a hundred equal divisions marked on it.

38° Celsius means 'thirty-eight degrees Celsius'. Eighty-five degrees Celsius would be written 85° Celsius or 85°C.

It is important to note that not all thermometers begin at 0° and end at 100°. Some begin below 0° and others end higher than 100°. There are still others, for example the clinical thermometer, used to measure body temperature, which only covers a relatively small section of the scale. It is, therefore, very important to ensure that the thermometer being used is designed to measure within the range needed.

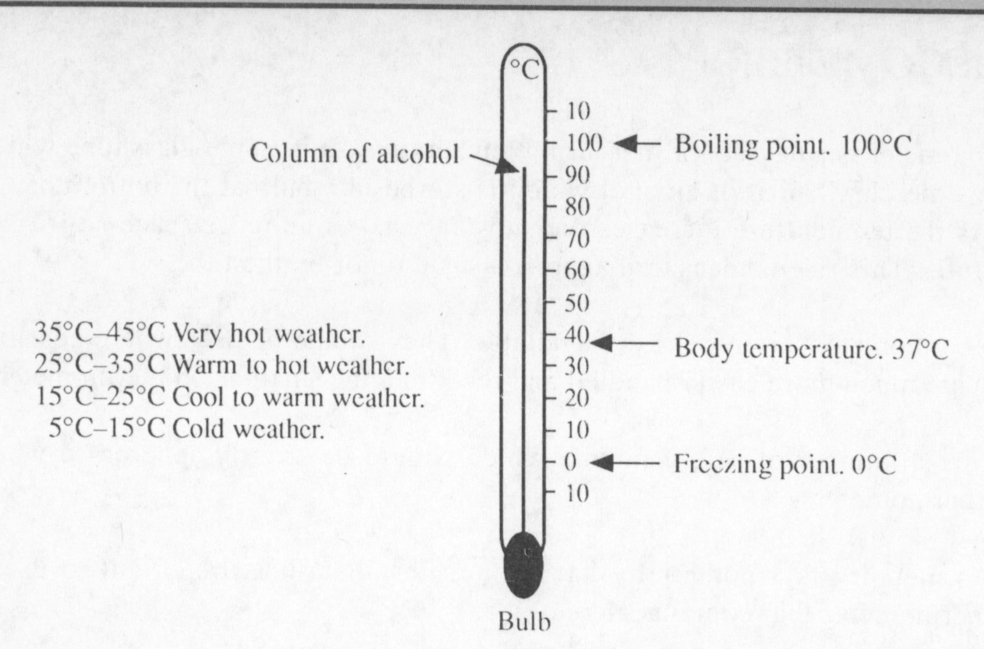

Students should be encouraged to undertake investigations into the different kinds of thermometer available, how they are made, what scales are used and the specific uses to which they are put.

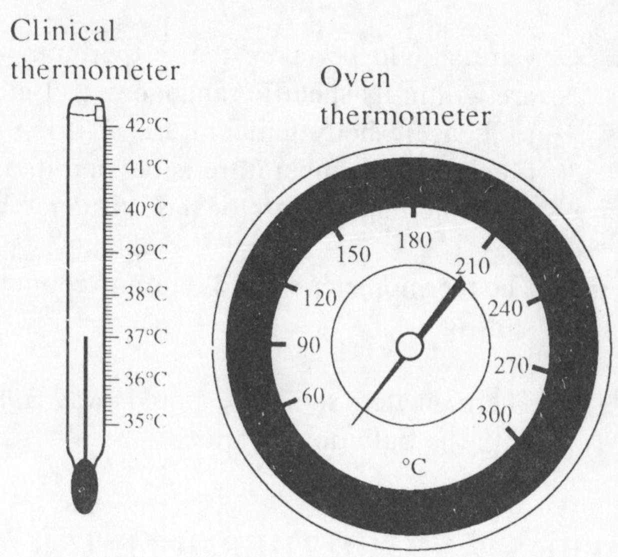

Examples:

Aquarium thermometers

Clinical thermometers

Cookery thermometers

Oven thermometer

Incubator thermometers

Maximum and minimum thermometers

The hygrometer which measures humidity could be investigated.

OTHER DEVICES FOR MEASURING TEMPERATURE

Examples:

Thermostats in:

Cars

Electric blankets,

Hair dryers

Refrigerators, etc.

There will be many opportunities where links can be made with the graphs sub-strand.

ACTIVITY:

Use the appropriate Celsius thermometer to measure the temperature in the room, in the schoolyard, of water, the body, etc. Graph the results.

FURTHER INVESTIGATIONS

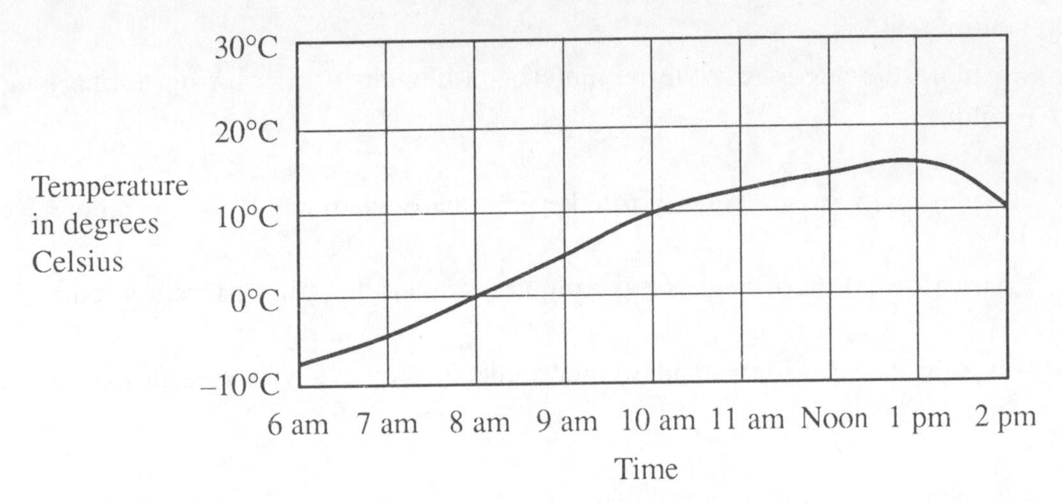

Example (i):
On a certain day the temperature in Malmo, Sweden, went from –7°C at 6 a.m. to 15°C at 1 p.m. What was the temperature rise?

Solution:
From –7°C to 0°C is a rise of 7°C.
From 0°C to 15°C is a rise of 15°C.
Therefore total rise is 7° + 15° = 22°C

Example (ii): Temperature in the backyard at 9 a.m.

Day	Mon	Tue	Wed	Thu	Fri	Sat	Sun
Temp	6°C	8°C	5°C	11°C	9°C	10°C	7°C

The temperature was recorded on each day of the week as shown in the table above. What was the average weekly temperature at 9 a.m.

Solution: Add up all the temperatures and divide the total by 7.

$$\text{Average temperature} = \frac{6 + 8 + 5 + 11 + 9 + 10 + 7}{7}$$

$$= \frac{56}{7}$$

$$= 8°C$$

VOLUME ASSESSMENT

Students should understand the following ideas:

Thermometers

- explain the need for a thermometer as a device for measuring hotness and coldness
- explain why it is necessary to take great care when handling thermometers
- use informal thermometers to compare temperatures in different situations
- explain the need for a standard thermometer as a device for measuring hotness and coldness
- demonstrate understanding of the Celsius range
- choose a thermometer with a suitable range to measure, compare and order temperatures in different situations
- graph the hourly temperature readings within a room for 12 hours, or daily at noon for a week
- recall the Celsius temperature for boiling point, freezing point, during the different seasons, normal body temperature, a hot drink, world temperature extremes
- describe and identify different thermometers, their specific uses and temperature range

LEVEL 1 — TEMPERATURE

EASIER QUESTIONS

Q1. What is a thermometer?

Q2. Where would you find temperatures above 100°C?

Q3.

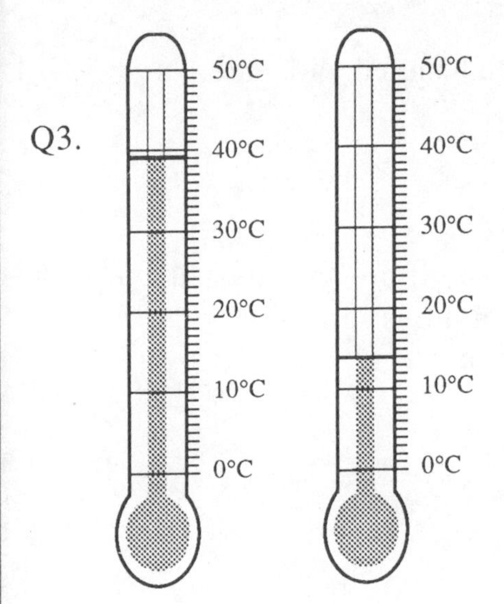

What is the difference between the temperatures shown on the thermometers?

Q4. (a) What kind of thermometer is shown on the right?

(b) Explain why it shows this particular temperature range.

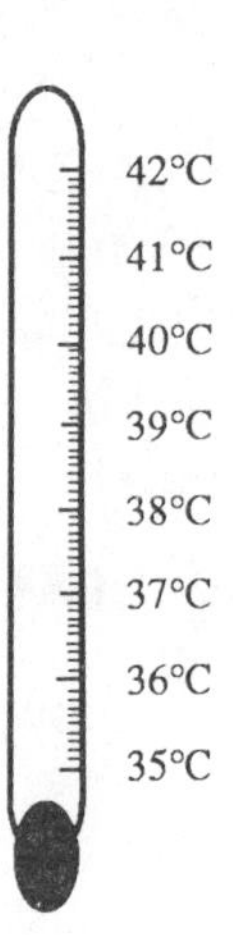

Q5. (a) At what temperature does water boil?

(b) At what temperature does water freeze?

(c) What is the normal body temperature?

LEVEL 2 — TEMPERATURE

AVERAGE QUESTIONS

Q1. Why is the Celsius scale also a centigrade scale?

Q2. Wherewould you find temperatures below 0°C?

Q3. Name 2 reasons why thermometers should be handled with care.

Q4.

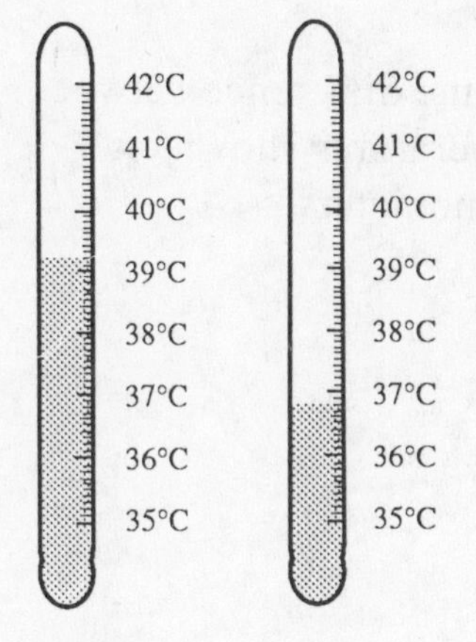

What is the difference between the temperatures shown on the thermometers?

Q5. (a) What kind of thermometer is pictured on the right?

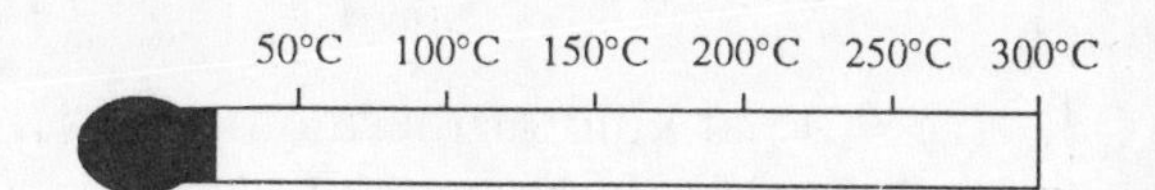

(b) Explain why it shows this particular temperature range.

Q6. Average temperature at noon over a 7 day period:

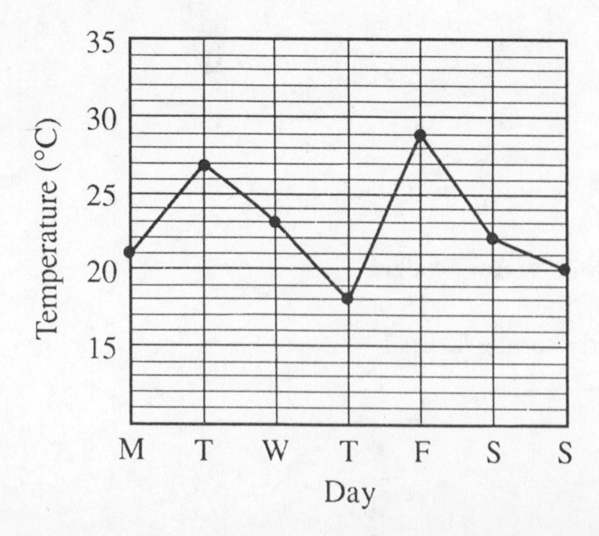

(a) What was the temperature on Wednesday?

(b) Which day was the warmest?

(c) What was the lowest temperature?

(d) How much warmer or colder was Tuesday than Saturday?

LEVEL 3 — TEMPERATURE DIFFICULT QUESTIONS

Q1. What is the difference between the temperatures shown on these thermometers?

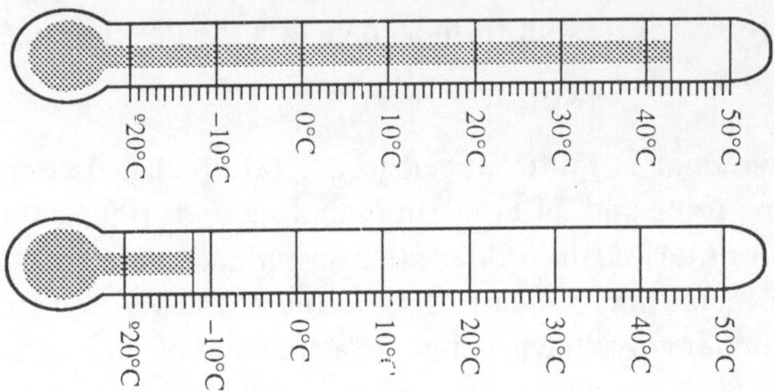

Q2. Explain briefly how a thermometer works.

Q3.

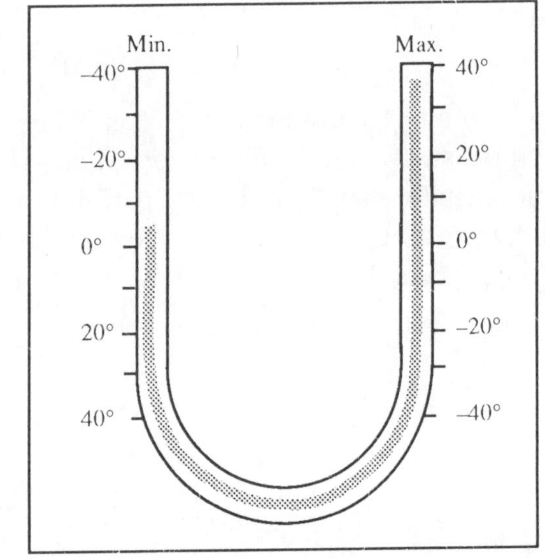

(a) What kind of thermometer is pictured on the left?

(b) Explain how it works.

Q4. Why is it important to use appropriate thermometers for specific situations?

Q5. Temperature of water in a kettle set to boil:

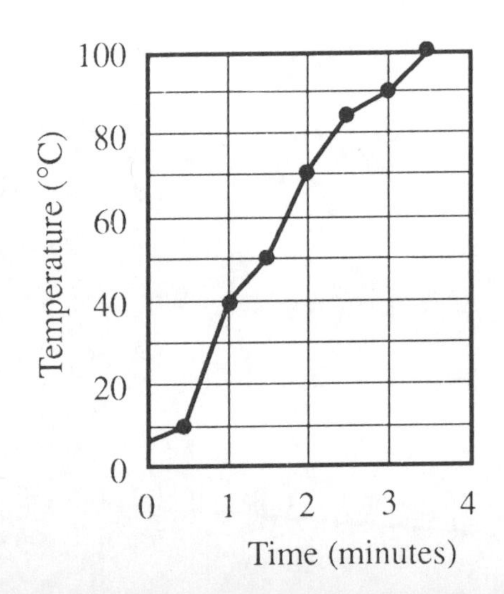

(a) What was the temperature of the water to begin with?

(b) How hot was the water after 2 minutes?

(c) After how many minutes did the water boil?

TIME

Time encompasses the past, present and future.

The first volume in this series suggests a number of activities which must be undertaken before progressing further to ensure the development of the concept of the passing of time.

A student is reintroduced to digital clocks, the terms a.m. and p.m., timetables, time lines and 24 hour time, and gains further experience estimating, comparing and ordering time intervals. A student should see the relationship between time units and have recall of time facts. In addition, many activities are undertaken which involve the accurate measurement of time using a stopwatch, and the concepts of speed, astronomical time and time zones are explored.

VOCABULARY

All stops, all stations, arrives, beginning, column, daylight saving, delay, departs, equator, equinox, express, fast, faster, fastest, finishes, Greenwich Mean Time, International Date Line, lap, latitude, longitude, meridian, mode, parallel, reset, revolution, quick, quicker, quickest, rapid, rate, row, semester, slow, slower, slowest, solstice, speed, start, stop, stopwatch, term, timetable, time zone, Tropic of Cancer, Tropic of Capricorn, vacation.

CONTENTS

A.M. AND P.M.

To avoid confusion between 9:00 in the morning and 9:00 in the evening when writing digital time, the terms a.m. or p.m. are written after the time.

a.m. = **ante meridiem** (Latin) meaning **before midday**
p.m. = **post meridiem** (Latin) meaning **after midday**

e.g.

9:00 a.m. means 9 o'clock in the morning.

9:00 p.m. means 9 o'clock in the evening.

Between 12 midnight and 12 noon times are a.m.

Between 12 noon and 12 midnight times are p.m.

Midday is most usually referred to as 12 noon or 12 midday rather than 12 p.m.

Midnight is most usually referred to as 12 midnight rather than 12 a.m.

Example:
Use a.m. or p.m. to write the following times:

(a) 10:47 in the morning . . . (10:47 a.m.)

(b) 8:26 in the evening . . . (8:26 p.m.)

(c) 12 in the middle of the night . . . (12 midnight or 12 a.m.)

ACTIVITIES:
Record the times of the main activities in the day as a.m. or p.m.

List occupations where people would be working at 10 a.m. In which occupations would people be working at 10 p.m.?

24 HOUR TIME

Another means of preventing confusion between 9:00 in the morning and 9:00 in the evening is to employ 24 hour time. Its use eliminates the need to specify a.m. or p.m. 24 hour time is used, for example, by airlines for their timetables, or by families to preset times for recording programs on a video recorder or for presetting the timer on the cooker so the meal is ready to eat when everyone gets home. Some digital clocks and watches use 24 hour tlme.

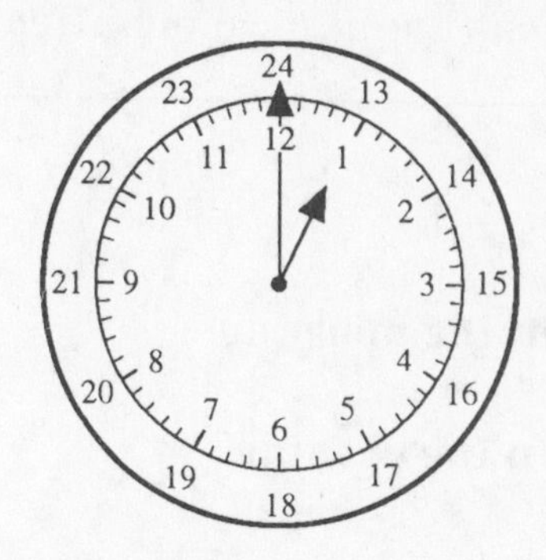

The day is divided into 24 hourly divisions which would be marked on a 12 hour clock face as the diagram above shows.

> 24 hour time is always given as a four digit number. The first two digits give the hours past midnight and the second two digits give the minutes past the last complete hour.

12 hour time	24 hour time	read as
2 a.m.	0200	oh 2 hundred hours
11 a.m.	1100	eleven hundred hours
1 p.m.	1300	thirteen hundred hours
2:20 p.m.	1420	fourteen twenty hours
11:51 p.m.	2351	twenty-three fifty-one hours

Example : Write and say the following times in 24 hour time:

(a) 8:25 a.m. (0825 oh-eight twenty-five hours)

(b) 8:25 p.m. (2025 twenty twenty-five hours)

Example:
Change the following 24 hour times to a.m. or p.m.

(a) 0930 (9:30 a.m.)

(b) 2130 (9:30 p.m.)

TIMETABLES

It is important to develop the ability to read and interpret the information given on timetables.

TRAIN TIMETABLE

FIVETOWN—CITY SQUARE LINE		MONDAY TO FRIDAYS	
FIVETOWN	11:24	11:30	11:45
SEVEN OAKS	11:27		
FOURBRIDGE	11:42		12:00
TENSTREET	12:05		
THREEFLATS	12:39		
CRESCENT BAY	12:55		12:58
HIGH OVAL	13:12		
CITY SQUARE	13:20	12:55	13:15

(a) How long does it take an all-stations train to travel between Fivetown and City Square?

(b) How long does the express train take to travel between Fivetown and City Square?

(c) How much longer does it take the all-stations train than the express train to make the journey between Fivetown and City Square?

(d) How long does it take the limited stops train to make the same journey?

(e) How much less time would a passenger spend travelling from Fourbridge to City Square by taking the 12:00 train rather than the 11:42 train?

(f) If you were a passenger travelling from Fivetown and you needed to be at Crescent Bay Station by 13:00, which train would you most likely take, and why?

Solutions:

(a) 1 hr 56 min.
(b) 1 hr 25 min.
(c) 1 hr 56 min—1 hr 25 min. = 31 minutes longer.
(d) 1 hr 30 min.
(e) 1 hr 38 min—1 hr 15 min. = 23 minutes longer.
(f) 11:45. The travelling time is shorter.

TIMELINES

Timelines are lines on which intervals of time are marked. They are a useful device for placing significant past events in chronological order. The line can perhaps represent a day, a year or even many centuries.

ACTIVITIES:

1. Construct a time line showing the significant events in the school's calendar. For example:

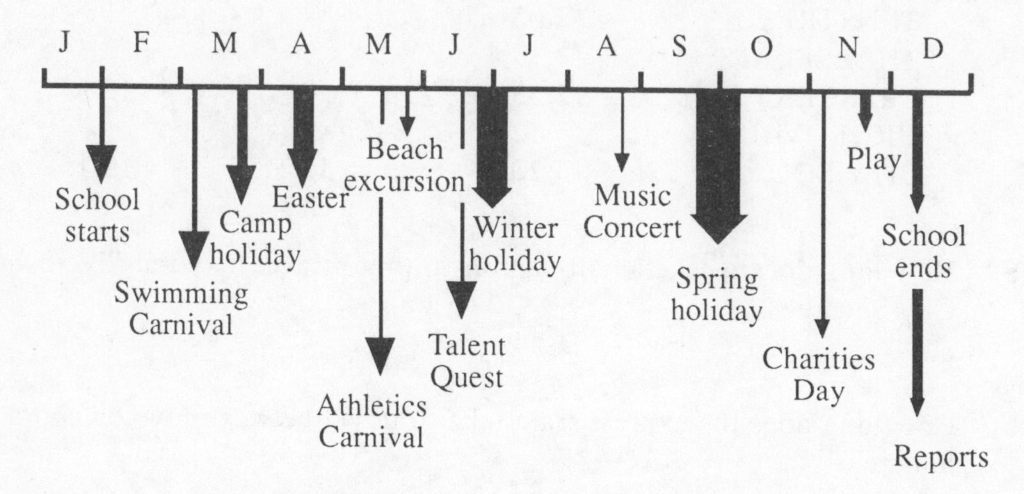

2. Research the significant dates in the development of Australia since European settlement. Construct a time line on which to record your findings.

3. Research significant dates in the history of flight since 1900. Record you findings on a timeline. For each date recorded, name a significant but unconnected happening, e.g. the death of Queen Victoria, Gallipoli, first use of the Salk vaccine against polio.

4. Construct a Prehistoric Time timeline marking in the advent of the dinosaurs, mammals, etc.

STOPWATCHES

When accurate measurements of time intervals are required, for example in sport when timing individual performances, stopwatches are used. They can give readings to hundredths of a second.

Examine as many different kinds of stopwatch as possible. The two basic kinds are illustrated below.

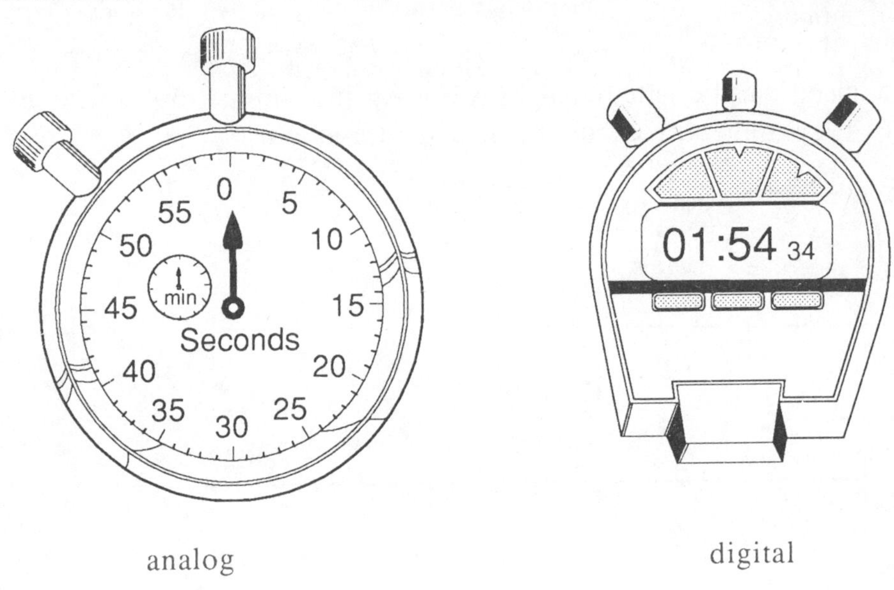

analog

digital

All stop watches have a start/stop button and a reset button.

ACTIVITIES:

1. Discuss the advantages and disadvantages of each type of stopwatch. Why are most stopwatches digital? (They give greater accuracy). How can digital watches be used as timing devices? (Calculate the difference between the recorded starting time and the finishing time).

2. Estimate what is the shortest time interval that can be measured using an analog Stopwatch. (Tenths of a second) Why is this?

3. If several students time the same event, there is likely to be a difference in the times recorded. This emphasises the difficulty of gaining accurate readings when dealing with such small intervals of time. How could this be minimised?

4. Use stopwatches in activities involving estimating the passage of various intervals of time.

SPEED

It is necessary to understand what is meant by the term speed. There are two kinds of speed, instantaneous speed and average speed.

Instantaneous speed is the speed at which, for example, a vehicle is travelling at any given moment. This can be read on the speedometer of the vehicle. On a normal journey, the instantaneous speed is constantly changing as the vehicle accelerates, cruises or brakes.

Average speed can be calculated by knowing the time it took to travel a given distance. The odometer records the distance travelled.

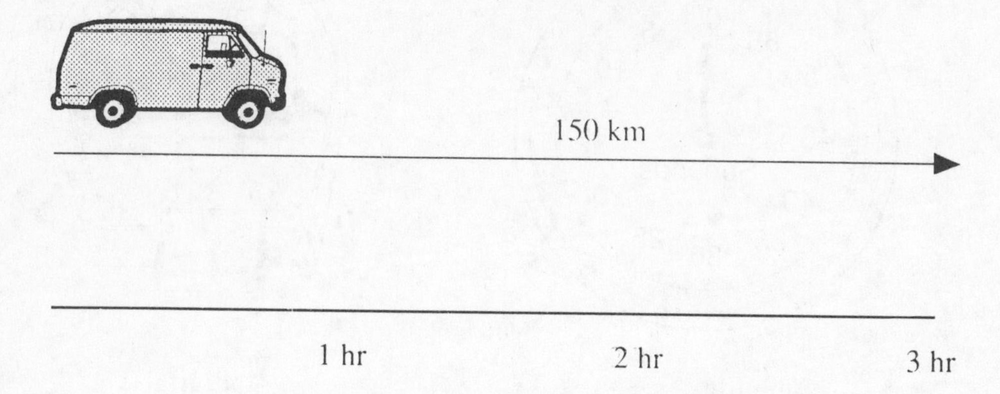

This van travelled 150 km in 3 hours. Its average speed was therefore 50 km per hour (50 km/h)

Example (i): A man walks at 6 km/h. How far will he walk in $2\frac{1}{2}$ hours?

He will walk 6 km in each of the 2 hours and 3 km in the half hour.
6 + 6 + 3 = 15. He walks a total of 15 km.

Example (ii): A cyclist travels 60 km in 3 hr. What is his average speed?

If the cyclist travelled 60 km in three hours he would have travelled an average of 20 km in each hour. His average speed was 20 km/h.

Example (iii): How long will it take to travel a distance of 300 km at an average speed of 60 km/h?

60 km are travelled each hour. It would take 5 hours to travel 300 km

ACTIVITIES:

1. Using a stopwatch, time a partner whilst e.g. walking 25 m, and later 50 m and perhaps 100 m. Work out the average speed at each distance. If 25 m was covered in 10 sec the—average speed was two and a half metres per second, ($2\frac{1}{2}$m/s). Use a calculator when necessary. (Link to decimals and fractions substrand for rounding off decimals). Discuss the results.

2. Link to graphs substrand to graph the comparative speeds of e.g. different forms of transport, (different forms of land transport, very fast air transport, the top speed of cars throughout their history) or the maximum speed of a variety of animals.

3. Discuss the advantages and disadvantages of travelling at high speeds. Investigate speed limiting devices on buses and trucks and also ways that the police try to limit all vehicles to safe speeds on the roads. (Traffic signs and radar).

4. Select an appropriate distance, e.g. 100 metres. Estimate, then time, how long it takes to cover that distance whilst walking, running and cycling. Discuss the accuracy of the estimates and then estimate and calculate the average speed in metres per second. (m/s)

WORLD TIME

It is important that students understand why there are different times around the world.

The earth spins on its axis from west to east taking 24 hours to complete one revolution. Imaginary lines—called meridians of longitude are drawn on maps; they run north/south. Since the earth turns through 360 degrees in 24 hours it will turn through 15° in one hour. Places which are 15° longitude apart will have a time difference of 1 hour.

Because different longitudinal sections of the earth are experiencing different times of the day at any given moment, longitudinal time bands called **time zones** have developed. These time zones do not strictly follow the meridians of longitude but vary with political boundaries (states or countries). Time is measured from the Greenwich meridian in England. The distance from the Greenwich Meridian determines the appropriate time zone. When it is noon in Greenwich it will be 10 p.m. in Sydney which is close to the 150° East meridian of longitude.

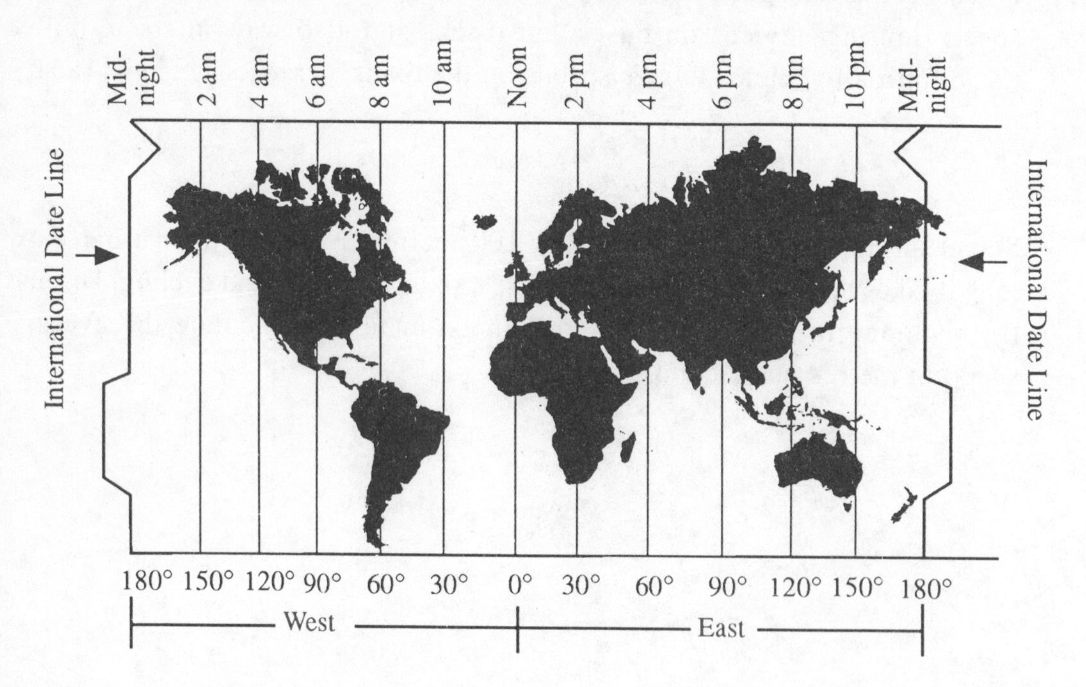

Times to the east of Greenwich will be ahead of the Greenwich Mean Time (GMT) until the 180° Meridian—the International Date Line is reached. Times here are 12 hours ahead of GMT. Times to the west of Greenwich will be behind GMT until the International Date Line is reached which will be 12 hours behind GMT.

At the International Date Line there is a 24 hour difference. Crossing to the west means crossing to the previous day (gaining a day). Crossing to the east means crossing to the next day (losing a day).

ACTIVITIES:

1. Place removable stickers on a globe to correspond with the time zones on the map on the previous page. Investigate what time it will be at various places around the world when it is 12 noon in Greenwich.

2. Use the globe and the removable stickers to investigate the International Date Line which roughly follows the 180 meridian and to find out why this line is not straight?

3. Investigate the orbit of the earth around the sun and how this determines the seasons. Use a globe to help with the investigations.

4. Research 'equinox and solstice'. What is the significance of each?

5. What are the Tropic of Cancer and the Tropic of Capricorn?

6. Research the orbits of the other planets in the Solar system. How does the length of the orbit of each compare with an earth year, the time it takes the earth to orbit the sun.

7. How can some airline passengers arrive at their destination before the time they have left the point of departure? Use a globe to help with the investigations.

8. Why does it take longer, using the same route, to fly from London to Sydney than from Sydney to London?

9. Research the Roman Calendar and the Gregorian Calendar.

10. Research famous people in history who have made significant contributions to the understanding of time.

AUSTRALIAN TIME ZONES

Australia is a huge continent spanning 40 degrees of longitude. Australia has 3 time zones—Western Standard Time, Central Standard Time and Eastern Standard Time. When it is 1.00 p.m. in Perth it is 2:30 p.m. in Adelaide and 3:00 p.m. in Sydney.

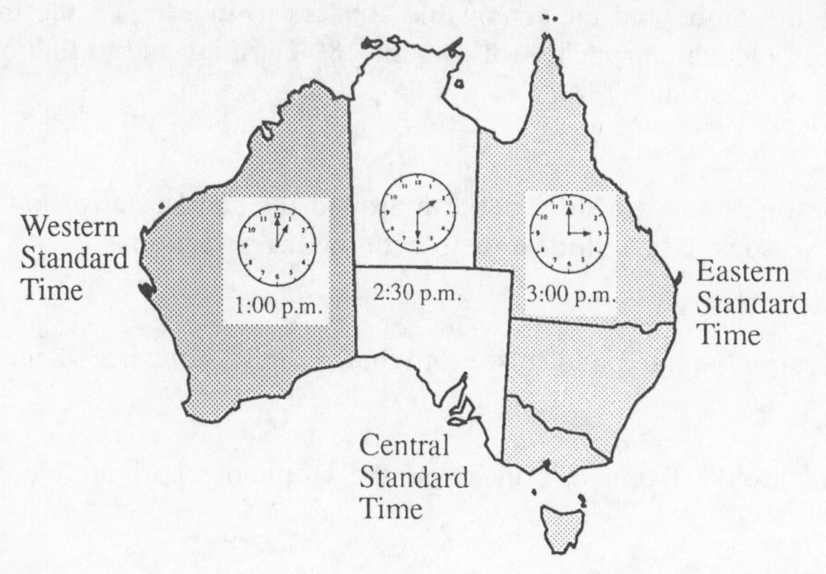

ACTIVITIES:

1. Why does Australia need 3 time zones?

2. What would happen if there was only one time zone over all of Australia?

3. Why does Broken Hill in New South Wales use Central Standard Time?

4. What problems are created by having 3 different time zones within one country? (Business hours, flight times, time tables, national radio and television broadcasts, etc.)

DAYLIGHT SAVING

Daylight saving involves moving (**spring**ing) the clock one hour ahead of standard time in the **spring** and moving it back (letting it **fall** back) in the **autumn** to take advantage of longer daylight hour during the summer. Daylight saving makes more daylight available in the evening instead of in the very early morning when most people are asleep.

ACTIVITY:

Not everyone supports daylight saving. Investigate the advantages and disadvantages. What is your opinion?

TIME ASSESSMENT

Students should understand the following ideas:

24 hour time

- mark 24 hour time on a 12 hour analog clock face by adding another ring of numbers
- convert a.m. and m. times to 24 hour time
- convert 24 hour time to a.m. or m. time
- describe when 24 hour time is used and by whom
- explain the advantages and disadvantages of the a.m./m. and 24 hour forms of recording time

Timetables and timelines

- collect, read and interpret bus, train, ferry and plane timetables
- research and construct a timeline from data collected
- interpret information on a timeline

Stopwatches

- demonstrate the use of the start, stop and reset buttons on both digital and analog stopwatches
- read times from both digital and analog stopwatches
- time activities with a stopwatch
- explain why most stopwatches are digital
- explain difficulties in obtaining accurate timing

Speed

- demonstrate understanding of what is meant by the speed of a vehicle
- recall common speed limits
- explain what instantaneous speed means and how it is found
- read the instantaneous speed of a vehicle from the speedometer
- calculate the average speed of a vehicle from given data of distance travelled and time taken
- calculate the distance travelled from given data of average speed and time taken

TIME ASSESSMENT Continued

World time

- calculate the time along any given meridian of longitude when it is e.g. 12 noon in Greenwich
- explain why we have day and night
- explain why the seasons occur
- explain the terms 'equinox' and 'solstice'

Australian time zones

- explain why Australia needs 3 time zones
- describe the problems of having 3 time zones in Australia
- calculate the time in one Australian time zone given the time in another Australian time zone
- give reasons for and against daylight saving

LEVEL 1 — TIME

EASIER QUESTIONS

Q1. Write the following in 24-hour time:

(a) 5 a.m. (b) 4:35 p.m. (c) 8:15 p.m. (d) 7:05 a.m.

Q2. Write these 24-hour times as a.m. or p.m.:

(a) 0515 (b) 2150 (c) 1232 (d) 1035

Q3. Below is a time line of Brian's life from birth to the age of 3.

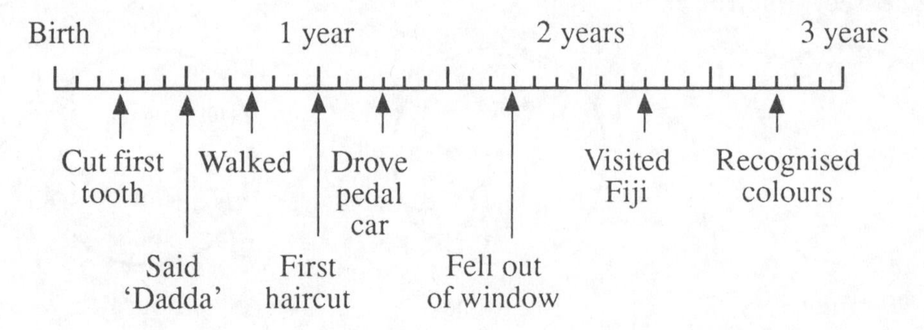

How old was Brian when he:

(a) said 'Dadda'? (b) had his first haircut?

(c) fell out of a window? (d) cut his first tooth?

Q4. On the stopwatch, Kylie's time was 12.05 seconds and Emma's was 10.52 seconds. How much faster was Emma than Kylie?

Q5. A car travels at an average speed of 82 km/h. How far will it travel between 7:30 a.m. and 10:30 a.m.?

Q6. What is the time in Sydney when it is noon in Greenwich?

Q7. In July, what is the time in Sydney when it is 4 p.m. in:

(a) Perth

(b) Adelaide?

LEVEL 2 — TIME

AVERAGE QUESTIONS

Q1. Write these as 24-hour time:

(a) 9 a.m. (b) 8:20 p.m. (c) 1:25 a.m. (d) 11:43 p.m.

Q2. Write these as a.m. or p.m.:

(a) 1625 (b) 0932 (c) 2135 (d) 1114

Q3. Each of the old clocks below is running either fast or slow. What should be the correct time for each?

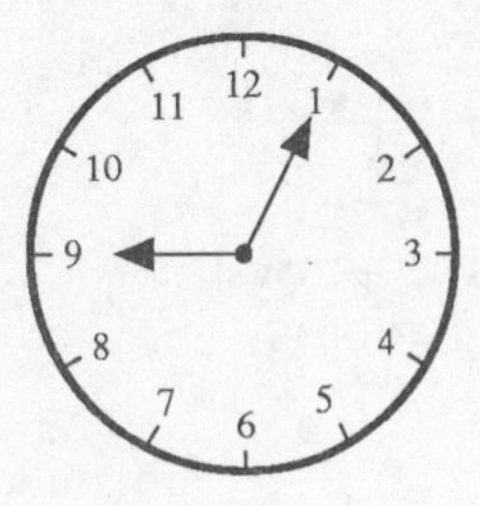

20 minutes fast

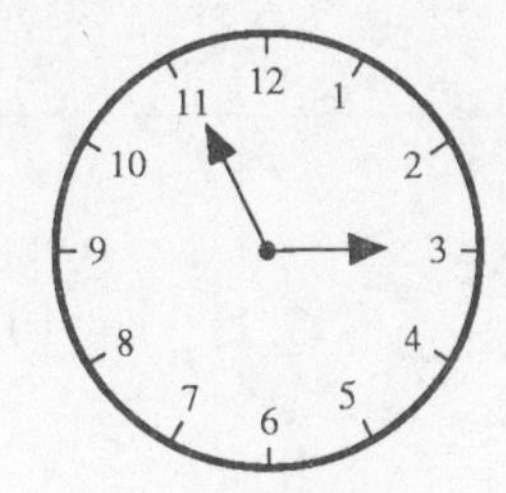

15 minutes slow

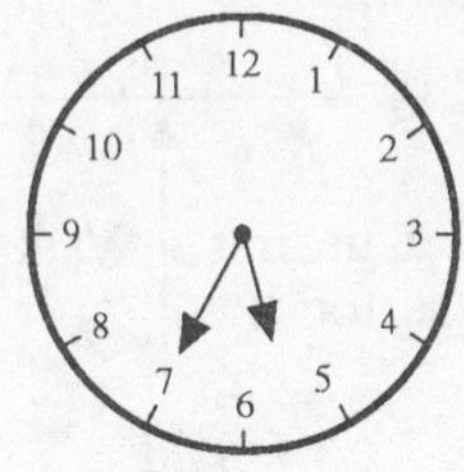

$\frac{3}{4}$ hour fast

Q4.

Bus Timetable	First bus		Last bus
Anne Rd	7:05 a.m.		10:35 p.m.
Peter Sq	7:12	Every	10:42
James Pl	7:22	half	10:52
William Dr	7:37	hour	11:07
Stephen Ave	7:48		11:18
Richard Rd	7:57		11:27
Timothy St	8:03		11:33

(a) How long does the journey take from Anne Rd to Timothy St?
(b) Which is the shortest stage of the bus route?
(c) At what time must a bus be caught at Anne Rd in order to arrive at Richard Rd by 9:30 a.m.?
(d) The 8:42 p.m. bus from Peter Sq is 10 minutes late. At what time does it arrive at Stephen Ave?

Q5. A car travels 240 km in 4 hours.

(a) What is the car's average speed in km/hr?
(b) How far would the car travel in 45 minutes?

LEVEL 3 — TIME

DIFFICULT QUESTIONS

Q1. The 24-hour clocks below have been set either fast or slow. What should be the correct time?

(a) 0136 — $\frac{3}{4}$ hour fast

(b) 1157 — 8 min slow

(c) 2341 — 30 min slow

Q2.

Train Timetable			
Easternville Crosstown Southam Western End Junction Bend Riversby	0608 0627 0712 0721 0739 0802	Every twenty minutes	2148 2207 2252 2301 2319 2342

(a) How long does the journey take from Easternville to Riversby?

(b) Which train from Crosstown should I catch to arrive at Junction Bend before 1530?

(c) The train which arrives at Western End at 1341, left late at Riversby. At what time did it arrive?

(d) The train which left Southam at 1152 arrived 10 minutes late at Riversby. At what time did it arrive?

Q3. When it is 2 a.m. on Tuesday in Greenwich, what day and time is it in Perth?

Q4. In winter, when it's 2341 on Sunday in Darwin, what day and time is it in:

(a) Perth?

(b) Sydney?

Q5. A train travels 90 km in 45 minutes?

(a) What is the average speed of the train in km/h?

(b) How far will it travel in 1 h 10 min.?

(c) How long will it take for the train to travel 150 km?

An extra page for additional notes

PROBLEM SOLVING

INTRODUCTION

Problem solving is an integral part of mathematics even in the early stages. It reinforces the process being learnt, promotes real understanding and, by using real-life relevant problems, gives a clear reason to students why mathematics is important and relevant to them as individuals.

With each new mathematical concept, a number of real-life relevant problems should be presented which require this understanding of the concept to find the solution. A student is given the opportunity to identify the need for understanding of this concept and also identifies it as a means of solving the problem.

The problems set should reflect the breadth of the interests within the given group of students.

Problem solving is a process or series of processes. It could almost be said that the answer is irrelevant. It is the choice of operation(s) and a suitable strategy that is the most important reason for problem solving experiences.

There are no clear rules. Problems can be solved from many different angles. Frequently, any one of a variety of strategies can be used. Teaching therefore involves giving an awareness of possible strategies, fostering the confidence to try them and encouraging the tenacity to see the problem through without giving up when difficulties are encountered. For adults assisting children who are really 'stumped' by a particular problem, simply rewording the question may unlock a pathway by which the student may find a solution.

Problem solving promotes reasoning and logical thought. It tests the ability to transfer from working through a type of algorithm to recognising the need for this operation as a means of solving the problem.

Students need practice in reading a problem so that they are able to extract the key question to be answered and the key words and phrases which will aid the solving process together with choosing the correct operation or combination of operations.

Problem solving is not a race against the clock. Challenging problems need time to 'simmer'. This can take hours and sometimes days.

Work through the problem yourself first. Now find at least one other way to solve it.

Share ways that others have used to solve the problem. Discussion and sharing develop understanding that there are many ways to reach a solution. Some open-ended problems have a number of possible solutions, that is, there is not one right answer but several. Discussing how a solution has been reached is a most important part of problem solving. True understanding only comes as a result of an exchange of ideas and methods. It encourages self-assessment and evaluation. These are life skills, important not only in Mathematics but throughout life in assessing every situation.

Don't be fazed if students are better at problem solving than you are! It gives them confidence to take risks and try different strategies when they realise that you too don't always know the answer first time and need to try again.

PROBLEM SOLVING IS AN ON-GOING PART OF THE LEARNING PROCESS. MANY STUDENTS' BOOKS WAIT UNTIL ALL THE OPERATIONS AND STRATEGIES HAVE BEEN LEARNED BEFORE INTRODUCING PROBLEM SOLVING. INSTEAD, IT SHOULD BE CONSTANTLY REINFORCED WHILST CONCEPT LEARNING IS IN PROGRESS, NOT LEFT TO THE END OF THE BOOK. LESS ABLE CHILDREN WITH LESS WELL DEVELOPED MATHEMATICS MEMORIES WILL HAVE FORGOTTEN THE PROCESS NEEDED BY THIS TIME.

STEPS IN PROBLEM SOLVING

There are four steps in the problem solving process.

1. Find out what the question is.
   Read the question carefully two or three times.

   By underlining key words and phrases a student learns to ask:

   (a) 'What is the problem? What have I been asked to find?'

   (b) 'What information have I been given that can help solve the problem.'

2. 'How do I go about finding the answer?' Choose a possible strategy—pictures, tables, drawings, working backwards, etc. N.B. If the first one doesn't work try others. If unsure, use 'guess and check'. DON'T GIVE UP!

3. Which operation, or combination of operations, is needed? What is an estimate of the answer?

   Show any working. Remember, credit is often given for choosing a suitable strategy even if an error is made in the answer. (When the correct strategy and operation have been identified, calculators can be used to simplify calculations.)

4. Write out the answer clearly. Evaluate whether the question has been answered and if the answer is reasonable in comparison with the question and the estimate. Look back on how the solution was reached and how others reached their solution.

STUDENTS NEED TO UNDERSTAND
THAT IF THE PROBLEM IS IN
THEIR BOOK IT IS SOLVABLE.

GUESS AND CHECK/TRIAL AND ERROR

Guess and check is a strategy where the answer is guessed using the given information. The guess is tested and further reasonable guesses made which move closer and closer to the solution. This strategy can be used on its own or in conjunction with others.

1. What have I been asked to find?
2. What information have I been given?
3. Guess the answer.
4. Check the answer with the original question. By checking whether your answer is too big or too small you can make a better guess next time.
5. Continue with this process until the correct answer is reached.

Example:
Derrick is 3 years older than Bobbie. Twice Derrick's age plus three times Bobbie's age is equal to 46. What are the ages of Derrick and Bobbie?

Solution:

Guess 1:	Derrick is 8 and Bobbie is 5.	
Check:	$(2 \times 8) + (3 \times 5) = 31$	This is too small.
Guess 1:	Derrick is 10 and Bobbie is 7.	
Check:	$(2 \times 10) + (3 \times 7) = 41$	Still too small.
Guess 1:	Derrick is 11 and Bobbie is 8.	
Check:	$(2 \times 11) + (3 \times 8) = 46$	Right!

Derrick is 11 and Bobbie is 8.

MAKE A LIST

Problem solving requires systematic recording of information. The strategy of making a list puts order into the solving process and allows easy reviewing of results to date.

1. What have I been asked to find?

2. What information have I been given?

3. Estimate the answer.

4. Make a list. Be systematic. Work through possibilities in an organised way.

5. Review the answer. Is it sensible?

Example:
Tony has $12 to spend at the newsagents. He sees magazines for $3.60 each, notebooks at $2.40 each and pens at $1.20 each. How many different combinations of magazines, and/or notebooks and/or pens could Tony buy?

Magazines ($3.60)	3 ($10.80)	2 ($7.20)	2 ($7.20)	2 ($7.20)
Notebooks ($2.40)	0	2 ($4.80)	1 ($2.40)	0
Pens ($1.20)	1 ($1.20)	0	2 ($2.40)	4 ($4.80) etc.

So far there are 4 combinations.

Solution:
14 combinations.

MAKE A TABLE

Making a table is similar to making a list. Information is organised in table form to record given information and to identify what data is missing. Tables often reveal patterns which lead to solutions.

1. What have I been asked to find?

2. What information have I been given?

3. Estimate the answer.

4. Construct a table. Be systematic. Work through possibilities in an organised way.

5. Review the answer. Is it sensible?

Example (i):
James needs to save $63 for a snorkel and mask. So far he has saved $19 dollars. From now on, each week he is able to save $6. How many weeks will he take to save enough for the snorkel and mask?

Weeks	0	1	2	3	4	5	6
Savings	19	25	31	etc.			

Solution:
It will take 8 weeks to save enough to buy the snorkel and mask.

Example (ii):
If James wanted to buy a snorkel, mask and fins costing $108, for how many weeks would he need to save?

Solution:
James would have to save for 15 weeks.

ACT IT OUT

Visualising by means of acting out a problem or using concrete materials can greatly simplify finding solutions. Concrete materials used to represent the objects in the problem need only be counters or even bits of paper if it is impractical or impossible to use the real objects.

1. What have I been asked to find?
2. What information have I been given?
3. Estimate the answer.
4. Act it out. Be systematic. Work through possibilities in an organised way.
5. Review the answer. Is it sensible?

Example:
Chris has been saving $1 and 50c coins in her money box. They total $11.50.

If she has 14 coins, how many of each has she?

Solution:
Chris has 9 × $1 coins and 5 × 50c coins.

Example:
If she has 18 coins, how many of each has she?

Solution:
Chris has 5 × $1 coins and 13 × 50c coins.

LOOK FOR A PATTERN

Regular, repetitive patterns of numbers, shapes, colours or combinations of these occur frequently in mathematics. Predictions based on such repetitious patterns can help in solving problems, often when used in combination with making a table.

1. What have I been asked to find?
2. What information have I been given?
3. Estimate the answer.
4. Organise information and look for a pattern. Be systematic. Work through possibilities in an organised way.
5. Review the answer. Is it sensible?

Example:
Find the sum of the counting numbers from 1 to 100
(i.e. 1 + 2 + 3 + 4 + 5 + 6 + 7 . . . . + 97 + 98 + 99 + 100)

Solution:
It would take a LONG TIME to add them all up.

Look for a pattern:

1 + 2 + 3 + 4 . . . . + 97 + 98 + 99 + 100

$$\begin{array}{r} 100 \\ +\ 1 \\ \hline 101 \end{array} \qquad \begin{array}{r} 99 \\ +\ 2 \\ \hline 101 \end{array} \qquad \begin{array}{r} 98 \\ +\ 3 \\ \hline 101 \end{array} \qquad \begin{array}{r} 97 \\ +\ 4 \\ \hline 101 \end{array}$$

There are 50 pairs each totalling 101.

Simply multiply 101 by 50

i.e.
$$\begin{array}{r} 101 \\ \times\ 50 \\ \hline 5050 \end{array}$$

The sum of the first hundred counting numbers is 5050

MAKE A PICTURE, DIAGRAM OR GRAPH

Drawing a picture or diagram of given information helps visualise a problem so that the data can be 'seen' and the next steps clarified.

1. What have I been asked to find?

2. What information have I been given?

3. Estimate the answer.

4. Draw a picture, diagram or graph. Be systematic. Work in an organised way.

5. Review the answer. Is it sensible?

Example (i):
Katie, Bronwyn and Jenny were contestants in a gymnastics competition. How many combinations of first and second place could there be?

Solution:

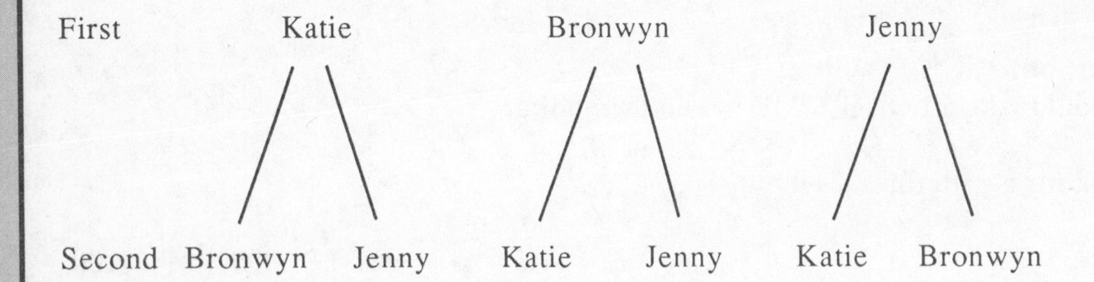

There are six possible combinations of first and second place winners.

Example (ii):
If Pauline had also competed, how many possible combinations of first and second place would there be?

Solution:
There would be 12 possible combinations.

WORK BACKWARDS

In some problems the beginning of the problem is not given. Instead, a series of steps or operations take students through to the final answer. To solve the problem begin with this final answer and work backwards through the steps, reversing operations to find the data at the beginning of the problem.

The opposite operation to adding is subtracting, and vice versa. The opposite operation to multiplying is division, and vice versa.

1. What have I been asked to find?
2. What information have I been given?
3. Estimate the answer.
4. Begin with the final answer and work backwards. Be systematic. Work through in an organised way.
5. Review the answer. Is it sensible?

Example:
Pat is 25 years younger than Justine and Graham is half Pat's age. Jason is 13 years older than Graham. If Jason is 41, how old is Justine?

Solution:
Work backwards from Jason's age.

Jason is 41.	Jason is 13 years older than Graham.
So, Graham is 28.	Graham is half Pat's age.
So, Pat is 56.	Pat is 25 years younger than Justine.
So, Justine is 81.	

MAKE IT SIMPLER

By solving a simpler similar problem, processes operations or patterns can become apparent, which help to solve complex problems often involving large numbers.

1. What have I been asked to find?

2. What information have I been given?

3. Estimate the answer.

4. Make the example as simple as possible Be systematic. Work through in an organised way.

5. Review the answer. Is it sensible?

Example:
There are 10 people at a party. If every person shakes hands with every other person, how many different handshakes will there be?
Start with only a few people.

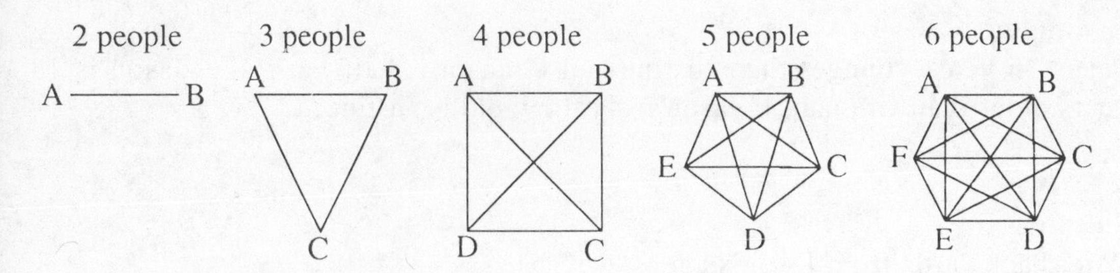

Can you see a pattern yet?

A definite pattern is emerging.

From 2 to 3 people, we added on 2 extra handshakes.

From 3 to 4 people, we added on 3 extra handshakes.

From 4 to 5 people we added on 4 extra handshakes, etc.

Number of people	2	3	4	5	6	7	8	9	10
Number of handshakes	1	3	6	10	15	21	28	36	45
Pattern		+2	+3	+4	+5	+6	+7	+8	+9

Solution:
There will be a total of 45 handshakes.

USE LOGICAL REASONING

Problems requiring logical reasoning often contain 'If . . . . . . then . . . . . .' although most problems need the use of logic. Logical reasoning means that you take one step at a time towards a solution, basing each step on the previous one.

1. What have I been asked to find?

2. What information have I been given?

3. Estimate the answer.

4. Be systematic. Work through possibilities in an organised way.

5. Review the answer. Is it sensible?

Example:
The world's finest male sprinters can run 100 metres in 10 seconds. How fast is this in kilometres per hour (km/h)?

Solution:

100 m in 10 seconds

=	600 m in 1 minute	(multiply by 6)
=	36 000 m in 1 hour	(multiply by 60)
=	36 km in 1 hour	(divide by 1 000)
=	36 km/h	

FIND ALL POSSIBILITIES

This kind of problem does not have just one answer. Investigations and recording must be completed systematically.

1. What have I been asked to find?
2. What information have I been given?
3. Estimate the answer.
4. Be systematic. Work through in an organised way.
5. Review the answer. Is it sensible?

Example:
List all the 2 digit numbers that can be formed using the digits 1, 2, 3 and 4 if each digit is only used once in each number.

Solution:

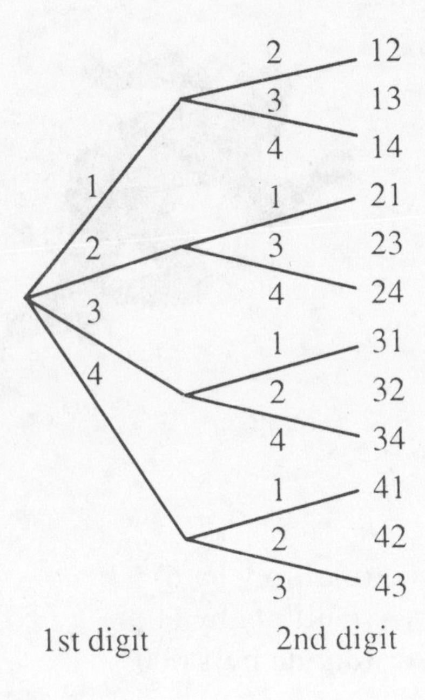

There are 12 two digit numbers which can be formed:

12, 13, 14, 21, 23, 24, 31, 32, 34, 41, 42, 43.

LEVEL 1 — PROBLEM SOLVING

EASIER QUESTIONS

Q1. 6 magazines cost a total of \$21.30. What is the cost of:

(a) 1 magazine? (b) 11 magazines?

Q2. Heidi went to the markets and bought 3 shirts at \$8.95 each, 5 bags of lollies at \$1.75 each, and 4 plants at \$6.80 each. How much change does she have left over from \$100?

Q3. If I think of a number, multiply it by 7 and then add 5, the result is 47. What is the number?

Q4. Find two numbers which add up to 16, and multiply to give 48.

Q5. Betty is 5 years younger than Marcia. Twice Betty's age plus Marcia's age equals 32. What are their ages?

Q6. Find a pattern and then solve these totals:

(a) $7 + 6 + 5 + 4 + 7 + 6 + 5 + 4 + 7 + 6 + 5 + 4 + 7 + 6 + 5 + 4$

(b) $30 - 29 + 28 - 27 + 26 - 25 + 24 - 23 + 22 - 21 + 20 - 19 + 18 - 17$

Q7. What are the 2-digit numbers that can be formed from the digits 5, 6, 7 and 8 , if each digit can only be used once?

Q8. Sugar is sold in 3 different sized packages. 1 kg for \$1.86, 500 g for \$1.05 and 2 kg for \$3.60. Which is the best buy?

Q9. The area of a rectangle is 12 cm^2. If the length and breadth are doubled, what is the area of the new (larger) rectangle?

Q10. Using 40 m of wire fencing and 4 posts, what is the largest area that can be enclosed?

LEVEL 2 — PROBLEM SOLVING

AVERAGE QUESTIONS

Q1. Mrs Fletcher took her husband and 3 children to the Museum. They were charged a total entrance fee of $28.50. If the adult fee was $7.50, what was the child fee?

Q2. Lisa and Eve are buying a new bike. Lisa is older and so has offered to pay 2/3 of the price. If the bike costs $195, how much does Eve have to pay?

Q3. Gabriel is 4 years older than Jonathan. Three times Gabriel's age minus four times Jonathan's age equals 3. What are their ages?

Q4. Divide 48 bubblegums between Chad and Sean so that:

(a) Sean gets twice as many as Chad.
(b) Chad gets three times as many as Sean.

Q5. Keith has pigs and chickens on his farm. He counted his animals and found that there were 15 heads and 44 legs. How many of each type of animal does Keith have?

Q6. Samantha has a collection of 20c and 50c coins. If the coins have a value of $9.40, and there are 29 coins, how many of each type of coin does she have?

Q7. How many matches are needed to make a line of 30 match triangles.

i.e. 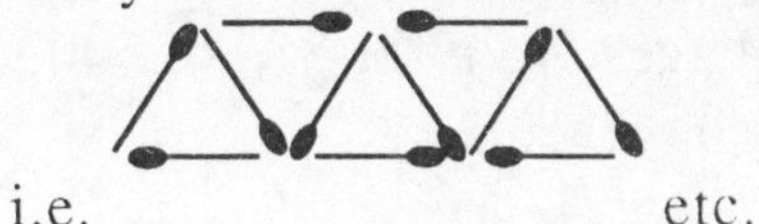 etc.

Q8. Jamie is 5 years younger than Becky, and Nicole is 6 years older than Becky. If the sum of their ages is 40, how old is each person?

Q9. I think of a number, add fourteen and double the new number. The result is 50. Find the number I first thought of.

LEVEL 3 — PROBLEM SOLVING

DIFFICULT QUESTIONS

Q1. Sandy baked a batch of macadamia biscuits. She gave half of them to Duncan who gave half of his to Gerard. Gerard gave half to Gudrun. Gudrun was given 3 biscuits. How many biscuits did Sandy bake?

Q2. Bronwyn wants to cycle 5 km in 35 minutes. She cycles the first 4 km at 8 km/hr. At what speed must she cycle the last kilometre?

Q3. Angelo was counting the football cards in his collection. He counted them by 2's, 3"s and 9's, and found that there was one left over each time. If the number of cards was definitely between 20 and 50, how many cards did he have?

Q4. 3 pairs of socks and 2 T-shirts cost a total of $31.50. If a T-shirt costs twice as much as a pair of socks, what is the price of a pair of socks?

Q5. Water is coming out of a tap at the rate of 72 L per hour. How many mL per second (mL/sec) is this?

Q6. James wants to cycle 10 km in 1 hour. He cycles the first 6 km at 12 km/h. How fast (in km/h) must he cycle for the next 4 km?

Q7. Find how many different 2-digit numbers can be formed from the digits 1, 2, 3, 4, and 5 if:

(a) each digit can only be used once?
(b) each digit can be repeated?

Q8. $350 is shared between Peter, Paul and Mary. Peter receives twice as much as Paul. Paul receives three times as much as Mary. How much money does each person receive?

Q9. 27 small cubes have been joined together to make one large cube. This large cube is then painted green all over. How many of the small cubes will have?

(a) 3 sides painted?
(b) 2 sides painted?
(b) 1 side painted?
(d) no sides painted?

APPENDICES

Isometric dot paper

Numeral expanders

	Thousands		Hundreds		Tens		Ones	

	Ones •		Tenths		Hundredths

	Ones •		Tenths

	Ones •		Tenths

	Tens		Ones •		Tenths		Hundredths	

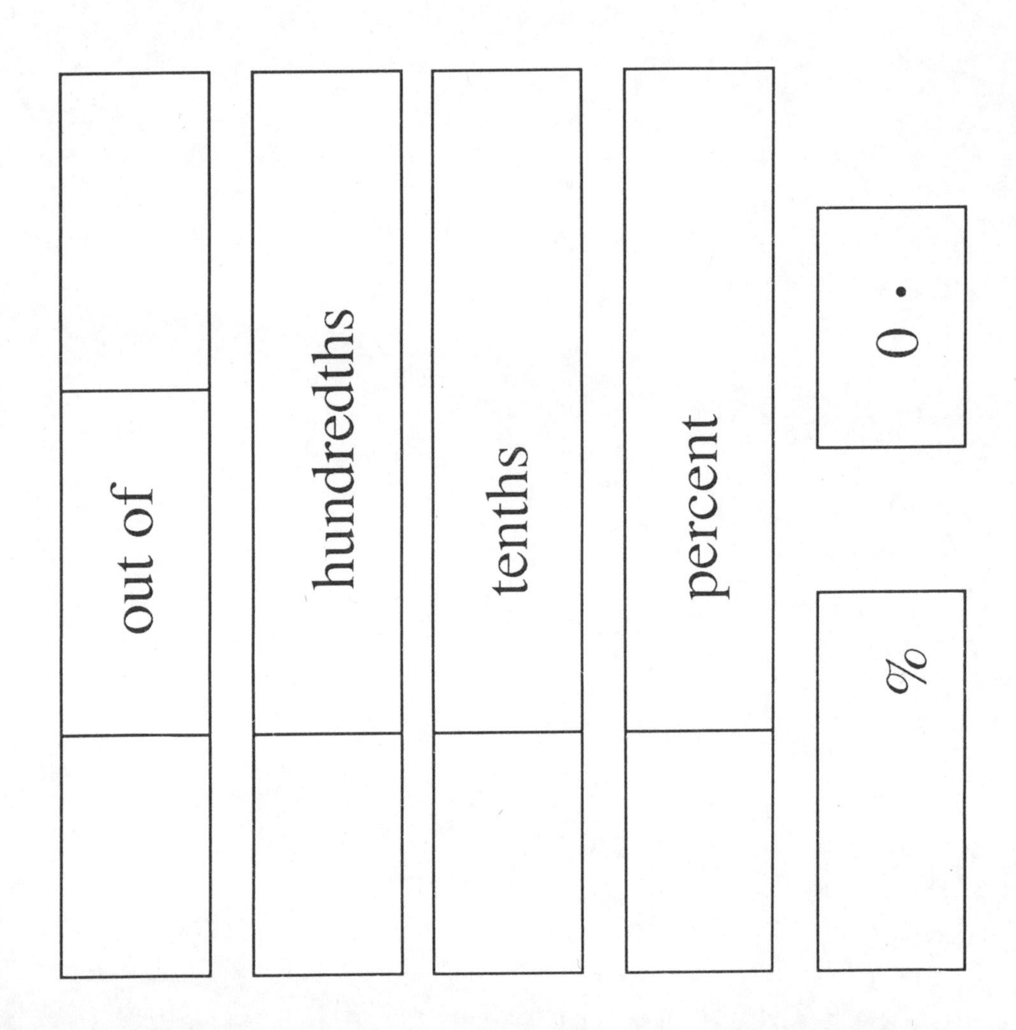

An extra page for additional notes

SOLUTIONS

Level 1 — Numeration

Q1. (a) 697 (b) 1 421
(c) 3 674 (d) 2 568

Q2. 27 027

Q3. (a) 3 hundreds (b) 3 thousands (c) 3 ones or units

Q4. 67 439

Q5. (a) 6000 (b) 11 000 (c) 27 000

Q6. (a) 148 239 (b) 73 012

Q7. 99 999, 376 428, 1 000 202, 2 563 180

Q8. (a) LXXIV (b) CXXVI (c) CDXIX

Q9. (a) 97 (b) 362 (c) 539

Level 2 — Numeration

Q1. (a) 3 950 (b) 4 001
(c) 7 969 (d) 2 050

Q2. (a) 50 737 (b) 21 048

Q3. (a) 3 ones or units
(b) 3 tens of thousands
(c) 3 hundreds of thousands

Q4. 37 250

Q5. (a) 60 000 (b) 110 000 (c) 380 000

Q6. (a) 18 017 (b) 209 377

Q7. 4 099 958, 4 199 986, 4 203 625, 4 400 000

Q8. (a) DXLIII (b) DCCXCVIII (c) MCCCXVI

Q9. (a) 1420 (b) 868 (c) 1995

Level 3 — Numeration

Q1. (a) 8024 (b) 10 001

Q2. 39 217

Q3. (a) 6 tens of thousands
(b) 6 hundreds of thousands
(c) 6 millions

Q4. (a) 25 360 (b) 51 498

Q5. (a) 500 000 (b) 600 000
(c) 1 300 000

Q6.(a) 149 725 (b) 99 999

Q7. (a) Fifty three million, four hundred and seventy three thousand, nine hundred and six
(b) 53 000 000

Q8. (a) CMLI
(b) MDCXIII
(c) MMCCCLXIX

Q9. (a) 1 020
(b) 3 601
(c) 2 704

Level 1 — Addition

Q1. (a) 98 (b) 379
(c) 144 (d) 512
(e) 977 (f) 1447

Q2. (a) $\begin{array}{r} 425 \\ +\ 239 \\ \hline 664 \\ \hline \end{array}$ (b) $\begin{array}{r} 376 \\ +\ 58 \\ \hline 434 \\ \hline \end{array}$ (c) $\begin{array}{r} 928 \\ +\ 156 \\ \hline 1\,084 \\ \hline \end{array}$

Q3. 1040 cans.
Q4. 111 Year 6 students.
Q5. 263 pieces.
Q6. 281 cars.
Q7. 482 drinks.

Level 2 — Addition

Q1. (a) 1 352 (b) 1 502
(c) 2 217 (d) 9 370
(e) 12 873 (f) 25 683
Q2. (a) 1 726
(b) 6 113
(c) 14 955
Q3. 35 696
Q4. 38 600 pieces of fruit.
Q5. $52 269
Q6. 85 636
Q7. $70 895

Level 3 — Addition

Q1. (a) 2 851
(b) 4 659
(c) 6 492
Q2. (a) 22 729
(b) 43 842
(c) 84 154
Q3. 694 464 newspapers.
Q4. 2 081 203 km^2
Q5. $270 968
Q6. $3 390 825
Q7. 12 563 350
Q8. $16 450 000

Level 1 — Subtraction

Q1. (a) 111 (b) 733
(c) 214

Q2. (a) 2 235 (b) 6 510
(c) 1 131

Q3. 61 372 more people live in Bassville.

Q4. 6 421 km.

Q5. (a) 17
(b) 26
(c) 126

Q6. 65 budgies left.

Q7. $43 left.

Q8. 593 adults

Q9. 353 girls

Q10. 625 stamps

Level 2 — Subtraction

Q1. (a) 518 (b) 285
(c) 799

Q2. (a) 1 361 (b) 2 718
(c) 2 754

Q3. (a) 17 570 (b) 50 522
(c) 112 071

Q4. 1 743 homes.

Q5. 11 789

Q6. $15 470

Q7. (a) 3 915
(b) 3 412

Q8. 367 passengers on board.

Q9. 4 347 L

Level 3 — Subtraction

Q1. (a) 176 (b) 348
(c) 326

Q2. (a) 4 545 (b) 8 042
(c) 8 149

Q3. (a) 8 078 (b) 1 792 386
(c) 40 601 453

Q4. 3397 km.

Q5. 86 740 books.

Q6. 287 825 square kilometres.

Q7. 50 002

Q8. 78 340 000 km

Q9. Beach Airlines made $847 000 more profit.

Level 1 — Multiplication

Q1. 30

Q2. (a) 60 (b) 162
(c) 932

Q3. (a) 1 022 (b) 504
(c) 1 075

Q4. 304 lollies.

Q5. 1 218 plants.

Q6. 1 440 passengers.

Q7. 300 eggs.

Q8.

Roll			Sandwich		
Salad	Cheese	Ham	Salad	Cheese	Ham

There are six different combinations.

Q9. nine different drinks.

Q10. Eight different shirts.

Level 2 — Multiplication

Q1. (a) 224 (b) 851
(c) 1296

Q2. 117

Q3. (a) 2 176 (b) 3 420
(c) 1 740

Q4. 3 850 loaves.

Q5. 1 330 km.

Q6. 1 728 oranges.

Q7. Tina can choose from 9 holiday combinations.

Q8. $6 272

Q9. 16 loaves.

Q10. 18 suits.

Level 3 — Multiplication

Q1. (a) 300 (b) 10 000
(c) 56 000

Q2. (a) 6 860 (b) 29 704
(c) 69 888

Q3. 1 275 bottles.

Q4. The Goard family have a choice of 18 holiday combinations.

Q5. (a) 234 meals per day.
(b) 3 276 meals.

Q6. $22 100 per year.

Q7. 20 150 km

Q8. 72 models.

Level 1 — Division

Q1. (a) 9 (b) 13
(c) 13 r 1 (d) 48
(e) 21 r 1 (f) 64

Q2. (a) 27 (b) 12

Q3. $32 to each charity.

Q4. 29 bottles.

Q5. (a) 21 pieces.
(b) 7 pieces left.

Q6. (a) 1 324 (b) 2 139
(c) 1 222 r 2

Q7 13 cards.

Q8. 225 g

Q9. 42 pupils.

Level 2 — Division

Q1. (a) 23 (b) 17 (c) 17

Q2. (a) 143 r 1 (b) 112 r 3 (c) 54

Q3. (a) 1 542 r 1 (b) 395 r 8 (c) 842 r 2

Q4. 96 layers.

Q5. 163 trees.

Q6. $1 501 each.

Q7. (a) 5 r 5 (b) 10 (c) 12 r 5

Q8. (a) 32 red and 38 blue.
(b) 8 red and 1 blue.

Q9. (a) 69 (b) 76 (c) 800

Q10. 115 bricks per hour.

Q11. Oranges cost 15c.

Level 3 — Division

Q1. (a) 7 r 8 (b) 90 (c) 75 r 3
(d) 42 r 6 (e) 83 r 2 (f) 125

Q2. (a) 85 (b) 67 (c) 259

Q3. (a) 121 (b) 3 102 r 2 (c) 480 r 22

Q4. 23 boxes.

Q5. 121 cattle.

Q6. $1 683 each.

Q7. 14 children.

Q8. 3 lollies.

Q9. 24 biscuits.

Level 1 — Order of Operations

Q1. (a) 33 (b) 21 (c) 11
(d) 4 (e) 10 (f) 13

Q2. (a) 2 (b) 3 (c) 15
(d) 24 (e) 2 (f) 44

Level 2 — Order of Operations

Q1. (a) 7 (b) 10 (c) 3
(d) 6 (e) 10 (f) 26

Q2. (a) 5 (b) 5 (c) 28
(d) 17 (e) 21 (f) 15

Level 3 — Order of Operations

Q1. (a) 43 (b) 45
(c) 17 (d) 32

Q2. (a) 94 (b) 32

Level 1 — Fractions and Decimals

Q1. 0.6

Q2. (a) 7 tenths
(b) 7 hundredths
(c) 7 tens

Q3. (a) 5.71, 5.7, 5.69
(b) 3.54, 3.47, 3.45

Q4. (a) $\frac{1}{2}$
(b) $\frac{3}{6}$ or $\frac{1}{2}$

Q5. (a) shade any 3 sections.
(b) shade any 5 sections.

Q6. 37%

Q7. Shade in any 87 squares.

Q8 (a) $\frac{31}{100}$ (b) $\frac{49}{100}$
(c) $\frac{7}{100}$ (d) $\frac{19}{100}$

Q9. (a) 17% (b) 45%
(c) 50% (d) 25%

Q10. (a) $\frac{8}{16}$ (b) $\frac{2}{6}$
(c) $\frac{6}{10}$

Q11. (a) 6.27 (b) 4.8
(c) 19 (d) 1.5

Q12. (a) 8 quarters (b) 5 halves

Q13. (a) $8.14 (b) $93.05

Q14. (a) $3 (b) 10 apples
(c) 10 students (d) 2 lollies

Level 2 — Fractions and decimals

Q1. 0.75

Q2. (a) 3 hundredths (b) 3 tenths

Q3. 4.07, 4.27, 4.7, 4.72

Q4. (a) $\frac{2}{5}$ (b) $\frac{9}{15}$ or $\frac{3}{5}$

Q5. (a) $\frac{1}{3}$ is equivalent to $\frac{2}{6}$ $\therefore$ shade in any 2 sections

(b) $\frac{3}{4}$ is equivalent to $\frac{6}{8}$ $\therefore$ shade in any 6 sections

Q6. 83%

Q7 60% = $\frac{60}{100}$ which is equivalent to $\frac{6}{10}$ $\therefore$ shade in any 6 sections

Q8. (a) 63% (b) 80%
(c) 60% (d) 80%

Q9. (a) 0.16 (b) 0.09
(c) 0.32 (d) 1.0

Q10. (a) $\frac{6}{9}$ (b) $\frac{6}{8}$
(c) $\frac{12}{15}$

Q11. (a) 78.91 (b) 53.42
(c) 87.5 (d) 2.3

Q12. (a) $\frac{1}{4}$ (b) $\frac{4}{7}$
(c) $\frac{3}{10}$

Q13. (a) \$224.74 (b) \$83.28
(c) \$74.20 (d) \$1.35

Q14. (a) 100g (b) 250 ml
(c) \$1.20 (d) 1.5 m

Level 3 — Fractions and Decimals

Q1. 0.07

Q2. (a) 7 ones (b) 7 hundredths

Q3. 1.43, 1.4, 1.34, 1.3, 1.04

Q4. (a) $\frac{7}{12}$ (b) $\frac{6}{9}$ or $\frac{2}{3}$

Q5. (a) Any 4 sections
(b) Any 10 sections

Q6. $\frac{8}{25} = \frac{32}{100} = 32\%$

Q7. Any 4 sections

Q8. (a) 16% (b) 32%
(c) 62% (d) 60%

Q9. (a) 25% (b) 82%
(c) 9% (d) 60%

Q10. (a) $\frac{12}{20}$ (b) $\frac{15}{20}$
(c) $\frac{6}{21}$

Q11. (a) \$142.65 (b) \$260.01
(c) \$4.72 (d) \$13.71

Q12. (a) $\frac{150}{1000} = \frac{15}{100} = \frac{3}{20}$ (b) $\frac{80}{400} = \frac{8}{40} = \frac{1}{5}$
(c) $\frac{125}{1000} = \frac{1}{8}$ other answers also acceptable

Q13. (a) 7.92 (b) 43.75 (c) 14.07 (d) 1.75

Q14. (a) 25% (b) 75% (c) 48%

Level 1 — Money

Q1. (a) $26.07
(b) 120.32
(c) $17.35
(d) $1.25
(e) $25.33
Q2. $31.46
Q3. (a) $5.83
(b) $14.17
Q4. (a) $10
(b) $11
Q5. $15
Q6. $20
Q7. $36.50

Level 2 — Money

Q1. (a) $439.61
(b) $1 047.16
(c) $55.88
(d) $30.27
Q2. $21
Q3. $2.94
Q4. $13 175
Q5. (a) $90 (b) $360
Q6. 5% p.a.
Q7. $15.50
Q8. Mangoes$1.60, oranges $1.20.

Level 3 — Money

Q1. (a) $97.92
(b) $5.67
(c) 0.90 or 90c
Q2. $459.04
Q3. $162
Q4. $180
Q5. (a) $54
(b) $75.60
(c) $121.50
Q6. (a) $88
(b) $231
(c) $385
Q7. $30 024
Q8. (a) $30.00
(b) 37.5% or $37\frac{1}{2}$%
Q9. 1.25 m

Level 1 — Chance and data

Q1. (a) 1 out of 2 (b) 1 out of 2

Q2. (a) 1 out of 3 (b) 1 out of 3

(c) 1 out of 3

Q3. (a) 1 out of 3 (b) 2 out of 3

Q4. (a) 1 out of 4

[No answers for (b) and (c) as results will differ. Discuss with an adult.]

Q5. Equal chance.

Q6. (a) 1 in 12 (b) 1 in 7

Q7. (a) 3 ways (b) 3 in 36 or $\frac{3}{36}$ or $\frac{1}{12}$

(c) 1 in 36 or $\frac{1}{36}$ (d) 6 in 36 or $\frac{6}{36}$ or $\frac{1}{6}$

Level 2 — Chance and Data

Q1. (a) Two coins can land in 4 different ways

i.e. Head Head or Head Tail or Tail Head or Tail Tail

(b) 1 out of 4 (c) 2 out of 4

Q2. (a) 2 out of 6 (b) 1 out of 6

(c) 3 out of 6

Q3. (a) 4 out of 16

[No answer for (b) and (c) as results will differ. Discuss with an adult.]

Q4. (a) 1 in 2 (26 in 52)

(b) 1 in 4 (13 in 52)

(c) 1 in 4 (13 in 52)

(d) 1 in 13 (4 in 52)

(e) 3 in 13 (12 in 52)

Level 3 — Chance and data

Q1. (a) Three coins can land in 8 different ways

i.e. HHH or HHT or HTH or HTT or THH or THT or TTH or TTT

(b) 1 out of 8 (i.e. HHH)

(c) 3 out of 8 (i.e. HHT, HTH and THH)

Q2. (a) (i) 3 out of 7

(ii) 4 out of 7

(b) Now there are 6 balls in the bag—3 white and 3 black

(i) 3 out of 6

(ii) 3 out of 6

Q3. Answers will vary.

Q4. (a) 1 in 2 (10 in 20)

(b) 1 in 20

(c) 1 in 4 (5 in 20)

(d) 1 in 10 (2 in 20)

(e) 1 in 5 (4 in 20)

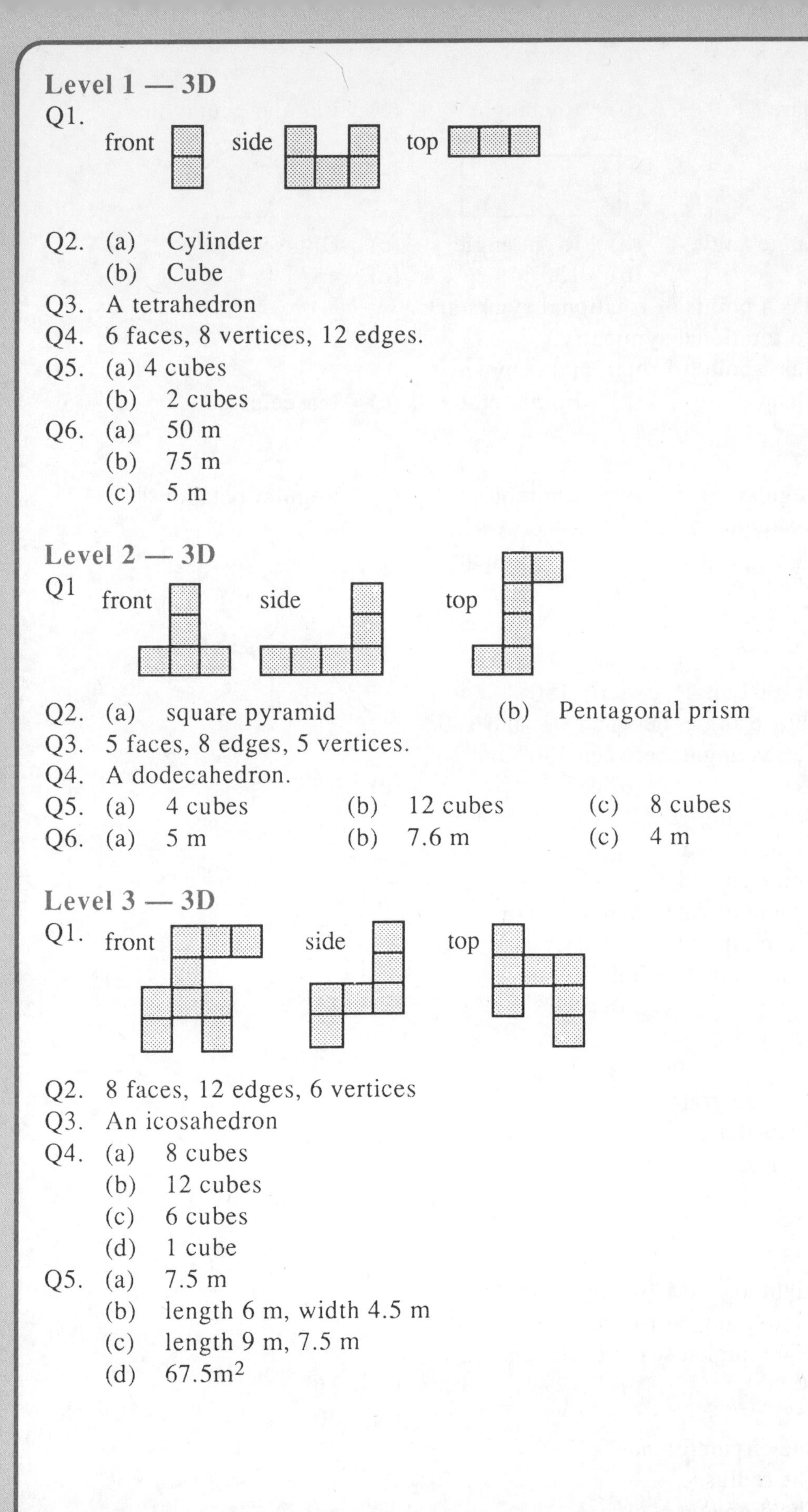

Level 1 — 3D

Q1. front side top

Q2. (a) Cylinder
(b) Cube

Q3. A tetrahedron

Q4. 6 faces, 8 vertices, 12 edges.

Q5. (a) 4 cubes
(b) 2 cubes

Q6. (a) 50 m
(b) 75 m
(c) 5 m

Level 2 — 3D

Q1 front side top

Q2. (a) square pyramid (b) Pentagonal prism

Q3. 5 faces, 8 edges, 5 vertices.

Q4. A dodecahedron.

Q5. (a) 4 cubes (b) 12 cubes (c) 8 cubes

Q6. (a) 5 m (b) 7.6 m (c) 4 m

Level 3 — 3D

Q1. front side top

Q2. 8 faces, 12 edges, 6 vertices

Q3. An icosahedron

Q4. (a) 8 cubes
(b) 12 cubes
(c) 6 cubes
(d) 1 cube

Q5. (a) 7.5 m
(b) length 6 m, width 4.5 m
(c) length 9 m, 7.5 m
(d) 67.5m^2

Level 1 — 2 D

Q1. (a) Square (b) Rectangle (c) Regular pentagon

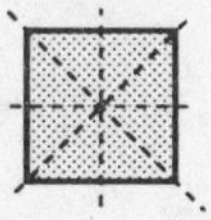

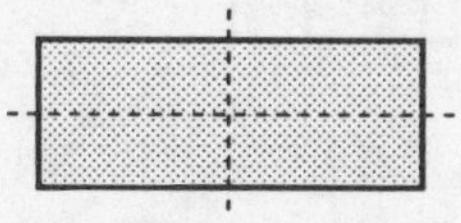

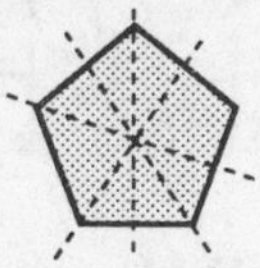

Q2. (a) Acute angle (b) Right angle (c) Obtuse angle

Q3. (a) 85° (b) 130° (c) 45°

Q4. (a) Has 4 points of rotational symmetry.
(b) No rotational symmetry.
(c) Has 1 point of rotational symmetry.

Q5. (a) Scalene (b) Equilateral (c) Isosceles

Level 2 — 2D

Q1.(a) Regular hexagon (b) Rhombus —no axis of symmetry (c) Regular octagon

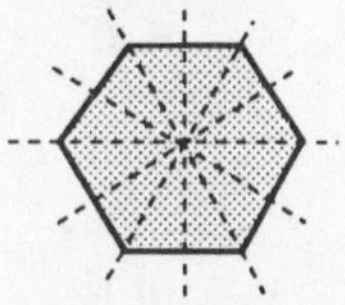

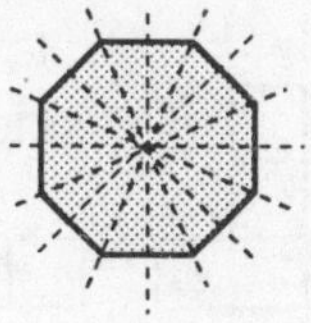

Q2. (a) straight angle, exactly 180°
(b) obtuse angle, between 90° and 180°
(c) Reflex angle, between 180° and 360°

Q3. (a) 153° (b) 68° (c) 25°

Q4. (a) Obtuse angled
(b) Right angled
(c) Acute angled

Q5. (a) 1 point of rotational symmetry.
(b) No rotational symmetry.
(c) 3 points of rotational symmetry.

Q6. (a) 60° (b) 55° (c) 59°

Level 3 — 2D

Q1. (a) Parallelogram
(b) Quadrilateral
(c) Hexagon

Q2. (a) 175°
(b) 235°
(c) 325°

Q3. (a) Right angled isosceles triangle
(b) Obtuse angled isosceles triangle.
(c) Right angled scalene triange.

Q4. (a) 60° (b) 129° (c) 36°
(d) 75° (e) 98° (f) 50°

Q5. (a) The circumference
(b) The radius.
(c) The diameter.

Level 1 — Position

Q1. (a) pencil
(b) flower
(c) car
(d) glasses
(e) square

Q2. (a) (i) Banksiaville (ii) Mutton Farm
(iii) Factory (iv) Crossroads
(b) (i) C6 (ii) E2 (iii) B4 (iv) E3

Q3.

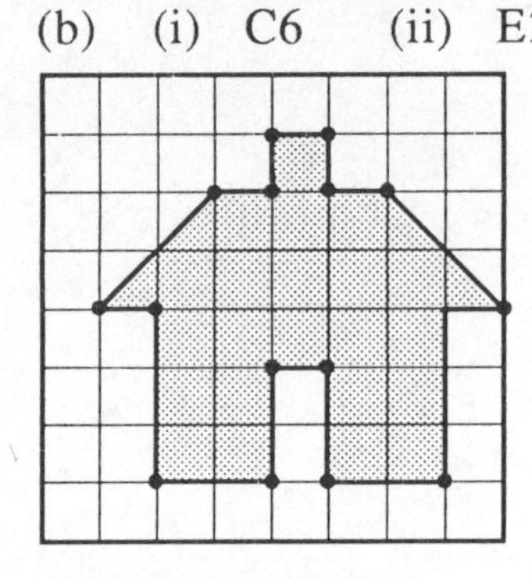

Level 2 — Position

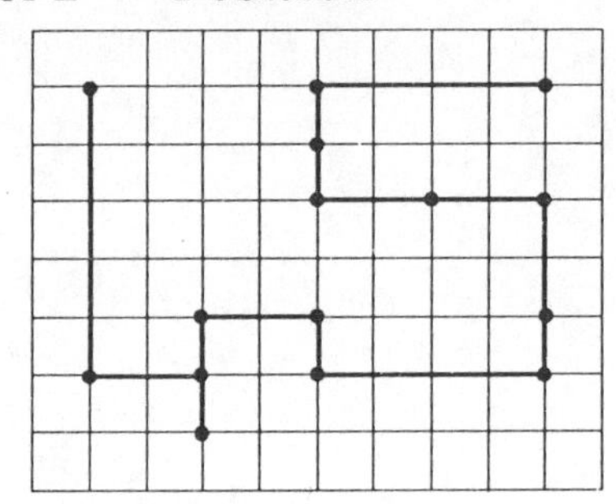

Q1. The number 45 is revealed.

Q2. (a) 115° (b) 65°

Level 3 — Position

Q1. (a) north (b) south
(c) west (d) east
(e) north-west (f) south-west
(g) south-east (h) north-west
(i) south-west

Q2. (a) 10 km (b) 25 km
(c) 20 km (d) 29 km
(e) 31 km

Q3. (a) 10 km (b) 11 km
(c) 17 km (d) 29 km

Level 1 — Graphs

Q1. (a) 50 cars
(b) 30 cars
(c) white
(d) black
(e) 186 cars
(f) lighter colours absorb less heat and reflect more heat, hence are cooler in summer

Q2. (a) 20 000 apples
(b) 1993
(c) 110 000 apples
(d) 27 500 more apples
(e) poor weather conditions, or increased insect pest infestation

Level 2 — Graphs

Q1. (a) 5 mm
(b) 80 mm
(c) October
(d) March, April, May
(e) 4 months
(f) 5 months
(g) January, August, October

Q2. (a) 38.8°C
(b) 1.8°C higher
(c) 40.2°C
(d) 4 a.m. to 8 a.m.
(e) 8 a.m.
(f) dropped by 2°C

Level 2 — Graphs

Q1. (a) 4 students
(b) $\frac{1}{8}$
(c) 4 more students
(d) True
(e) 4 times

Q2. (a) 14 kangaroo paws, 14 banksias
(b) 28 rosebushes
(c) 14 more eucalypts
(d) 14 fewer banksias
(e) 25%

Level 1 — Length

Q1. (a) 145 cm
(b) 15 cm

Q2.	(a)	40 mm	(b)	8 000 m	(c)	7 cm
	(d)	5 km	(e)	300 cm	(f)	4 m
Q3.	(a)	18 cm	(b)	32 cm	(c)	28 cm

Q4. 7000 cm = 70 m

Q5.	(a)	50 cm	(b)	75 cm	(c)	250 m

Q6. 11.7 m
Q7. 7 rulers
Q8. 50 cm
Q9. 156 m

Level 2 — Length

Q1.	(a)	20 cm	(b)	65 mm	(c)	0.5 km
	(d)	4.5 cm	(e)	3 400 m	(f)	9.25 km

Q2. 150 m longer
Q3. 50 steps
Q4. (a) 120 km
(b) 180 km
Q5. 9.35 m

Q6.	(a)	48 cm	(b)	90 m	(c)	56 cm

Q7. (a) 270 cm or 2.7 m
(b) 5 mm or 0.5 cm
(c) 2400 m or 2.4 km
Q8. 56 cm
Q9. 36 cm

Level 3 — Length

Q1. (a) 56.7 mm
(b) 43.2 cm
(c) 420 cm
Q2. (a) 60 cm or 0.6 m
(b) 1 800 m or 1.8 km
(c) 35 mm or 3.5 cm
Q3. (a) 600 m
(b) 8 lengths
Q4. 3993 m or 3.993 km
Q5. 7.85 km or 7 850 m
Q6. 10.8 km = 10 800 m of fencing
Q7. (a) 124 m
(b) 168 cm
Q8. Width is 7 cm
Q9. 6 more circuits.

Level 1 — Area

Q1. (a) $14\ cm^2$
(b) $16\ cm^2$

Q2. (a) $10\ 000\ cm^2$
(b) $10\ 000\ m^2$
(c) 2 ha

Q3. (a) km^2
(b) m^2
(c) m^2
(d) cm^2
(e) cm^2
(f) cm^2

Q4. (a) $40\ cm^2$
(b) $36\ cm^2$
(c) $36\ cm^2$

Q5. $70cm^2$

Q6. $14\ m^2$

Q7. $18m^2$

Q8. $45\ cm^2$

Level 2 — Area

Q1. (a) $23\ cm^2$
(b) $19\ cm^2$

Q2. (a) $5\ m^2$
(b) $50\ 000\ m^2$
(c) 100 ha

Q3. (a) $168\ cm^2$
(b) $256\ m^2$
(c) $212\ cm^2$

Q4. $35\ 000\ m^2$

Q5. $1170

Q6. $510\ m^2$

Q7. (a) 45 ha
(b) $150\ 000\ cm^2$
(c) $10\ km^2$

Level 3 — Area

Q1. (a) $30\ cm^2$ (b) $25\ cm^2$

Q2. $23\ 000\ cm^2$

Q3. (a) 7.5ha (b) $8\ 300\ cm^2$
(c) $320\ 000\ cm^2$

Q4. (a) $402\ m^2$ (b) $311\ cm^2$

Q5. (a) 10 m (b) 8.6 cm
(c) 13.2 m

Q6. 45 blocks

Q7. 520 tiles

Level 1 — Volume

Q1. (a) 1 L (b) 2 000 mL
(c) 0.5 l L (d) 3 500 mL
(e) 2.51

Q2. (a) 10 spoonfuls (b) 70 spoonfuls

Q3. (a) 8 cm^3 (b) 6 cm^3

Q4. (a) 650 cm^3 (b) 55 g
(c) 1000 ml (d) 356 cm^3

Q5. (a) 30 cm^3 (b) 64 cm^3

Q6. (a)

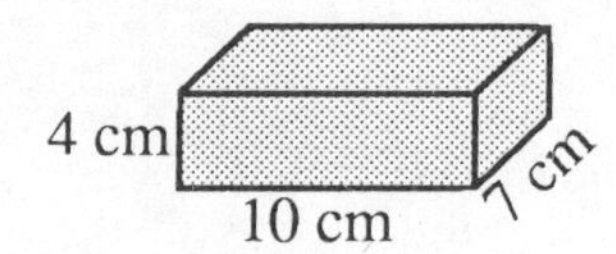

(b) 280 cm^3

Level 2 Volume

Q1. (a) 0.25 L (b) 3 250 ml
(c) 2.75 L

Q2. 900 ml

Q3. 1 L for $1.20

Q4. (a) 13 cm^3 (b) 18 cm^3

Q5. (a) 300 m^3 (b) 360 cm^3

Q6. (a) 2 kg (b) 3 L
(c) 5 000 cm^3 (d) 1 250 g

Q7. 5 m wide

Level 3 — Volume

Q1. (a) $0.70
(b) $9.80

Q2. Volume = 350 m^3 = 350 000 L

Q3. 1 L takes 20 min $\therefore$ 5 L takes 1 hr 40 min

Q4. (a) 24 cm^3
(b) 24 cm^3

Q5. (a) 3 cm
(b) 5 m
(c) 15 cm

Q6. Volume of full box = 120 m^3 $\therefore$ depth is 4 m

Q7. Volume when full is 1600 mL $\therefore$ width is 8 cm

Remember 1 m^3 = 1000 L

Level 1 — Mass

Q1. (a) 1000 g
(b) 1 t
(c) 2 kg
(d) 500 kg
(e) 5 500 g
(f) 0.5 kg
Q2. 5.25 kg
Q3. 4.95 kg
Q4. 1 kg at $2.88
Q5. 5 apples
Q6. 69 g
Q7. 4500 kg or 4.5 t
Q8. 43.5 kg
Q9. 2.8 kg

Level 2 — Mass

Q1. 4.41 kg
Q2. 13.5 kg left
Q3. (a) 2.75t
(b) 3600 g
(c) 5 250 kg
(d) 5.1 kg
(e) 900 g
(f) 0.2 t
Q4. 21.6 kg
Q5. 4557.6 kg
Q6. (a) 600 g
(b) 300 kg
(c) 48 g
Q7. 5 cans
Q8. 340 kg

Level 3 — Mass

Q1. 2 kg
Q2 156 minutes or 2 h 36 min
Q3. 575 g
Q4. 18.75 kg
Q5. (a) 800 g
(b) 375 g
(c) 600 kg
Q6. 70 g
Q7. (a) 14 g
(b) 10.5 g
(c) 336 g
Q8. 800 g or 0.8 kg

Level 1 — Temperature

Q1. A thermometer is a device for measuring temperature (i.e. hot or cold).

Q2. In ovens, furnaces, kilns, etc. [discuss further with an adult].

Q3. 39°C – 14°C = 25°C

Q4. (a) A clinical thermometer i.e. measures people's body temperature.
(b) The range covers the extremes of human body temperature.

Q5. (a) Water boils at 100°C
(b) Water freezes at 0°C
(c) Body temperature is 37°C

Level 2 — Temperature

Q1. Celsius scale is based on 100° (centi means 'hundred').

Q2. In freezers, at the Artic and North Pole, anywhere with snowy or icy weather conditions. [discuss with an adult].

Q3. 1. Mercury is a potentially toxic substance.
2. Glass can be easily broken.

Q4. 2.4°C

Q5. (a) an oven thermometer.
(b) this is the range required for warming or cooking food.

Q6. (a) 23°C
(b) Friday at 29°C
(c) Thursday 18°C
(d) 4° colder

Level 3 — Temperature

Q1. 55°C

Q2. The substance (mercury or alcohol) stored in the bulb of the thermometer expands in size when temperature rises, and so it moves up the glass tube. The rise in substance is measured on the scale.

Q3. (a) A maximum/minimum thermometer.
(b) The mercury or alcohol moves around the u-shaped tube, pushing markers which indicate the maximum or minimum temperatures recorded over a period of time. [Discuss further with an adult].

Q4. Inappropriate thermometers will break as they are not capable of handling temperatuares outside of their range.

Q5. (a) 7°C
(b) 70°C
(c) $3\frac{1}{2}$ minutes

Level 1 — Time

Q1. (a) 0500 (b) 1635
(c) 2015 (d) 0705

Q2. (a) 5:15 a.m. (b) 9:50 p.m.
(c) 12:32 p.m. (d) 10:35 a.m.

Q3. (a) 6 months (b) 1 year
(c) 21 months (d) 3 months

Q4. 1.53 seconds faster

Q5. 246 km

Q6. 10 p.m.

Q7. (a) 6 p.m
(b) 4:30 p.m.

Level 2 — Time

Q1. (a) 0900 (b) 2020
(c) 0125 (d) 2343

Q2. (a) 4:25 pm (b) 9:32 a.m.
(c) 9:35 p.m. (d) 11:14 a.m.

Q3. (a) 8:45 (b) 3:10
(c) 4:50

Q4. (a) 58 min
(b) Richard Rd to Timothy St
(c) 8:35 a.m.
(d) 9:28 p.m.

Q5. (a) 60 km/h
(b) 45 km

Level 3 — Time

Q1. (a) 0051
(b) 1205
(c) 0011

Q2. (a) 1 hr 54 min
(b) 1407 train
(c) 1247
(d) 1252

Q3. Tuesday 10:00 a.m.

Q4. (a) 2211 Sunday
(b) 0011 Monday

Q5. (a) 120 km/h
(b) 140 km
(c) 1 h 15 min

Level 1 — Problem solving

Q1. (a) \$3.55
(b) \$39.05

Q2. \$37.20

Q3. The number is 6

Q4. 4 and 12

Q5. Betty is 9 and Marcia is 14

Q6. (a) 88
(b) 7

Q7. 56, 57, 58, 65, 67, 68, 75, 76, 78, 85, 86, 87.

Q8. 2 kg for \$3.60

Q9. 48 cm^2

Q10. 100 m^2

Level 2 — Problem Solving

Q1. \$4.50 per child

Q2. Eve pays \$65

Q3. Gabriel is 13 and Jonathan is 9

Q4. (a) Sean 32, Chad 16
(b) Chad 36, Sean 12

Q5. 7 pigs and 8 chickens

Q6. 17 × 20c and 12 × 50c

Q7. 61 matches.

Q8. Jamie is 8, Becky is 13 and Nicole is 19.

Q9. 11

Level 3 — Problem Solving

Q1. Sandy baked 24 biscuits.

Q2. 12 km/hr

Q3. 37 cards

Q4. \$4.50

Q5. 20 mL/sec

Q6. 8 km/h

Q7. (a) 12, 13, 14, 15, 21, 23, 24, 25, 31, 32, 34, 35, 41, 42, 43, 45, 51, 52, 53, 54. Total 20.
(b) All the numbers from (a) plus 11, 22, 33, 44, 55. Total 25.

Q8. Peter \$210, Paul \$105 and Mary \$35.

Q9. (a) 8 cubes
(b) 12 cubes
(c) 6 cubes
(d) 1 cube